HUMAN TROPHOBLAST

A Monograph in

THE CARL VERNON WELLER LECTURE SERIES

HUMAN TROPHOBLAST

By

ARTHUR T. HERTIG, M.D.

*Shattuck Professor
of Pathological
Anatomy and
Chairman of the Department of Pathology
Harvard Medical School
Boston, Massachusetts
Consultant in Pathology
Boston Hospital for Women, formerly Free Hospital for Women
Brookline, Massachusetts
Boston Lying-in Hospital
Boston, Massachusetts*

CHARLES C THOMAS · PUBLISHER
Springfield · Illinois · U.S.A.

Published and Distributed Throughout the World by

CHARLES C THOMAS • PUBLISHER

BANNERSTONE HOUSE

301-327 East Lawrence Avenue, Springfield, Illinois, U.S.A.

NATCHEZ PLANTATION HOUSE

735 North Atlantic Boulevard, Fort Lauderdale, Florida, U.S.A.

© *1968, by* CHARLES C THOMAS • PUBLISHER

Library of Congress Catalog Card Number: 68-13760

Printed in the United States of America

C-1

DEDICATION

I DEDICATE this Weller Lecture Monograph to the late Doctors S. Burt Wolbach, Fredrick C. Irving, Frank A. Pemberton, George L. Streeter, and to Doctors George W. Corner and John Rock on whose shoulders I have stood individually and collectively for these many years.

PREFACE

THIS Weller monograph on human trophoblast has had a very long gestational period—over thirty years—and has suffered from a certain amount of inertia, desultory labor, and dystocia during its preparation for delivery. The writing and plate making have been done during the past three summers since a busy administrative and academic schedule has precluded productive writing during those school years after the Weller Lecture itself was given on December 12, 1964. Support for the original work and its publication has come largely from USPHS Grant HD-00137.

Many persons have been patient and/or helpful in the preparation of this monograph. I am most grateful to them, individually and collectively, for without their forebearance and assistance the manuscript and illustrations would never have been prepared. Special thanks are due Dr. Hazel Gore, who has taken my handwritten manuscript and molded it into a finished product. Mrs. Virginia W. Leahey has helped significantly by typing the final manuscript as has Miss Edith A. Lowry, our departmental secretary, in typing the final bibliography. Mrs. Nancy Coté has also helped in the typing during the necessary final revisions of the manuscript.

The pictures have resulted from the skill and devotion of several photographers: Mr. Chester F. Reather, formerly at Carnegie's Department of Embryology but now at the Johns Hopkins Hospital, made many of the superb original gross photos and photomicrographs of the early human embryos as well as all of the illustrations on angiogenesis. Mr. Richard D. Grill, the present Carnegie photographer, made the remainder of the original pictures and the majority of the fine prints of the embryological specimens here reproduced. Mrs. Audrey Hadfield, my departmental research photographer, made the many excellent prints

vii

of material submitted to me in consultation and prints of histo-chemical material originally photographed by Mr. Leo Goodman of the Boston City Hospital. Finally, the photographic department of the Armed Forces Institute of Pathology in Washington, D.C. kindly furnished prints of pathological material through the courtesy of its Director, Brigadier General Joe M. Blumberg.

To several colleagues in the Department of Pathology I am greatly indebted for significant assistance. Miss Eleanor C. Adams made the original meticulous plastic reconstructions of the early human previllous ova. These reconstructions were then made into the magnificent half-tone drawings by the late James F. Didusch, artist for the Carnegie Department of Embryology. Miss Adams also skillfully performed the histochemical reactions on the various stages of human placentation. Dr. Tien-Wen Tao's material on differentiation of trophoblast has been a real contri-bution to the biology of that tissue as well as to this monograph. The contribution of pathological material from colleagues throughout the country is collectively acknowledged.

I am grateful to Dr. James D. Ebert, Director of the Depart-ment of Embryology of the Carnegie Institution of Washington, for free access to the photographic files of that unique collection of human and primate embryos. To Dr. George W. Corner, Sr., former Director, I am indebted for his helpful suggestion as to the originator of the term *trophoblast*. Also, Dr. Corner's help and encouragement in the early human embryo program over the years is again here gratefully acknowledged.

The permission to reproduce the four placental sheets in the appendix was obtained from Dr. Zekin A. Shakhashiri, Acting Chief of the Perinatal Research Branch of the National Institute of Neurological Diseases and Blindness. For such permission I am grateful.

The staff of the Francis A. Countway Library of Medicine has been most helpful in matters bibliographical, especially Miss Catherine L. Binderup, Assistant Librarian for Reference.

To my patient and long-suffering family thanks are certainly due. Our summer cottage at Gloucester, Massachusetts, where the monograph was planned, the literature reviewed, the manuscript written, and the plates assembled will no longer be cluttered with the impedimenta of the author. Our small, aged sailboat can now be repaired and readied for the grandchildren. Our daughter-in-law, Anne-Rose Hertig, is here publicly thanked for her translation from German to English of Hubrecht's original comments on *trophoblast* and the reasons why he so named this fascinating tissue.

Thanks are given to the officers of the Michigan Society of Pathologists for inviting me to give this Weller Lecture. Without this stimulus to assemble my thoughts on, and experience with, human trophoblast, this monograph would certainly never have been written.

And finally, I am grateful to Mr. Payne E. L. Thomas for his help during preparation of this manuscript and its final publication.

Boston, Massachusetts   ARTHUR T. HERTIG

CONTENTS

HUMAN TROPHOBLAST

CHAPTER I

INTRODUCTION

A S the Ninth Carl V. Weller Lecturer, I am well aware of the great honor bestowed upon me. Dr. Weller was one of the outstanding general pathologists of his day—a "compleat" pathologist. His academic stature, his diagnostic skill, and his editorial ability are so well known as to require no further comment. Therefore, it is with some trepidation that I chose *Human Trophoblast* as the subject of this lecture and this monograph to honor such a distinguished general pathologist.

Trophoblast and its definitive organ, the placenta, are undoubtedly at the bottom of any (pathological) totem pole as regards their interest to the majority of pathologists. I am well aware that placentas and abortuses are often only grossly examined, if at all, by pathologists. The reason for such disinterest on their part is not difficult to explain. The placenta is an organ which has functioned, albeit vitally, for only a limited time, and the diagnosis of its pathological lesions seldom helps the mother or baby during that particular pregnancy. The general pathologist is expected to be diagnostically skillful in all fields of tissue pathology—a manifest impossibility. Facility in the diagnosis of trophoblastic lesions, as with all other lesions, requires the combination of abundant material, the necessity for the tissue diagnosis, and the value of that diagnosis to the patient. These criteria are seldom met except in a very large general or a special obstetrical hospital. The striking exceptions to this statement concern the hydatidiform mole and choriocarcinoma, uncommon and rare lesions respectively. Few pathologists see enough of such lesions, except in consultation, to gain familiarity in their interpretation, diagnosis, and prognosis.

On the other hand, the placenta is primarily seen by, and is of interest to, the obstetrician whether he delivers his patient at home or in a small, large, or special hospital. This busy, tired, and often harassed practitioner of medicine is always genuinely interested, for the sake of his patient's safety, in the intactness of the placenta. Should some part of it remain behind, he knows of the frequent, potentially serious sequelae of retained placental tissue. Therefore, he looks at the maternal surface and notes its apparent intactness, little realizing that the frequently lacerated placenta often defies determination of its completeness without proper submersion in several changes of clear fluid, preferably saline. This enables the natural contours of the organ to be observed and the defects to be noted. Actually, a more accurate procedure would be to fix the placenta for several hours in 10% formalin to bring out natural and unnatural contours.

Even the scholarly obstetrician usually shows little interest in placentas unless their potential pathology may impinge upon a particular maternal disease of special interest to him. I frequently remember the classic remark of the late Dr. Foster B. Kellogg, an eminent clinical obstetrician at the Boston Lying-in Hospital. His outstanding interest in and knowledge of the hypertensive toxemias were nationally recognized. Regarding placentas in general, he once said to me, "I've seen ten thousand placentas and have never looked at a damned one of them!"

Anatomists as a group have shown some interest in the placenta from a developmental, comparative, or functional standpoint. The classic studies of Otto Grosser,[31] the late George B. Wislocki,[148-151] the late George L. Streeter,[130-137] the late Chester H. Heuser,[65-71] George W. Corner,[16-18] E. C. Amoroso,[1a] Bent G. Böving,[8] and S. R. M. Reynolds[113] are a few examples of such productive scholarship. Placental physiology, endocrinology, histochemistry, ultrastructure, and immunology are receiving ever-increasing attention from basic scientists. The number of recent symposia and conferences on the placenta or trophoblast attests to the increasing interest in and knowledge of this vital tissue. Nevertheless, pathologists are in a minority among those interested in the placenta, except for such modern students as Elizabeth M. Ramsey,[112] Donald G. McKay,[95-102] Kurt Benirschke,[4-6] William B. Ober,[106] Shirley G. Driscoll,[6] Wadi G. Bardawil,[3] and Aaron Szulman.[139] These pathologists became interested in the placenta through their daily work in an embryological laboratory or a maternity hospital.

How then did your lecturer become interested in trophoblast and the placenta? Why, moreover, has he the temerity to make it the subject of a Weller Lectureship and its associated monograph? The answer lies in his professional activities and interests for the past thirty-five years. In a broad sense, the answers to these questions will necessarily be somewhat autobiographical as well as biographical: the former with respect to his own interests and the latter with respect to trophoblast. Interwoven will be a certain amount of philosophy and a few comments on how chance plays a significant role in what anyone—in this case a pathologist —does, and, consequently, in what subject he becomes particularly interested.

Chance played its first role when I went to China in 1925 as a medical entomological assistant to my brother Marshall. He and the late Dr. Charles W. Young, under the auspices of the China Medical Board of the Rockefeller Foundation, were investigating the insect transmission of kala-azar in Hsùchowfu, Kiangsu Province, and later in Peking. This endemic visceral leishmaniasis was sharply localized to the region in northeast China north of the Huai River which flows through the provinces of Anhwei and Honan. While in Peking, I chanced to meet the then Dean of the Harvard Medical School, the late Dr. David L. Edsall, when he visited the Peking Union Medical College. I learned later of a conversation with his son Geoffrey and my brother Marshall which indicated that our technique for artificially feeding sand-flies[51] (demonstrated to Dr. Edsall) helped to influence my admission to the Harvard Medical School. This occurred in 1928 when I was a third-year transfer student from the University of Minnesota.

Through my brother Marshall, I met Professor S. Burt Wolbach, with whom he had worked on the bacteroids of the cockroach during the summers of 1922 and 1923. These organisms are related to the Rickettsiae and other pathogenic and nonpathogenic bacteria-like parasites of insects. This association between S. Burt Wolbach and Marshall Hertig, two men of widely diverse interests, pathology and medical entomology respectively, was based on a common interest, namely, intracellular parasites of insects and their relation to human disease.

My acquaintance with Dr. Wolbach led to a summer job in 1929 at Woods Hole and on the islands of Naushon (owned by the Forbes family) and Martha's Vineyard. Dr. Wolbach's many friends in that region were desirous of ridding the area of wood ticks and were willing to contribute enough money for the project. The latter consisted of the feasibility of wood tick control by the introduction of the Chalcid wasp, *Ixodiphagus caucurtei*, which was known to parasitize the wood tick.

This hymenopterous parasite was discovered by the famous French professor, E. Brumpt, and was described by M. R. du Buysson in 1912. Brumpt suggested in 1913[12] that this parasitic wasp might be used to control the wood tick vector of Rocky Mountain spotted fever and other diseases. The parasite was brought to Harvard's Department of Pathology by Dr. F. Larrousse, Brumpt's assistant, in May of 1926. The strain was obtained from one parasitized nymph among ninety-four *Ixodes ricinus* infesting the deer in the Forest of Fontainebleau. Dr. Wolbach's group—consisting of Dr. F. Larrousse and Mr. Arthur G. King, a medical classmate of mine—successfully introduced this parasite on Naushon Island. Moreover, it survived during the winter of 1926-27. A more or less simultaneous experiment on a much larger scale under the direction of Professor R. A. Cooley was undertaken in Montana where Rocky Mountain spotted fever was endemic in the Bitter Root Valley. These data are given in great detail in the paper by Larrousse and associates.[84] It was from the United States Public Health Laboratory in Hamilton, Montana, that Dr. Wolbach obtained the hundreds of parasitized nymphal ticks which I used during the summer of 1929.

It was my job to determine (a) whether the parasite had survived the winters of 1927-28 and 1928-29 and (b) what proportion of the immature wood ticks, parasitic on the ears of field mice, were so parasitized. Moreover, I was to liberate some twenty or more thousands of these tick parasites in the hope that they would become permanently established on the islands of Naushon and Martha's Vineyard. Suffice it to say, the parasites survived the winters in the proportion of only one parasitized tick out of four hundred, secured as nymphs from trapped field mice and then reared to maturity. This was hardly a sufficient rate of parasitization to control these bothersome pests. My meeting with and the chance to work for Wolbach, however, led me into the field of pathology and hence ultimately to the Ninth Weller Lectureship, a happier and more permanent relationship.

The internship in pathology at the Peter Bent Brigham Hospital under Dr. Wolbach was followed by a year at the Boston Lying-in Hospital. Dr. Frederic C. Irving, newly appointed professor of obstetrics, wanted a laboratory of pathology established in that hospital. I was its first resident pathologist under Dr. Wolbach. Available to the very fledgling pathologist were two empty laboratories, planned by a retired pediatrician of small physical stature, along with a tiny storeroom and a small autopsy room. The staff consisted of a part-time secretary from the record room and an experienced but temperamental technician. My obstetrical and pathological colleagues were almost uniformly pessimistic about a future in obstetrical pathology. After all, childbirth was a normal function; there was little pathology anyway—and of what there was, so what? This all in spite of the fact that during the spring of 1931, overlapping with my Brigham internship, I performed fourteen adult autopsies in a hospital devoted to a so-called physiologic function!

Dr. Irving was, however, most encouraging. He perceived that the solution of those pathologic problems in obstetrics would at least educate the staff and hence ultimately would help the patients. His classic remark that "the pregnant patient can have any disease that any other woman can have except sterility" epitomizes both his wit and his wisdom. Owing to Dr. Irving's help and encouragement, I decided to make obstetrical pathology my field of special interest.

The following year was spent in pediatric pathology with Dr. Wolbach and Dr. Sidney Farber at the Children's Hospital. During this year of 1932-33 the Depression was in full bloom, the banks were closed, and we went off the gold standard. Since Dr. Irving wished me to and I wanted to continue in obstetrical pathology, the choice of additional training had to be made. Would it be further training in general pathology, special training in obstetrical-gynecological pathology with the late Robert Meyer in Berlin, or training in embryology with the late George Linius Streeter in Baltimore?

Here chance or luck played a very large role. Dr. Farber indicated to me in February of 1933 that the Brigham residency in general pathology was committed to Dr. George Hass, who preceded me by six months in the internship. I have been grateful to Drs. Farber and Hass ever since, although I was bitterly disappointed at the time. Therefore it seemed best to seek training in embryology rather than in the special pathology of obstetrics and gynecology. The reasoning which lay behind this decision was simple. Dr. Irving and I decided that I could probably learn female genital pathology as I pursued this special field, but I could not hope to become even an amateur embryologist on a "do-it-yourself" basis.

Dr. Irving was baffled, as were other obstetricians, by the cause(s) of spontaneous abortion or miscarriage. His frustrating experience in seeking help in this matter can best be expressed in his own words: "The pathologists say this is embryology, and the embryologists say it is pathology." The usual diagnosis for such a case was "products of conception," which the obstetrician knew or strongly suspected before he sent the material to the pathologist. Dr. Streeter was the only embryologist, together with his colleague Dr. Chester H. Heuser, who seemed to know or even care about the pathogenesis of spontaneous abortion. Hence, it was decided that someone should learn his techniques and methods of approach to the problem accounting for at least 15 per cent of fetal wastage.

Chance again played a large role. The late Dr. George B. Wislocki, a close personal friend of Dr. Irving and a long-time Baltimore colleague of Dr. Streeter, was professor of anatomy at Harvard. Although he did not know me personally, and there was little to know professionally (4 papers published and 1 submitted for publication), he recommended me to Dr. Streeter because of Dr. Irving's wishes.

Fortunately I was able to secure a National Research Council Fellowship to work with Dr. Streeter at the Department of Embryology of The Carnegie Institution of Washington in Baltimore. The project upon which I wished to work was the pathogenesis of hydatidiform swelling or "degeneration" so common in the chorionic villi of abortuses. I wished to investigate the relationship between the swelling of villous stroma and disappearance of its blood vessels.

The National Research Council representative in Boston was none other than the late eminent physiologist, Walter B. Cannon. He was kindly, sympathetic, and patient as he listened to my plans. Sometime later, after my return from Baltimore, he admitted to me that the project sounded so esoteric that he thought the council might well take a chance on it.

When I arrived in Baltimore in the early fall of 1933, I explained to Dr. Streeter the project upon which I wished to work. His response was gentle but firmly negative. He indicated that any observations that I might make on the blood vessels in the placenta, whether normal or abnormal, would be difficult to interpret because the embryological development of placental blood vessels was then largely unknown. At this point I began my training as a morphologic embryologist, albeit a trophoblastic one. I spent the year working on angiogenesis in the early human and macaque chorion. Here I learned the fundamental principles and techniques of morphologic embryology, the methods and value of serial sections, and how structures followed in serial sections were reconstructed so that they might be studied in three dimensions.

In addition to this research project on the development of placental blood vessels, I was assigned the routine job of examining and describing all of the human embryologic material accessioned to the collection—a fine apprenticeship.

During this exciting year, I had daily contacts with Dr. Streeter and absorbed his wonderful philosophy about embryology and life in general. His wise but offhand question, "Hertig, why do you suppose the Lord made the cervix?" is a good sample of the informal give-and-take between the greatest morphologic embryologist of his day and the amateur neophyte in his field. He was gently but firmly scornful of the concept of three independent germ layers of the embryo. He pointed out their gradual evolution, one from another, and likened differentiation in general to the use of toothpaste. "Hertig," he said, "when toothpaste is in the tube it is potentially usable, but when squeezed out it's good only for brushing your teeth." Also, in describing the early action of macaque trophoblast on maternal tissue, he stated that "trophoblast eats the maternal tissue as a person eats grapes, by sucking out the juice and spitting out the seeds." The accuracy of this comparison is somewhat debatable. Certainly, however, the early trophoblast of the monkey appears to do something analogous to Dr. Streeter's homely simile. Moreover, the early human trophoblast ingests and digests maternal tissue as I shall describe later in the text.

During this year of 1933-34, the brilliant and imaginative program of securing early primate (macaque) embryos was just getting well-started. Dr. Carl Hartman, affectionately dubbed "the monkey gynecologist" by his colleagues, was interested in reproductive physiology. Dr. Chester H. Heuser developed his elegant techniques for finding and preparing this uniquely precious material, while Dr. Streeter was in charge of the overall program. My first conversation with him typifies Dr. Streeter's innate modesty. In describing the small but distinguished group of research workers, he said, "Lewis looks after the tissue culture, Metz the genetics, Hartman the physiology and Heuser and I see to the embryology." The professional competence of this group was equally matched by the outstanding skills of several technical associates. The late James F. Didusch was a superb artist. (He later succeeded Max Brödel as professor of art in medicine at Johns Hopkins.) Moreover, he was an excellent embryologist. He refused to draw a histologic detail on the surface of a three-dimensional reconstruction unless he was personally convinced, from examination of the tissue sections, that the cells were as represented by the scientist for whom he was drawing the picture. After all, he said simply, "I sign my name to the picture, don't I?"

Mr. Chester H. Reather, now heading the photographic department at the Johns Hopkins Hospital, was a master photographer. His skills are amply demonstrated in the pictures of Carnegie origin.

Mr. Osborne O. Heard,[35] in charge of the modeling and photography of serial sections, was a superb artisan in wood and metal. He was trained as a pattern maker and so was able to help design and make the unique stereo camera used in the photography of the embryos. Some examples of the beautiful gross specimens originally photographed stereoscopically under fluid are to be seen in the text.

I describe the general atmosphere of the Carnegie Laboratory of Embryology and its staff since it and they are wholly responsible for my early and continuing interest in trophoblast. Therefore, I pay tribute now to that original staff and to those persons who came later: Dr. George W. Corner who succeeded Dr. Streeter as director and to Dr. James D. Ebert, who in turn succeeded Dr. Corner. Without their stimulation, encouragement, and help this lecture would not have been given nor this monograph written.

The determination to find early stages of human pregnancy stems from this contact with the original group in Baltimore. In studying angiogenesis of early human chorions, I was impressed by the paucity of material even in that magnificent world-famous collection. The opportunity to search for and find a series of such conceptuses was implemented in 1938 after completing twenty months of clinical obstetrical training under Dr. Irving. At that time, I became pathologist to the Free Hospital for Women where my former teacher in obstetrics, John Rock, was busily pursuing his broad researches on human reproduction. We had started a program of searching for early human embryos upon my return from Baltimore in 1934, but this was not wholly successful. We did, with the late Dr. Gregory Pincus' help, learn something of the difficulties of finding preimplantation stages of human embryos, and we practiced the techniques taught me by Dr. Heuser. Particularly, did we learn that there are many artifactitious objects of maternal origin that mimic, at least so it seemed to us inexperienced observers, a human morula or blastula.

At this point, in connection with the recognition of early conceptuses, I am reminded of the colorful and dynamic Carl Hartman, then of the Carnegie staff, to whom I referred earlier. Quite pointedly, referring to an artifact that looked like monkey ovum, he said, "If there's any doubt about it, 'tain't an egg!"

This wise aphorism was to be borne out many times in our long search for early human beings of two weeks of age or younger. (It can also be applied to general pathologic diagnoses.)

It now becomes clear that as pathologist of two women's hospitals, the Boston Lying-in Hospital devoted to obstetrics and the Free Hospital for Women devoted to elective gynecology, my initial interest in trophoblast grew to the point of justifying it as a subject for the Ninth Weller Lecture.

Much of what I have to say concerns *normal* trophoblast; this requires no apology. The pathologist uses and contributes to normal anatomy constantly. It is well recognized that an infinite number of subtle and not so subtle gradations between the normal and the abnormal exist. The appreciation of these gradations is what, to me, makes pathology fun. The mere diagnosis of a tissue lesion, although satisfying, does not complete the spectrum of satisfaction in pathology. Dr. Wolbach, in gently deprecating some pathologist, used to say, "Oh, he is content to put a name on a condition and then forget about it."

This lecture, along with the associated monograph, is in no sense a complete treatise on trophoblast and its many ramifications into pathology, histology, physiology, and endocrinology. It merely represents the highlights of my own personal experience, or that of my closely associated colleagues, with this interesting tissue. It is, however, a summary of trophoblast by and for pathologists. What is to follow has already been published elsewhere but usually not in the literature customarily read by or available to pathologists. In a very real sense, the title and subject might just as well be "Afterthoughts on the Afterbirth" or "Thirty Years at the Bedside of the Placenta."

CHAPTER II

HISTORICAL REVIEW

TROPHOBLAST (Fig. 1) is derived and defined by Skinner[127] in his *Origin of Medical Terms* as follows: "Greek τροφή, nourishment plus βλαστός, germ or sprout. The forerunner of the placenta or nourishing organ of the embryo. The name was given to this embryonic formation by Hubrecht in 1889." Actually, Hubrecht first used this term in 1888[74] and thereafter elaborated upon its significance, development, and phylogeny in a series of papers, the first and last of which, published in 1889[75] and 1895[76] respectively, are germane to trophoblast. The first is in English and the second in German.

Because of the historical interest in, and early understanding of, this remarkable tissue, it seems worthwhile to quote what Hubrecht actually said about trophoblast in 1888[74] when he used this term for the first time before the Anatomical Society of Würtzburg. He said:

Die äussere Wand der Keimblase ist verdickt (drei- bis vierschich-

TROPHOBLAST

τροφή = nourishment
βλαστός = germ

FIGURE 1. A graphic representation of the Greek derivation of the term *trophoblast*. The latter refers to a composite tissue and not to a specific type of trophoblastic cell, of which there are several. I am indebted to Dr. George Diamandopoulos, Department of Pathology, Harvard Medical School, for the proper Greek roots from which the term, trophoblast, is derived.

tig) und besitzt wabige Lacunen. Für diese äussere (epiblastische) Schicht sei der Name Trophoblast gewählt).

Translated, this says, "The outer shell of the blastocyst is thickened (three to four layered) and possesses honeycombed lacunae. For this outer shell (epiblastic) the name trophoblast may be chosen."

The footnote at the bottom of page 511 then goes on to say,

1) Es ist meiner Ausicht nach zweckmässig, sich bei der Säuge-tier-embryologie diesen Namen zu wählen, um damit den nicht zum Aufbau des Embryos verwendeten Epiblast auzudeuten. Das, was man bis jetzt als REICHERT'sche und RAUBER'sche Zellen, als Träger, als Deckschicht, Ektodermwulst, Hufeisenwucherung etc. angedeutet hat, wäre alles, weil dem peripherischen Epiblast der Keimblase angehörend, zum Trophoblast zu rechnen. Sogar beim Opossum beschreibt SELENKA Wucherunger der epiblastischen Keim-blasenwand. Die Rolle dieses nicht formativen Epiblastes spielt sich also in erster Linie bei der Nahrungszufuhr zum Embryo ab, weshalb der Name Trophoblast gewählt wurde.

Translated, this says, "In my opinion it is practical to choose this name concerning mammalian embryology, in order to indi-cate the epiblast which is not used for the building up of the embryo. That which until now has been designated as Reichert's and Rauber's cells, as carriers, as the upper layer, as the ecto-dermal pad, as the horseshoe-shaped growth etc., all would be counted as being part of the trophoblast. Even in the case of the opossum, Selenka describes growth of the epiblastic shell. The part of this nonformative epiblast primarily consists in helping to supply the embryo with nourishment; that is why the name TROPHOBLAST had (has) been chosen."

The interested reader is referred to Hubrecht's 1889 paper in English on page 392 for details of the placental nomenclature used by various embryologists prior to that time.[75] The references to these earlier classic scholars go back to 1827 to the writings of Von Baer.[2] (The late Dr. George L. Streeter once told me that Von Baer was the first embryologist to discover in the dog the recently ovulated mammalian oocyte or unfertilized egg. Dr. Streeter went on to say with a twinkle in his eye that that was about the time the Baltimore and Ohio Railroad was built.)

The interested reader is also referred to the following extensive writings, reviews, and symposia on the placenta: Grosser's classic monograph[31] published in 1927; the book on the placenta and its membranes edited by Villee,[143] which followed a conference in November of 1958 and which contains eight formal papers, the transcript of the conference, and 2,700 pertinent references; the proceedings of the three Rochester conferences[88-90] on trophoblast held in 1961, 1963, and 1965 respectively and edited by Lund and Thiede; and the symposium[111] on the placenta edited by Plentl.

The reader is particularly referred to the classic placental papers of the late George B. Wislocki, one of the great comparative placentologists of all time. The four papers worthy of review are as follows: the one written on the development of the monkey placenta,[151] the one with Bennett on the histology and cytology of human and monkey trophoblast,[148] the one on electron microscopy of the human placenta written with Dempsey,[149] and the one on histochemistry written with Padykula.[150] The most recent text is the superb "Pathology of the Human Placenta" by Benirschke and Driscoll.[6]

Within these writings, the reader can find all that there is to be known at present about trophoblast and its definitive organ, the placenta. The subjects range from comparative placentology by Amoroso, through primate trophoblastic development and/or pathology by Hertig and Benirschke, to immunologic aspects by various authors including Billingham, Simmons, and Schlesinger. The reader is advised, if interested, to peruse the proceedings of the Third Rochester Trophoblast Conference and to work backward, in time, through the other references cited.

Again, it should be stressed that the present monograph is neither an exhaustive treatise on human placental trophoblast nor a review of its extensive literature. Rather, it highlights the author's interest in this organ against his background as a pathologist at the Boston Lying-in Hospital and as searcher for early human embryos at the Free Hospital for Women.

CHAPTER III

ORIGIN OF TROPHOBLAST

A DEFINITION of trophoblast in *Dorland's Illustrated Medical Dictionary*[23] is as follows: "A layer of extra-embryonic ectodermal tissue on the outside of the blastodermic vesicle. It attaches the ovum to the uterine wall and supplies nutrition to the embryo. The inner cellular layer of the trophoblast is called *cytotrophoblast* and its outer syncytial layer *syntrophoblast*." (Syncytiotrophoblast is older and, in the author's opinion, more acceptable in its usage.)

It is evident that there are at least two main types of trophoblast. Therefore it is incorrect to refer to either type of trophoblastic cell as "a trophoblast," when used in the sense of "a fibroblast," since the tissue, by definition and function, is a composite one. The author realizes that he is fighting a losing battle about "trophoblasts" since his colleagues persist in misusing the term. Actually the cytotrophoblast gives rise to or differentiates into a number of quite different tissues such as syncytiotrophoblast as well as all of the auxiliary supporting tissues of the placenta.

Thus, trophoblast is a multipotential tissue. It gives rise, by *in situ* delamination from primitive cytotrophoblast, to placental connective tissues (mesoblast), blood vessels, and amniotic epithelium. The primitive mesoblastic or fibroblastic tissue in turn forms the primary and definitive yolk sacs, exclusive of the endodermal portion of the germ disk. It also contributes largely, if not wholly, to the mesenchyme or connective tissue of the body stalk or umbilical cord. The definitive epithelium of the immature placenta further differentiates into several other epithelial structures. The cytotrophoblast forms the Langhans' epithelium of the villus and its cell column together with the basal plate or "floor" of the placenta. These structures serve to anchor or attach the placenta to the maternal *decidua basalis*. The syncytiotrophoblast gives rise to syncytium which covers the villi or, conversely, lines the intervillous space. Both epithelial elements appear to contribute to the giant cells of the placental site. All of these derivatives of the trophoblast are well formed or forming by the time the true mesoderm, the third germ layer of the embryonic disk, has begun to form during the fourteenth to fifteenth days of development. These relationships explain why some blighted or pathologic ova (abortuses) contain no embryonic derivative and yet have all or many of the definitive structures of purely trophoblastic origin. This aspect of trophoblastic differentiation will be considered in Chapter IV, Differentiation of Trophoblast.

Trophoblast is the first definitive tissue to be recognizable in the segmenting mammalian ovum. Although it is possible that the first cleavage results in the formation of blastomeres of trophoblastic and embryonic potential respectively, present data do not prove it. O. van der Stricht, quoting Lams,[83] gives some morphologic evidence in the early fertilized ovum of the guinea pig that the cytoplasm of one blastomere, following the first cleavage, is wholly male and the other wholly female. This concept would seem logical in view of the fact that the trophoblast, possibly derived from one of the two blastomeres following the first cleavage, should be of pure female constitution since it is, in the mouse, for some time immunologically incompetent.[83, 138]

O. van der Stricht[138] says:

Persistance de la queue du spermatozoïde dans un des deux premiers blastomères.—La persistance de cette queue présente une grande importance. Cet élément, substratum des mitochondries et du cytoplasme mâles, se désagrège exclusivement dans l'ooplasme d'une des deux sphères de segmentation. Comme le dit LAMS (13) on peut considérer cette cellule "comme entièrement mâle et femelle, tandis que le cytoplasme de l'autre est resté exclusivement femelle." Depuis de nombreuses années, je définis, dans mon cours d'embryologie, la fécondation des oeufs des mammifères, en prenant pour type ceux de chauve-souris et de cobaye, en disant qu'elle se passe en deux temps. Lors de la période de fécondation proprement dite s'opère la conjugaison des pronucléus et plus tard, dans le blastomère contenant la queue du germe mâle, s'opère le mélange des mitochondries paternelles et maternelles. Si les recherches de Ed. Van Beneden sont exactes, au suject de la formation chez la lapine de son "endoderme," le feuillet embryonnaire proprement dit, aux dépens du "plus petit blastomère" et de la genèse de son "feuillet externe," aux dépens du plus grand, qui se divise le plus rapidement, il est logique d'admettre pour la chauve-souris une évolution semblable pour les deux premières sphères de segmentation. L'une, à vitellus exclusivement femelle, engendrerait le feuillet externe du blastocyste (27, p. 76) "l'ectoblaste placentaire," l'autre, entièrement fécondée, une "masse interne ou feuillet interne primitif, correspondant à l'ébauche du feuillet externe définitif ou de l'ectoblaste définitif proprement dit et du feuillet interne" de l'embryon.

Freely translated, this means: The persistence of the (sperm) tail is of importance. This element, substratum of the mitochondria and of male cytoplasm, disaggregates exclusively in the ooplasm of one of the two spheres of segmentation. As LAMS has said (13), one can consider this cell "as entirely male and female, while the cytoplasm of the other remains exclusively female." For several years, I described, in my course of embryology, the fertilization of the eggs of mammals, taking as type specimens those of the bat and guinea pig, saying that they took place in two stages. At the time of fertilization, strictly speaking, the conjugation of the pronucleus occurs and then later, in the blastomere containing the tail of the male germ cell, the mixing

$\rightarrow$

FIGURE 2. *(Upper)* The living ovum recovered from the fallopian tube and photographed under phase microscopy after adding a few drops of hyaluronidase (150 units/ml) to the saline used in flushing the tube. The vertically oriented sperm tail is seen to the right, just below a centrosome. The two pronuclei, one slightly smaller than the other, are seen above a plane slightly above that made by the two centrosomes. The zona pellucida and few remaining granulosa cells are readily seen ($\times$ 600, approximately).

FIGURE 3. *(Lower)* The two pronuclei from the same specimen as shown in Fig. 2 but after fixation in Lacmoid® (resorcinol blue). Note unequal size of pronuclei, the smaller presumably the male. Note also the sperm tail between the two pronuclei but slightly nearer the smaller one. ($\times$ 1500. The apparent discrepancy in magnification is due to some shrinkage in the fixed preparation.)

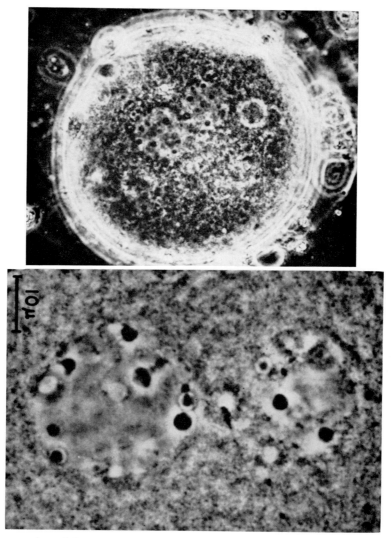

FIGURES 2 and 3 represent the earliest stage of human development thus far observed, the pronuclear ovum. Published by Noyes *et al.*[105] (Courtesy Dr. R. W. Noyes, and American Association for the Advancement of Science.)

FIGURE 4. *(Upper)* This legend is a direct quotation from Heuser and Streeter,[70] 1929: "Fig. 6. Wax-plate models of the pig egg showing the formation of the segmentation cavity and the differentiations of the trophoblast (stippled). The dark cells represent the more primitive part of the egg, and what is finally left of this material becomes the inner cell-mass and germ-disk. The distribution of color in eggs a-c is only introduced tentatively, for there is no reliable way for distinguishing trophoblast cells at that time. The eggs from which these models were reconstructed ($\times$ 400) are as follows: a, 286-3; b, 288-B; c, 288-A; d, 281-1; e, 281-3; f, 281-4; g, 284-6; h, 284-8, and i, 291-5." In this reproduction, magnification is about 270 diameters. Previously published by Heuser and Streeter.[70] (Courtesy of Carnegie Institution of Washington.)

FIGURE 5. *(Center left)* An intact monkey blastocyst as viewed by transmitted light. This specimen is 9 days of age and represents one of the four immediate preimplantation stages of the primate blastocyst in existence. Note eccentrically placed, dark, inner cell mass (embryo) and thickened cells of the polar trophoblast. The thin, mesothelial-like trophoblastic cells of the blastocyst wall are easily seen. See Figs. 6 and 12 for histologic details. Carnegie No. C-522, $\times$ 160. Published originally by Heuser and Streeter.[71] (Courtesy of Carnegie Institution of Washington.)

FIGURE 6. *(Lower right)* A microscopic section of a 9-day implantation stage of the monkey blastocyst, the gross of which was seen in Fig. 5. Note inner cell mass with primitive endoderm, the thickened polar trophoblast at the embryonic pole, and the thinner trophoblast elsewhere. Higher-power details of embryonic (implantation) pole may be seen in Fig. 12. Carnegie No. C-522, $\times$ 300. Compare with slightly younger human preimplantation blastocyst in Figs. 7 and 11. Published originally by Heuser and Streeter.[71] (Courtesy of Carnegie Institution of Washington.)

FIGURE 7. *(Lower left)* An intact 107-cell human blastocyst (4½ days' developmental age) photographed by transmitted light. Note, as in the monkey blastocyst, the inner cell mass, thickened polar trophoblast, and the thin trophoblast elsewhere. Carnegie No. 8663, sequence 1, $\times$ 300. For histological details see Fig. 11. Published originally by Hertig *et al.*[62] (Courtesy of Carnegie Institution of Washington.)

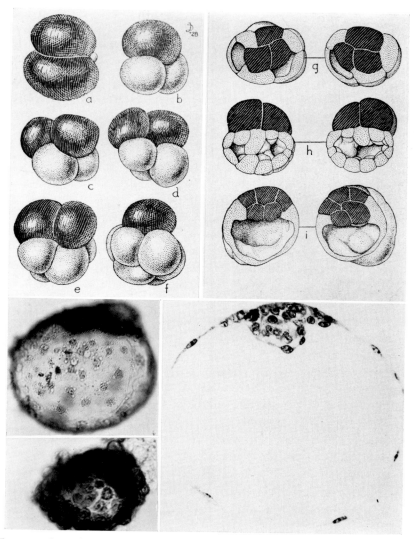

FIGURES 4 to 7 represent segmenting eggs of the pig, monkey and man.

of paternal and maternal mitochondria takes place. If the researches of Van Beneden on the subject of the formation of the endoderm of the rabbit are accurate, the germ layer, strictly speaking, depends on the smaller blastomere; the formation of the external layers depends on the larger which divides more rapidly. It is logical to admit a similar evolution of the first two segmentation blastomeres in the bat. One, exclusively female, forms the external layer of blastocyst, the ectoblast of placenta; the other, completely fertilized, forms an internal primitive germ layer or the ectoblast of the embryo.

It is of interest that Noyes and associates[105, 22] have recently (1965) published the earliest stage of the human fertilized ovum, one in the pronuclear phase. This critical stage is seen in Figures 2 and 3. The sperm tail is seen in both figures, the living and the fixed ovum respectively.

It has long been recognized morphologically that there has been little, if any, maternal cellular reaction to the presence of normal placental trophoblast. That the placenta is generally tolerated by the mother for nine months has been known for as long as man has understood anything about gestation. That it is a homograft, however, and yet is not rejected is a fairly modern concept. The immunological reasons why the placenta is well tolerated for a gestational period of nine months is under investigation in many laboratories at the present time.[125, 126] The interested reader is referred to the proceedings of the Second Rochester Trophoblast Conference, held in 1963, for data on this important aspect of placental biology.

Heuser and Streeter, in their classic monograph on the early stages of the pig embryo, published in 1929,[70] show that trophoblast is morphologically identifiable by the sixteen-cell stage. The blastocyst is then just over four days of age and is beginning to form a segmentation cavity. Thus, the trophoblast is the first definitive tissue; the segmentation cavity, the anlage of the extraembryonic coelom or chorionic cavity, is the first definitive structure formed by that tissue. This fundamental concept is shown in Figure 4 (Fig. 6 in the monograph of Heuser and Streeter).

These authors, in discussing on page 15[70] the early segmentation of pig eggs, say:

> The outstanding feature in the cleavage of the pig egg is the disparity in the volume that soon shows itself in the component cells, and correlated with this is a definite difference in rate of subdivision of different parts of the egg, the part that is to be trophoblast undergoing more precocious subdivision than the part that will form the embryo. This difference in cleavage rate is the only obvious sign of localization of special substances and qualities in egg cytoplasm. The sorting-out of the special substances may very well be the explanation of the disparity in size that is so noticeable in the "halves" with each cell division. (The reader will recall that O. van der Stricht[138] cites the observations of Beneden on segmenting rabbit eggs showing that the embryo comes from the smaller blastomere.)

Such inequality of the "halves" is shown by volumetric data from one of their eight-cell eggs (No. 284-9), the eight-cell components constituting 31, 18, 16, 11, 11, 5, 4, and 4 per cent respectively. These changes are beautifully shown in my Figure 4, although the specific egg (284-9) is not in that drawing of the several eggs reconstructed by the classic wax-plate method of embryologists. Subfigures g and h, however, are reconstructions of five other late morulae (early blastulae) from the same litter whose fertilization age was four days, three and one-half hours. The data of the nine segmenting pig eggs shown in Figure 4 (a-i) are as follows in Table I.

The segmenting eggs of all mammals are of approximately

TABLE I

NUMBERS, STAGES, AND FERTILIZATION AGES OF PIG EGGS

No.	Stage	Fertilization Age
286	2-cell, tubal	2 days, 3½ hours
288	4-cell, uterine	3 days, 2 hours
281	6- to 8-cell, uterine	3 days, 18 hours
284	Morula, uterine	4 days, 3½ hours
291	Segmentation cavity, uterine	4 days, 18 hours

These pig eggs were reconstructed and are shown in Figure 4. Adapted from Heuser and Streeter's table.[70]

FIGURE 8. *(Upper left)* A two-cell stage found in the middle third of the fallopian tube about 60 hours after a single recorded coitus. From endometrial dating and degree of ovular development, the specimen is judged to be about 1½ days' developmental age. Note zona, artifactitiously broken, the unequal size and variation in shape of the two blastomeres, and the presence of the two polar bodies. This picture of the intact specimen was taken by transmitted light after Bouin's fixation and dehydration up to 70 per cent alcohol. It may be compared with the picture of the same specimen taken by phase contrast photomicrography in Fig. 9. Carnegie No. 8698, sequence 12, × 500.

FIGURE 9. *(Upper right)* The same two-cell human ovum as in Fig. 8 but photographed under phase microscopy. The few remaining granulosa cells of the corona radiata, the zona pellucida, and the two polar bodies are well visualized. The nuclei, however, are less distinct than in Fig. 8. The greater mass of the upper blastomere is well seen. Whether this is the one of trophoblastic potential is unknown but it is probable. Carnegie 8698, sequence 14, × 550.

FIGURE 10. *(Lower left)* A transpolar section, one of eleven in series, through a human morula of about 96 hours' developmental age found within the uterine cavity and possessing 58 cells: 5 embryonic and 53 trophoblastic. Note partially eroded zona, two polar bodies, early segmentation cavity, slightly eccentrically situated embryonic mass, and uniform nature of the polyhedral trophoblastic cells. Carnegie 8794, section 7, × 500.

FIGURE 11. *(Lower right)* A transpolar section, one of fifteen in series, through a human uterine blastocyst of 4½ days' developmental age and consisting of 107 cells: 8 embryonic and 99 trophoblastic. Note several types of cells in embryonic disk, which forms an integral part of the blastocyst wall. Compare the thin trophoblast of this preimplantation specimen with that of the thick, less well-differentiated trophoblast of the younger specimen in Fig. 10. Carnegie 8663, sect. 9, × 600.

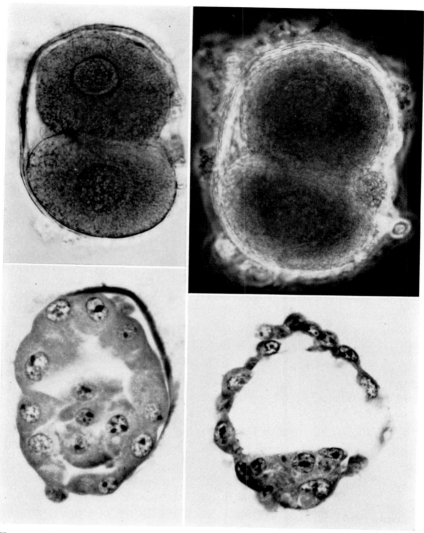

FIGURES 8 to 11 represent three segmenting human ova ranging from about 30 hours to 4½ days of age. All were originally published by Hertig *et al.*[62] (Courtesy of Carnegie Institution of Washington.)

the same size. The proportion of cellular components, time of disappearance of zona pellucida, time of implantation, et cetera are, in general, the same. All have a zona pellucida; all form trophoblast early, perhaps immediately with the first cleavage; all form a segmentation cavity; and all have an embryonic mass with primitive endoderm and potential ectoderm at the implantation (embryonic) pole during early implantation. Some stages of segmenting primate ova, the macaque monkey and man, comparable to those already mentioned for the pig, are seen in Figures 5 through 11.

In man (Figs. 8-11), the initial cleavage occurs in the tube some time between twenty-four and thirty hours after fertilization, as shown by the observations of Hertig and associates in 1954.[62] The two blastomeres, one presumably of trophoblastic potential, are of unequal size as we had been led to suspect from Heuser and Streeter's observations on the developing pig embryos. The larger blastomere, clearly seen in both Figures 8 and 9, probably will divide first and hence may well be the potential trophoblastic blastomere.

By the fourth day of development, the human ovum is within the uterine cavity as an early blastula or late morula. It consists of fifty-eight cells, of which five are of embryonic potential all morphologically identical and fifty-three are of trophoblastic potential as seen in Figure 10. The polar bodies are still present, and the zona pellucida is beginning to be eroded or dissolved. Although the inner cell mass has not yet assumed its polar position where it will act as a "bung" or plug in the blastocyst wall, the five embryonic cells are slightly eccentrically placed within the segmentation cavity. There is, as yet, no polar preimplantation trophoblast. All potentially trophoblastic cells are of a fairly uniform cuboidal or polyhedral nature about the periphery of this early blastocyst. If anything, the ones nearest the embryo are a trifle thinner than those elsewhere. Whether these thinner cells play a role in the erosion of the zona or whether the latter is due to maternal enzymatic action or other factors is not known. Suffice it to say that the human blastocyst at this stage is beginning to increase its diameter and cell population, especially with respect to its potential trophoblast.

Within the next twenty-four to thirty-six hours, the ovum has approximately doubled its number of potentially trophoblastic cells (99), has formed a respectable segmentation cavity, and has differentiated its germ disk as seen in Figure 11. The embryonic mass now has eight cells of three types: obvious primitive, vacuolated ectoderm; flattened primitive endoderm; and a large indifferent cell, presumably a germ cell. (It will be recalled that the mammalian germ cell does not arise in the gonad but is first recognized in the gut endoderm—Witschi,[152] McKay, Hertig *et al.*[96]

The potential trophoblast of this four-and-one-half-day preimplantation blastocyst consists of ninety-nine cells; most of them are somewhat thinned out, but those near the embryonic disk are somewhat thicker. The latter are designated as polar trophoblast to denote their proximity to the implantation or embryonic pole. It is this thickening and presumed differentiation of the polar trophoblast (possibly by induction from proximity to the embryonic mass and/or maternal epithelium) that undoubtedly plays a role in the implantation of the ovum. Although the embryo orients the ovum vis-à-vis its implantation pole—the embryonic mass being exposed—it is the polar trophoblast that actually secures the blastocyst to the endometrial or other mucosal or serosal surfaces. This process is called implantation and will be discussed more fully in Chapter IV. The interested reader is referred to the proceedings of the symposium on implantation held in Brussels in 1960.[27]

CHAPTER IV

DIFFERENTIATION OF TROPHOBLAST

A. MORPHOLOGIC OBSERVATIONS

THIS section will consist of morphologic observations on some of the Hertig-Rock early fertilized ova of seven to seventeen days' developmental age. Two specimens of eighteen and nineteen days will also be illustrated.

This Hertig-Rock material has all been published definitively over a period of years from 1941 to 1954. The individual descriptions of most of the specimens appear in five monographs of the Carnegie Contributions to Embryology (Nos. 184, 200, 201, 221, and 240).[54, 56, 69, 57, 62] A complete summary of the morphology, developmental ages, clinical histories, and interpretations of these thirty-four normal and abnormal specimens was published in 1956 as part of the Festschrift volume honoring Dr. George Washington Corner.[60] Various papers stressing clinical applications but using some of this same material have appeared in the clinical obstetrical and allied literature.[37, 41, 55, 58, 59, 61, 116] The histological and histochemical aspects of the corpora lutea associated with many of these specimens was published by White and associates in 1951.[145] The histologic correlation of the trophoblast, endometria, and corpora lutea was published by the author in 1964.[42]

The interested reader is referred to one of these published reports by Rock and Hertig in 1942[115] for details as to the operative surgical material from which these specimens were recovered at the Free Hospital for Women. The techniques by which the specimens were found are given in the 1944 reference.[55] Suffice it to say, over two hundred uteri were carefully searched during a sixteen-year period to find the thirty-four specimens: twenty-one ova being normal and thirteen abnormal. The tubes were routinely flushed, in the direction of normal tubal ovular transport, with physiological saline or Locke's solution. The uterus was bivalved through the bases of the broad ligaments, and the uterine cavity opened under this same type of fluid in order to recover unimplanted blastocysts or morulae. After bivalving the uterus in the frontal plane (see posterior uterine wall of specimen yielding a specimen of 7½ days, Fig. 15), each half of the uterine wall, with intact endometrium, was inspected under fluid before and after fixation in Bouin's solution. Specimens up to and including the eight-day stage were seen *only* after fixation, whereas all later stages were clearly evident prior to fixation due to their size with surrounding congestion and/or hemorrhage. Refer to Figures 26 and 27, the eleven-day specimen, as a good example of the gross appearance of an easily visible implantation site.

Unless the pathologist is very fortunate, the classic technique of opening a uterus by the Y-shaped or straight vertical incision will either damage the early implantation site or cause it to be obscured or even completely hidden. An example of a large, easily visible implantation site of about eighteen days, sent to the author in consultation, is to be seen in Figures 43 and 44. The anterior incision fortunately exposed the early ovum, but it could just as well have been hidden in either cornu or on the anterior uterine wall.

Whether pathologists are interested in early ova, per se, or not, it is their obligation to open all uteri carefully so as to expose the entire uterine mucosal surface. Early cancers of the endometrium, or other pathologic lesions thereof, are easily missed unless the uterus is carefully bivalved in the manner originally taught the author by the late Dr. Chester H. Heuser. He devised the technique in searching for early macaque monkey ova but neglected even to mention it, let alone describe its details, in the classic monograph of 1941 by him and Streeter.[71]

The author would like to admonish gently all pathologists of any age or experience not to rub or scrape mucosal surfaces of any organ, let alone the endometrium prior to fixation. It spoils any lesion, whether cancer or an early implanted ovum.

The material in this section of the chapter is represented by two specimens from the macaque monkey and nine of human

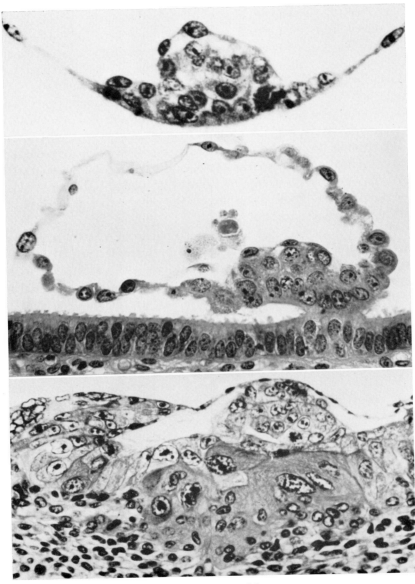

FIGURE 12 to 14

FIGURE 12. *(Upper)* The embryonic or implantation pole of a 9-day monkey blastocyst in its preimplantation stage. Note the two types of embryonic cells, endoderm and ectoderm, and the polar trophoblast. The latter covers the embryonic mass and shows a gradient of differentiation or development. Carnegie No. C-522, × 600. Adapted from Heuser and Streeter.[71] (Courtesy of Carnegie Institution of Washington.)

FIGURE 13. *(Center)* Recently implanted 9-day blastocyst of a macaque monkey. Note the one point of contact or implantation to the right of the embryonic mass. The cytoplasm of the maternal epithelium and newly coalesced syncytiotrophoblast are now homogenous. The embryonic disk is exposed, and the polar trophoblast merges gradually into that of the remaining blastocyst wall. Carnegie No. C-560, section 2-4-4, × 500. Previously published by Heuser and Streeter.[71] (Courtesy of Carnegie Institution of Washington.)

FIGURE 14. *(Lower)* A well-, but recently (36 hrs), implanted human blastocyst of about 7½ days' developmental age. Note gradient of trophoblastic development and differentiation from thin blastocyst wall (exposed) to a thick plaque (attached) showing an admixture of primitive dark syncytiotrophoblastic and light cytotrophoblastic cells. The embryo has induced amniogenesis in the immediately adjacent cytotrophoblast. Note further the edematous endometrial stroma and lack of cellular response. For better orientation at lower power, see Fig. 17. Gross views and reconstructions of this specimen are seen in Figs. 15, 16, and 18, 19 respectively. Carnegie No. 8020, section 6-5-9, F.H.W. S-42-908, × 333. Previously published by Rock and Hertig.[115] (Courtesy of the C. V. Mosby Company, and Carnegie Institution of Washington.)

FIGURE 15. *(Upper left)* The posterior half of a human uterus opened by Heuser's bivalve technique and photographed in 70% alcohol after Bouin's fixation. Some of the submucosal myometrium has been removed, leaving a slab of endomyometrium about 6 to 7 mm thick. The 7½-day implantation site is barely perceptible at the right branch of the Y-shaped furrow (arrow). Carnegie No. 8020, sequence 2, F.H.W. S-42-908, natural size. Other views of this specimen are seen in Figs. 14, 16, 17, 18, and 19.

FIGURE 16. *(Upper right)* Recently implanted (36 hrs) human blastocyst. The opaque embryonic mass is in the center, surrounded by the double, folded layer of developing trophoblast. The circumvallate pits are mouths of uterine glands. The endometrial surface shows early normal wrinkling or furrowing. Carnegie No. 8020, sequence 6, F.H.W. S-42-908, × 35. Previously published by Hertig and Rock.[55] (Courtesy of the C. V. Mosby Company, and Carnegie Institution of Washington.)

FIGURE 17. *(Lower)* A medium-power photomicrograph of human ovum of 7½ days shows superficial implantation, primitive solid trophoblast, edematous endometrium without leukocytic infiltration, and beginning regeneration of surface epithelium of endometrium. A higher-power detail of the histology may be seen in Fig. 14 and its reconstructed form in Figs. 18 and 19. The dilated gland, due to surface blockage, is common in this age (38 yrs) and is unassociated with the implantation of the ovum. Carnegie No. 8020, F.H.W., section 6-5-9, F.H.W. S-42-908, × 175. Previously published by Rock and Hertig.[115] (Courtesy of the C. V. Mosby Company, and Carnegie Institution of Washington.)

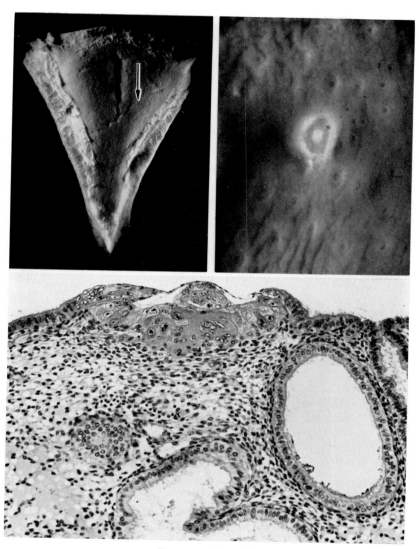

FIGURES 15 to 17

origin. The two monkey ova (Figs. 12 and 13) represent the immediate preimplantation and postimplantation stages of the blastocyst since comparable human material has never been reported by any investigator. The monkey, paradoxically, implants three days later than the human being, although its gestation is three months shorter. The human material ranged from the blastocyst of seven and one-half days, implanted about thirty-six hours, to the conceptus of about nineteen days, or five days after the first missed menstrual period (Figs. 14-47).

As a general note, in orienting these specimens, the mucosal surface of the endometrium is uppermost. The only exceptions are in those specimens whose reconstructions (Figs. 18, 19, 21 and 34), already labeled by Mr. James F. Didusch, are oriented in the opposite direction. The embryologist prefers to orient all specimens so that the ectoderm is uppermost, thus making the endometrium "upside down" as far as the pathologist is concerned. Hence apologies are due to both embryologists and pathologists who chance to read this lecture monograph.

It should be noted further that all Carnegie tissue sections were fixed in Bouin's, dehydrated in the usual manner, embedded by the double celloidin-paraffin technique, cut serially on a

→

FIGURE 18. *(Upper)* A plastic reconstruction of half of the ovum of 7½ days shown in Figs. 14 to 17. This is drawn to show the vascular pattern of the endometrium, the irregular lobulated outer surface of the solid plaque of trophoblast, and the external contour of the endometrial glands. Carnegie No. 8020, F.H.W. S-42-908, × 250. The cut surface of the same specimen in mid-cross section is seen in Fig. 19. Previously published by Hertig and Rock.[56] (Courtesy of Carnegie Institution of Washington.)

FIGURE 19. *(Lower)* The vertically cut surface of the implantation site and ovum of a 7½-day human gestation as reconstructed by the plastic or glass-plate method. The ovum is drawn so as to orient the ectoderm dorsally and the endoderm ventrally. The solid plaque of primitive trophoblast is stippled, as are the cut surfaces of glandular epithelium. The surface epithelium is represented by parallel lines. The maternal vessels stand out in bold relief as though the endometrial stroma had been digested away from an injection-corrosion specimen. Carnegie No. 8020, F.H.W. S-42-908, × 250. Previously published by Hertig and Rock.[56] (Courtesy of Carnegie Institution of Washington.)

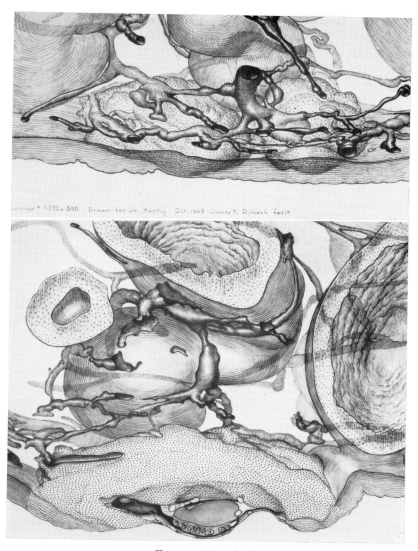

FIGURES 18 and 19

sliding microtome, and stained by hematoxylin and eosin. All gross specimens were photographed under 70 per cent alcohol by the stereo camera designed and made at the Carnegie Institution of Washington's Department of Embryology in Baltimore. This instrument was first illustrated in Heuser and Streeter's 1929 monograph.[70]

Mr. O. O. Heard, long-time modeler and machinist in that laboratory, helped in the design and execution of the several models of that camera.[35] He has published a fine paper on the techniques designed and used by the late Dr. Heuser during his long tenure in that laboratory. Mr. Heard played a significant role in the execution of Heuser's design of the instrument or technique in question.

All reconstructions (Figs. 18, 19, 21, 28, and 34) were made by the so-called plastic- or glass-plate method by Miss Eleanor C. Adams. Simply stated, this classic technique of the embryologist requires a perfect series of serial sections. Each section is oriented to its two contiguous sections by the three-point principle. The glass (or wax) plate then has transferred to it the object to be reconstructed; a drawing is made on the glass or the object is cut out of the wax plate. Two of the edges of the plate at right angles coincide with the two orienting lines on the series of serial photographs or camera lucida drawings. Thus when the plates are stacked together in proper orientation, the series of serial sections produces a three-dimensional model. The medical artist, the late Mr. James F. Didusch, made all of the superb drawings here used.

An amusing anecdote may be told about the reconstruction (such a drawing is not a DIAGRAM—as was once stated by an embryological colleague who should have known better) shown in Figure 19. This appeared in the January 29, 1945 issue of *Time*[87] with the following caption: "The embryo proper is the irregularly shaped kernel in the oval sac at the top (cut in half by the edge of the picture). The rest of the drawing is devoted to the bulbous, contorted uterine glands and sections of blood vessels developing to nourish the embryo." Mr. Didusch was justifiably put out that his unique artistry should have had such inaccurate reporting—even if by a lay press. Although the author has been a long time subscriber to *Time,* he has not, since 1945, necessarily believed that all of its writings are infallible!

Implantation, Early, Superficial

The general, low-power gross and microscopic features of the preimplantation monkey blastocyst have been seen in Figures 5 and 6, Chapter III. At somewhat higher magnification, the future implantation pole (Fig. 12) shows clearly the inner cell (embryonic) mass consisting of two types of cells: the primitive flattened endoderm facing the segmentation cavity, and the potential or primitive ectoderm lying between the endoderm and polar trophoblast. Two morphologically different types of potential trophoblast are evident: the thin mesothelial type away from the implantation pole which forms most of the blastocyst wall, and the somewhat thickened polar type which covers and blends with the cells of the embryonic mass. Mitosis may be seen in either type of trophoblast.

At, or soon after implantation, the embryonic mass is exposed and acts as a plug or "bung" in the blastocyst wall as seen in Figure 13. The gradient of differentiation or transformation of nonpolar into polar trophoblast is accentuated as compared to the free blastocyst. Nearly all of the trophoblastic cells surrounding the embryonic mass show varying stages of this transformation, or about one fourth to one third of all trophoblastic cells. This is probably due to inductive forces lying within the embryo, although proximity to the endometrial surface cannot be ruled out as a factor. It would appear from Figure 13 that, at the instant of implantation, the few polar trophoblastic cells fuse or lose their cytoplasmic identity and simultaneously fuse with the cytoplasm of the endometrial epithelium. In this way the blastocyst becomes adherent to and inextricably mixed with the mother's tissue. (There is histological and histochemical evidence that syncytiotrophoblast continues to ingest and digest maternal tissues as it becomes further implanted. The reader is referred to the author's detailed observations on the thirteen-day human ovum studies published in 1958,[47] although pertinent illustrations from this study will appear in the latter part of the present chapter.)

Of the three primate blastocysts available for study of the process of implantation, the earliest (Carnegie C-560) is here illustrated in Figure 13. The other two (C-520 and C-610), not illustrated, are somewhat later, but are all of eight to nine days' developmental age. As implantation progresses, more and more foci of syncytiotrophoblast develop and simultaneous fusion with the maternal tissue takes place. By graphic reconstruction of these three specimens, Heuser and Streeter[71] showed that the implantation poles possess one, six, and nine foci, respectively, of attachment such as the one illustrated in Figure 13.

The monkey and the human blastocysts collapse at or just before implantation, as does a toy balloon when pricked by a pin. Subsequently they become redistended. The macaque monkey blastocyst remains within the uterine cavity forming two placentas, whereas the human and chimpanzee become interstitially implanted and form placental tissue about the entire periphery. The initial collapse of the human blastocyst during implantation is well shown in Figures 14 and 19, whereas its redistention, interstitial type of implantation, and peripheral trophoblastic development are well illustrated in stages beyond the eight-day one shown in Figure 22.

The monkey blastocyst (C-610), not here illustrated, shows beautifully that the initial syncytiotrophoblast, formed from the coalescence of polar trophoblast, continues to be added to by subsequently developing trophoblast now designated as cytotrophoblast. In the human, there had been no clear-cut morphologic evidence of the derivation or origin of syncytiotrophoblast until Tao,[140] working in the author's laboratory, showed by organ culture methods that syncytiotrophoblast was derived from cytotrophoblast epithelium. Reference, with illustrations, will be made to this matter later in this chapter, section C.

It must be emphasized at this point that the human and the macaque monkey blastocysts, and inferentially those of other primates, implant on edematous, nondeciduous endometrium. In man, this takes place on day 20 of the classic menstrual cycle of twenty-eight days. At this time, the blastocyst is about six days of age or is in its seventh day of development. The glands have largely finished their secreting, apparently of functional use in the development of the preimplantation morula and blastula. (The fertilized ovum reaches the uterine cavity when it is a morula of 12 cells or when it is about three days of age, as shown by Hertig and associates in 1954.) The estrogen and progesterone levels have their respective peaks during the secretory phase of the cycle. The edema of the stroma is presumably associated with the known fact that estrogenic substances cause an increase in wet weight of the rodent uterus, presumably mediated through capillaries made more permeable by estrogen. Whether the juicy endometrium of the implantation stage in man makes implantation "easier" is of course unknown. The author, being a teleologist, likes to think so.

Holden, in 1939,[72] first suggested that the imbibition of water results from vasodilatation and from changes in the permeability of the walls of the blood vessels in the uterus. This theory has been modified by Spaziani and Szego,[129] who believe that estrogens induce the local release of histamine or histamine-like substances in the rat uterus and that these substances alter the permeability of blood vessels and secondarily produce vasodilation and edema.

Cole, in 1950,[14] suggested that water imbibition is due to increase of osmotically active groups from within the uterine tissue following estrogenic stimulation. But no osmotically active units have been identified.

Kalman, in 1955,[79] suggested that estrogens increase uterine permeability based on adsorption data using I^{131}-labeled albumin.

The mechanisms of implantation have interested a great many embryologists, physiologists, and chemists over the years. Whole symposia have been devoted to the subject. The author has participated in two during 1958 and 1960. His contribution to the first one, held as a part of the West Point Conference on "Mechanisms Concerned with Conception," may be read in Chapter VII of the volume of the same name, edited by Dr. Carl G. Hartman, a leading scholar in the physiology of reproduction.[34]

That part of the conference devoted to implantation (Chapter VII) had as its chairman Dr. Bent G. Böving, a leading scholar of the subject. His own classic work on the rabbit is well worth reading since it gives in detail all that is known about the mechanisms of rabbit blastocyst implantation. There is, moreover, a superb set of references.

With respect to implantation in general, the interested reader is urged to peruse Chapter VII which summarizes all that was known about mammalian implantation up to the time of the conference in 1958 and during the following five years when the proceedings were being prepared. A few facts are cited from this chapter to give the pathologist-reader an idea of the complexity of implantation mechanisms. On page 331, regarding rabbit blastocyst implantation, it says, "whereas progesterone (P) is required by many of the components and thus is a general prerequisite for implantation, it is the interplay of mechanisms that explains the consistent orderliness of the implantation process." It goes on to cite illustrative details of the above statement:

1. Five to seven days after mating as a consequence of progesterone action, the blastocyst enlarges rapidly.

2. The distention of each blastocyst stimulates the progesterone-dominated uterus to contract, and waves of contraction move neighboring blastocysts as far away as possible, thus resulting in even spacing.

3. Continued progesterone-dependent expansion of the blastocyst makes it too big to move, it being then "grasped" and rotated.

4. Seven days after mating, progesterone-dependent increase of *endometrial carbonic anhydrase* accelerates CO_2-removal by way of accessible maternal vessels and thereby causes a *rise of pH locally over those vessels*. This in turn influences the orientation of the blastocyst, its adhesion and the simultaneous loss of cohesion in uterine epithelial cells over these vessels thereby allowing trophoblastic knobs to penetrate and spread.

In contrast, decidualization is necessary in the rat *prior* to implantation; in man and guinea pig, it forms after implantation. Thus on page 377 of Chapter VII, Shelesnyak, the leading scholar of the subject, without insisting that histamine is the stimulus supplied by the rat blastocyst, considers that histamine is somehow involved in the decidual reaction. The general hypothesis of implantation based on mechanisms of rat decidualization holds that

1. Progesterone domination of pregnancy is briefly interrupted by an "estrogen surge" in the rat at four to five days.
2. The histamine released by the estrogen causes decidual transformation of stromal cells.
3. Lysis of such decidual cells occurs, without morphologic evidence, and makes a site receptive to phagocytic invasion by the trophoblast.

If the reader is conversant with French, the proceedings of the Brussels conference on implantation of 1960 may be of interest.[41] Many of the same investigators spoke at this conference as had spoken in 1958 at West Point. From what has been cited of that conference and from what the author has endeavored to say, the pathologist-reader will readily agree that implantation is a complicated process. That it is not completely understood is a gross understatement.

It is highly unlikely that endometrium is absolutely necessary in the human being, otherwise we would not see such pathological states as ovarian, tubal, cornual, abdominal, and cervicovaginal pregnancies. It seems to the author that the human egg implants at about six days, wherever it chances to be. If it never gets out of the ovary, then the fertilized egg finds its nest amid the debris of the ruptured graafian follicle and so on through other nonendometrial environments.

The crude analogy with the hand grenade has always seemed apropos to the author in thinking about implantation. When the pin is pulled by the soldier, he has about seven seconds to get rid of it. It matters not to the hand grenade whether it is still in the infantryman's hand, at the foot of one of his buddies, or in the enemy's foxhole (trench of earlier wars); it explodes about seven seconds after the pin has been pulled. The chemistry of the exploding hand grenade has been largely worked out, but the detailed chemistry of the implanting blastocyst awaits further study.

Returning to the simple facts as known about the earliest

human implantations, there are only two specimens in the entire world literature available for study. Both specimens (7½ days of age) are largely on the surface of the endometrium, measure 0.3 to 0.45 mm in diameter, and were discovered by the author *only* after Bouin's fixation of the endometrial surface. The gross and microscopic views of one specimen are seen in Figures 15 and 16, and Figures 14 and 17 respectively. The other, used later in this chapter to illustrate amniogenesis from trophoblast, is to be seen microscopically in Figure 68.

The trophoblast forms a solid plaque intimately attached to the edematous, nondeciduous endometrium. The predominating trophoblast is of primitive syncytial type. It is multinucleated and contains the large, anaplastic-appearing intrinsic nuclei together with the ingested and more or less digested nuclei of endometrial origin. There is a beautiful gradient of differentiation of tropho-blast from the thin mesothelial-like cell of the still free blastocyst wall, through the indifferent trophoblast of the polar type at the superficial maternal-ovular junction to the admixture of primitive cytotrophoblast and syncytiotrophoblast so well seen in Figures 14, 17, and 68.

Although mentioned before in Chapter II, it is worth empha-sizing again that there is no leukocytic cellular response to the presence of this invading tissue, nature's first "physiologic cancer."

The author has never seen incontrovertible evidence of the transition between cytotrophoblast and syncytiotrophoblast, al-though it must occur at this early stage. Suffice it to say, cyto-trophoblast and its more differentiated derivatives—Langhans' epithelium, cell islands, cell columns, and placental basal plate or "floor"—all undergo mitosis. The primitive syncytiotrophoblast and its definitive derivative, syncytium, however, never undergo mitosis. In retrospect, now that Tao[140, 142] has shown by H[3]-thymidine uptake and other morphologic studies how syncy-tiotrophoblast is derived from cytotrophoblast, it would be un-reasonable to expect mitoses to appear in syncytiotrophoblast, a differentiated tissue. For the same reason, it would be unreason-able to expect mitoses to appear in mature squamous epitheliel cells, although evidence of such growth is seen in basal cells as a matter of course!

Implantation, Later, Interstitial

The beginning of this phase coincides with the ninth day of development when the ovum is eight days old (Figs. 20-22). It lies barely beneath the surface of the endometrium: impossible to discern in the fresh, and probably often unrecognizable even after fixation. That this is true is shown by the fact that only one specimen, the one illustrated, is available for study although sought many times at the proper time of the menstrual cycle. Even this specimen escaped detection, initially, in spite of the fact that its implantation site was searched during several different days following fixation. The histologic appearance of the endometrium and corpus luteum plus the combination of persistent search, the correct angle of illumination, and a great deal of luck finally contributed to finding the implantation area. There was an imperceptible elevation, a tiny ulcer and a certain glistening refractility of the surface, but no congestion or hemorrhage in the surrounding stroma (Fig. 20). None of the laboratory staff was convinced of its validity as an implantation site until the serial sections were completed. (This stage has also been seen by chance once in the author's consultation material: an endometrial biopsy done on the twenty-third day of the cycle during a patient's sterility studies. This illustrates why the onset of menstrual flow is the safest time to do an endometrial biopsy during the investigation of female sterility.)

This phase is further characterized by the persistence of some features of the original blastocyst: a tiny chorionic cavity and solid trophoblast. The latter is, as to be expected, most highly developed at the implantation pole. This specimen, however, shows beautifully the same gradient of trophoblastic differentiation as mentioned in the two seven-day specimens. The exposed abembryonic trophoblast still maintains the mesothelial character of blastocyst wall cells. Just beneath the maternal epithelium, there is a transition from primitive cytotrophoblast to primitive syncytiotrophoblast. This appearance is quite comparable to that of the early implanting monkey blastocyst (Fig. 13). In all probability, the early human trophoblast at the moment of implantation would look like this transitional zone, although it has

Figure 20. *(Upper left)* The surface view of a recently implanted (about 60 hrs) human ovum of approximately 8 days' developmental age. The tiny ulceration in the center of the irregular elevation is barely visible, even at this magnification. The ulcer is due to the exposed abembryonic pole of the ovum. The surrounding gland mouths are prominent. Carnegie No. 8155, sequence 4, F.H.W. S-43-763, × 50. Previously published by Hertig and Rock.[57] (Courtesy of Carnegie Institution of Washington.)

Figure 21. *(Upper right)* A drawing made from a plastic or glass-plate reconstruction of the same specimen as seen in the preceding and following figures. Note lobular outline of external surface of ovum, its position beneath the endometrial surface, and proximity to enlarging capillaries and endometrial stroma. Carnegie No. 8155, F.H.W. S-43-763, × 200. Previously published by Hertig and Rock.[57] (Courtesy of Carnegie Institution of Washington.)

Figure 22. *(Lower)* A mid-cross section of the same specimen as seen in the two preceding figures. Note gradient of trophoblastic differentiation from exposed abembryonic pole to thick solid trophoblast at embryonic (implantation) pole. The bilaminar embryonic disk has curved dorsally to form the amniotic cavity, but amniogenesis has not yet begun. Note further the actively secreting glands in a very edematous, essentially leukocyte-free, stroma. (One polymorphonuclear leukocyte is seen at "4 o'clock.") The prominent, though still largely empty, uncongested vessels are also noteworthy. Carnegie No. 8155, F.H.W. S-43-763, × 300. Previously published by Hertig.[37] (Courtesy of *Yale Journal of Biology and Medicine,* and Carnegie Institution of Washington.)

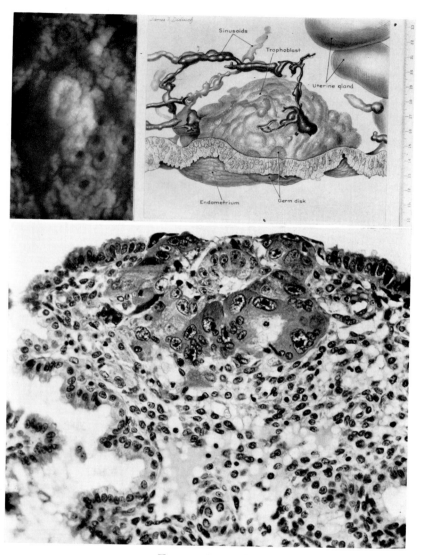

FIGURES 20 to 22

never been seen. This transitional zone has undoubtedly been in contact with endometrial stroma for only a few hours. It illustrates that the blastocyst wall never takes on its definitive trophoblastic form, even though solid, until it is in actual contact with, and fused to, maternal tissue.

At the implantation pole the invasive, ingestive, and digestive nature of primitive syncytiotrophoblast may be readily appreciated. The small nuclei are those of ingested endometrial stroma, whereas the larger anaplastic ones are of intrinsic trophoblastic type. Even now, at this early phase of trophoblastic development, the ultimate peripheral location of the syncytiotrophoblast is becoming evident. Although cytotrophoblast appears to have some invasive qualities, it is far outdistanced by those of the syncytiotrophoblast. The latter, during the first week of implantation, literally eats its way into the maternal stroma.

It would appear that during this initial, critical phase of becoming interstitially implanted, the blastocyst becomes as small as possible, consistent with trophoblastic growth. Although the external diameter of the ovum (0.306 mm, maximum) is no greater than that of the original blastocyst, the trophoblastic growth is prominent, apparently at the expense of the chorionic cavity. Thus the bilaminar germ or embryonic disk is crowded within a tiny cavity surrounded by rapidly growing and differentiating trophoblast. The latter still resembles that of the earlier superficially implanted seven-day ova of the eighth day (Figs. 16 and 17).

The external contours of the trophoblast show fine and coarse lobulation when the specimen is reconstructed (Figs. 18 and 19). Some of the irregularity of external form is due to growth per se and some due to juxtaposition to enlarging capillaries, connecting the single spiral arteriole and venule. All implantation sites during the first two weeks of development show this relationship of trophoblast to one of the approximately 4,000 vascular units of the endometrium: an arteriole and a venule with its anastomosing capillary network. This is correlated with the anatomic fact that all ova implant on solid endometrium. (It need only be recalled that the blastocyst can implant on various nonendometrial surfaces.) Irrespective of why the implanting ovum implants over a neat, ready-made vascular unit, it is fortunate that this is so. The capillary network gradually undergoes dilatation and hyperplasia before being eroded by the invading trophoblast to begin the first sluggish phase of uteroplacental circulation. It is only later, when the ovum has villi and is about fourteen days old, that a true arteriolar-venous circulation is established by steady encroachment of the trophoblast on its implantation site. This phase will be discussed more in detail when considering the villous ovum.

As in the preceding phase of implantation, the endometrial stroma is edematous, not appreciably congested in spite of slight dilatation of capillaries, and essentially free of infiltrating leukocytes. There is one polymorphonuclear leukocyte in a sequestered area of stroma being surrounded and engulfed by syncytiotrophoblast. The glands are just beginning to show persistence or reactivation of secretion in the presence of marked stromal edema. This morphologic feature, a recrudescence of a phase of secretion ordinarily tapering off at twenty days of the nonpregnant cycle, is highly suggestive of the earliest (gestational) hyperplasia of pregnancy. Indeed, the examination of routine sections of endometrium and corpus luteum prior to finding the ovum convinced the author that an implanted ovum must be present as was subsequently confirmed. It is doubtful whether these slight changes would be routinely noticeable unless the observer had a series of such gestationally hyperplastic endometria and corpora lutea for comparison. Certainly the author was unaware of such changes until he began routinely searching for early human pregnancies prior to the first missed menstrual period. The reader is referred to the author's 1964 paper for histological details of gestational hyperplasia of corpus luteum and endometrium.[42]

Lacuna Formation in Trophoblast

This stage of trophoblastic differentiation begins in the nine-day ovum or in its tenth day of development (Figs. 23-25). At this time, the ovum is easily visible to the naked eye because of its size—up to approximately 0.6 mm in its greatest diameter (Fig. 23). Moreover, the endometrium is beginning to show congestion of the continuously proliferating and expanding capillary network about the ovum. All implanted ova, in the author's experience, are in the upper half of the *corpus uteri.* The normal ones tend to be on the posterior wall in the ratio of 12 to 5, whereas the abnormal ones tend to implant anteriorly. Of further interest is the fact that normal ova tend to implant nearer their corpora lutea of origin in the ratio of 10 to 6, only one egg landing precisely in the middle of the posterior wall. The abnormal ova seem not to care on which side they implant with respect to the ovary from which they came.

The endometrium shows more clearly the evidence of gestational hyperplasia: active glandular secretion in the presence of inspissated mucus, slight congestion, marked edema, and an early though variable decidual reaction. The latter is general and not particularly prominent about the ovum. The prominent capillary network about the ovum shows incorporation into and digestion by the invading trophoblast (Fig. 24). This joining of maternal

→

FIGURE 23. *(Upper left)* Surface view of gross implantation site. Note exposed, thin wall of the abembryonic pole of the ovum appearing as an ulcer or defect in the surface epithelium. Although the gland mouths are still prominent, they are beginning to be encroached upon by progressive wrinkling of surface epithelium. Sequence 7, × 22. Previously published by Hertig and Rock.[55] (Courtesy of the C. V. Mosby Company, and Carnegie Institution of Washington.)

FIGURE 24. *(Upper right)* A histologic detail of the trophoblast at the equatorial region of the ovum to show lacunae within syncytiotrophoblast and its effect upon the dilating though nearly empty capillaries. The early decidual transformation of the endometrial stroma is seen at the right lower corner, and the epithelium is at upper right. Section 11-4-4, × 300. Portion of picture previously published by Hertig and Rock.[55] (Courtesy of the C. V. Mosby Company, and Carnegie Institution of Washington.)

FIGURE 25. *(Lower)* A low-power section through the ovum and surrounding endometrium. Note gestational hyperplasia of the endometrium and sponge-like nature of the developing trophoblast. Communication between opened maternal capillaries and primitive intervillous space may be seen in the "8 o'clock" region of the ovum. First evidence of primitive villus formation is seen just beneath the embryonic disk. Section 11-4-7, × 100. Previously published by Rock and Hertig.[115] (Courtesy of the C. V. Mosby Company, and Carnegie Institution of Washington.)

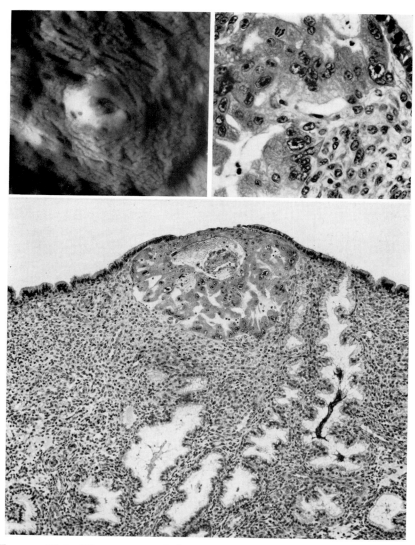

FIGURES 23 to 25 represent a 9-day ovum in its tenth day of development. Carnegie No. 8004, F.H.W. S-42-672.

vessels to trophoblast is the essence of the uteroplacental circulation of the so-called hemochorial type.

The syncytiotrophoblast begins to form isolated lacunae within its cytoplasm (Fig. 24). These lacunae soon coalesce to become the continuous intervillous space, the latter joining very neatly with the opened maternal vessels. A simplified version of what happens is this. The trophoblast, through mechanisms not well-understood, causes dilatation of the capillaries first and larger blood vessels later. There is a concomitant hyperplasia of endothelium, as shown by Hertig and Rock, 1941, and presumably of other vessel wall elements later. The trophoblast then surrounds and partially digests the vessels, allowing a controlled flow of blood into the simultaneously forming intervillous space. The minimal congestion of maternal vessels about the ovum may be either active or passive. Only physiologic data would help to decide this point. During the tenth day of development, the circulation within the sponge-like trophoblast must be minimal. It seems more like a reflux or capillary oozing than true circulation. (Later, at the time of the missed menstrual period, there is actually a miniature arteriolar-venular circulation: the very early placenta with tiny unbranched villi acting as a miniature arteriovenous aneurysm, so to speak.)

While the syncytiotrophoblast is busy fashioning the intervillous space (it actually lines this space and thus covers the villi), the cytotrophoblast is actively proliferating in sprout-like fashion to form primitive chorionic villi. This process of the evolution of the intervillous space and the chorionic villi takes place during the previllous phase or from the tenth through the thirteenth days of development. It will be considered in more detail in the next section.

Previllous Trophoblast

This phase begins during the tenth day of development (9-day ovum) but reaches its maximum during the eleventh to thirteenth days or when the ovum is developmentally ten to twelve days of age. The author has not personally seen an example of the ten-day stage, but presumably it is intermediate in size and development between the specimens shown in Figures 25 and 29.

The previllous ovum is completely interstitially implanted. It is equidistant from surrounding glands, a relationship beautifully illustrated in the reconstruction of the eleven-day specimen in Figure 28. The position of these glands about the ovum reminds the writer of the old-fashioned "Tiffany setting" in an engagement ring—a comparison more familiar to the ladies than the gentlemen.

The endometrium shows only a moderate gestational hyperplasia: slight congestion, marked edema, active glandular secretion, and moderately prominent decidual ("predecidual") reaction about the spiral arterioles and beneath the surface epithelium. It is important to note that the decidual reaction is no more prominent, relatively, about the ovum than elsewhere. This is in keeping with the fact that the gestational hyperplasia is a function of the direct or indirect effect of the trophoblast on the corpus luteum and not directly upon the endometrium.

The abembryonic trophoblast, the last to gain maternal contact, is naturally not as well-developed as that at the embryonic (implantation) pole. The endometrium is doing its best to heal the surface wound made in the epithelium during implantation. Success in such healing is only partial at best. There is often a small ulcer associated with necrotic maternal tissue, an oozing coagulum, and epithelial proliferation. These features are well seen in Figures 26 to 29 (11 days) and in the reconstruction of the twelve-day specimen in Figure 34.

This constant attempt on the part of maternal tissues to heal the endometrium persists until well into the second menstrual month of gestation when the conceptus is of six weeks' developmental age. That the patient may bleed from such a necrotic area covering the implanted ovum is documented clinically as well as anatomically. A patient may occasionally bleed at the time of her missed period, thus confusing the practical matter of her estimated date of confinement (E.D.C.). She may bleed as late as the sixth week of development and complicate the medicolegal aspects of bleeding (threatened abortion) coincident with, but not caused by, trauma of one sort or another. These features will later be discussed and illustrated more fully.

The implantation site of the well-developed previllous ovum

FIGURES 26 and 27. *(Upper left)* Two surface views of the implantation site after fixation and partial dehydration but illuminated to show various gross features. The upper shows the hemorrhage surrounding the implantation site; the lower emphasizes the surface contours. Easily seen are the stellate ulcer and tiny teardrop of coagulum. Sequences 1 and 8 respectively, × 8.

FIGURE 28. *(Upper right)* The external view of the reconstruction made to emphasize the plexiform pattern of the primitive or potential intervillous space. Note the vascular network, especially the arteriole at lower left, the venule at the lower right, and the intervillous space. The fibrinous coagulum is easily seen and its microscopic nature appreciated in Fig. 29. The lighter areas are the glands surrounding the ovum. × 87.5.

FIGURE 29. *(Lower)* A mid-cross section through the ovum to show all of the significant histologic features of the ovum and its surrounding endometrium. Note regenerating surface epithelium beneath coagulum or "scab." The endometrium, although gestationally hyperplastic, has not advanced as far as that surrounding the younger specimen in Fig. 25. The early decidua ("precidua") is no more advanced about the ovum than elsewhere (e.g., about the spiral arteriole). Note hemorrhage to left of ovum, a feature seen grossly in Fig. 26, and the encroachment of trophoblast upon the gland. The ovum shows peripheral syncytiotrophoblast containing the intervillous space within which are blood-derived leukocytes. The inner cytotrophoblast is proliferating outwardly to form the anlagen of chorionic villi and inwardly to form the mesoblastic structures about the bilaminar embryonic disk. × 100.

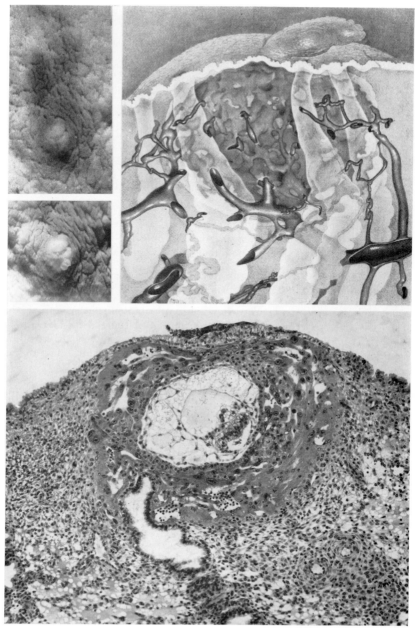

FIGURES 26 to 29 represent various features of an 11-day human ovum, Carnegie No. 7699, F.H.W. S-39-161. Previously published by Hertig and Rock.[54] (Courtesy of Carnegie Institution of Washington.)

FIGURE 30. *(Upper left)* An 11-day human ovum transilluminated after cedar oil clearing to show the dark largely empty potential intervillous space within the light trophoblastic shell of the specimen. The dark circular area in the center is the chorionic cavity. Carnegie No. 7699, F.H.W. S-39-161, sequence 14, × 22.

FIGURE 31. *(Center left)* The 12-day specimen, prepared and photographed comparably to the 11-day ovum in Fig. 30, showing the flooding of the potential intervillous space by maternal blood. Sequence 9, × 22.

FIGURE 32. *(Upper right)* Lateral view of 12-day specimen to show elevation of implantation site. Sequence 8, × 22.

FIGURE 33. *(Center right)* Top view of implantation site. Much of the surface is covered by necrotic endometrium. A flattened, ear-like tab of coagulum, comparable to that in Fig. 28, is seen at left. Note crowding of endometrium by expanding ovum as shown by concentric furrows in surface. Sequence 3, × 22.

FIGURE 34. *(Lower)* A plastic reconstruction, drawn in halftone, showing one half of the ovum and surrounding endometrium. Note vessels (probably misnamed by the author originally as "sinusoids"), the arteriole on right, and the venule on left. Several connections of the maternal capillaries with the potential intervillous space are seen: one at "2" and one at "10 o'clock." The shape of the intervillous space within the trophoblastic shell surrounding the chorionic cavity is readily appreciated. The chorionic cavity contains the bilaminar embryonic disk held in place by delicate, interconnecting, mesoblastic tissue. Histologic details are to be seen in Figs. 35 and 36. Approximately × 100.

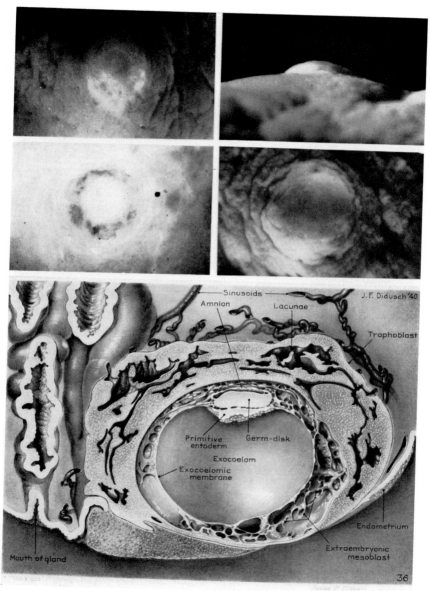

FIGURES 30 to 34 illustrate the gross and reconstructed features of a 12-day human ovum (Carnegie No. 7700, F.H.W. S-38-2655) and include one view of an 11-day ovum (Fig. 30) to contrast the empty potential intervillous space with the blood-filled one of the older specimen (Fig. 31). Previously published by Hertig and Rock.[54] (Courtesy of Carnegie Institution of Washington.)

is easily seen in the freshly opened uterus without magnification. The area is approximately a millimeter in diameter with more or less congestion and/or hemorrhage about the ovum (Fig. 26). Of the five specimens of this stage discovered by Hertig and Rock, the maximum diameters of the fixed and sectioned ova vary from 0.750 to 1.026 mm. The earliest previllous stage at nine days, of which these authors have three specimens, possesses maximum diameters ranging from 0.422 to 0.582 mm. Thus, the range in size of the entire previllous phase ranges from approximately a half millimeter to one millimeter, irrespective of whether the fresh implantation site or the fixed section is measured. Since the undisturbed implantation site of an ovum of nine days or older is clearly recognizable, it is the duty of all pathologists to consider any uterus in the childbearing age to be potentially pregnant. The point need not be belabored that the pathologist is the only physician-scientist to see such material. The anatomist may be interested, but the author is unaware of any anatomist, past or present, who discovered *de novo* an intact human pregnancy of whatever age.

It is a matter of passing interest that only two colored pictures of the fresh implantation size of a human pregnancy prior to the first missed menstrual period are known by the author to exist. One, Carnegie No. 8905, not illustrated, was discovered incidentally by Dr. James A. Merrill* when he was the author's resident pathologist at the Free Hospital for Women, in Brookline, Massachusetts. The other was photographed by the Chief Medical Examiner of Maryland, Dr. Russell S. Fisher, while doing a medicolegal autopsy on a homicide victim. (She was murdered by her "boy friend.")

The various implanted ova found by Hertig and Rock were not photographed in the fresh, either in black and white or in color, because it was deemed important to secure fixation as soon as possible. At the time of this study, 1938-1954, the early stages of human reproduction were largely unknown.

The previllous trophoblast is now oriented so that the primitive syncytiotrophoblast is peripheral, whereas the primitive cytotroph-

---

* Now Professor of Obstetrics and Gynecology at the University of Oklahoma School of Medicine, Oklahoma City, Oklahoma.

oblast is central. This relative position is maintained through-out the remainder of pregnancy. Such a relative position of these two tissues is in keeping with the fact that the syncytial elements of the living shell of the ovum are busily invading the maternal tissue, opening blood vessels, and forming the future intervillous space. In contrast, the cytotrophoblast is proliferating to form knobby projections of villous potential outwardly and the various mesoblastic or auxiliary elements of the placenta inwardly. (The subjects of mesogenesis, angiogenesis, and amniogenesis will be considered in another section of this chapter.)

The intervillous space now forms a single irregular plexiform space with many connections to the surrounding maternal capil-lary network. This is well illustrated in the halftone reconstruction of the eleven-day specimen seen in Figure 28. In spite of such vascular connections as the anlage of the future uteroplacental circulation, there is little maternal blood yet within the inter-villous space. Such blood cells as are present are mainly of leukocytic type. This is seen microscopically in Figure 29 and was appreciated even in the gross as seen in Figures 26, 27, and 30. The intervillous space soon becomes flooded with blood to form a striking circle composed of red dots. It is as though an artist had taken a fine crow-quill pen and ringed with a dotted line the edge of the ovum in brilliant crimson ink. Though nowhere nearly as beautiful, the adequate black and white representation of the beginning of the uteroplacental circulation is seen in Figures 30 and 31. These contrast, by transillumination of the cedar oil-cleared specimen, the lack of and the presence of blood within the intervillous space of the eleven- and twelve-day specimens respectively. The three-dimensional representation of the inter-villous space of the twelve-day specimen is well seen in the reconstruction of that ovum in Figure 34. No attempt has been made by the artist to differentiate the two types of trophoblast.

The spaces, discontinuous on the cut surface but actually inter-communicating, all lie within the syncytiotrophoblast. The knob-by masses of inner trophoblast pushing into the outer trophoblast are all of the cytotrophoblastic variety. These constitute the primitive solid anlagen of the chorionic villi. Hence, this phase is designated as previllous by the author. The late Dr. George L.

Streeter designates the phase in his classic monograph on "Developmental Horizons in Human Embryos" as "V. Ovum implanted but still avillous."[137]

The histologic details of this important previllous phase of the ovum and its endometrium are seen in Figures 35 and 36. Details may be summarized as follows:

1. The endometrium shows advanced gestational hyperplasia with prominent, dilated, and rapidly growing capillaries which appear to leak and contribute to the massive stromal edema. Early decidua is evident about the ovum as well as around arterioles and beneath the surface. The glands are secreting into lumina already containing inspissated secretions.

2. The ovum is now essentially globular and possesses a rapidly proliferating mesoblastic tissue forming the exocoelomic membrane (Heuser's), the primitive chorionic supporting tissue, blood vessels, and amnion. Heuser's membrane is the primitive yolk sac and will be replaced within the next twenty-four to thirty-six hours by the definitive one which will be relatively much smaller.

3. The trophoblast is differentiating into Langhans' epithelium and anlagen of primordial villi. The intervillous space is largely formed, although some discontinuous lacunae are still to be seen in primitive syncytiotrophoblast. The inter-

→

FIGURE 35. *(Upper)* The ovum is distended and still shows the gradient of differentiating trophoblast from abembryonic to embryonic pole. The endometrium is markedly edematous and possesses large plasma-filled vascular spaces. Decidua is moderate in its development. Section 6-1-8, × 50.

FIGURE 36. *(Lower)* A portion of the implantation site and trophoblast from the equatorial region illustrated in Fig. 35. Note flattened mesoblastic nature of Heuser's (exocoelomic) membrane—the primitive yolk sac. It is attached to and derived from the primitive mesoblast, the latter of trophoblastic origin. Note early Langhans' epithelium, irregular masses of cytotrophoblast forming villous anlagen, and blood-filled future intervillous space within the syncytiotrophoblast. There still remain within the syncytiotrophoblast a few isolated lacunae which have not yet coalesced with the main intervillous space. At "8 o'clock" is clearly seen a maternal vessel in continuity with the intervillous space. Section 6-3-2, × 250.

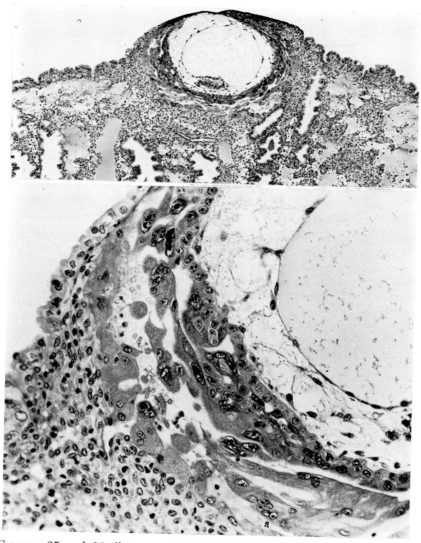

FIGURES 35 and 36 illustrate the 12-day ovum and its surrounding endo-metrium for purposes of general orientation and histological detail re-spectively. Carnegie No. 7700, F.H.W. S-38-2655. Previously published by Hertig and Rock.[54] (Courtesy of Carnegie Institution of Washington.)

FIGURE 37. *(Upper left)* Surface view to show elevation made by the underlying ovum, the fibrinopurulent hemorrhagic exudate covering the ovum, and the recent hemorrhage escaping from the intervillous space. Note wrinkled endometrial surface characteristic of early decidua. Sequence 2, × 8. Previously published by Hertig and Rock.[55] (Courtesy of the C. V. Mosby Company, and Carnegie Institution of Washington.)

FIGURE 38. *(Upper right)* A moderately detailed histologic view of the developing chorion at the implantation or embryonic pole. The embryonic disk is above, and the basal plate of the chorion is below. Note evolution of primitive unbranched villi from simple columns of trophoblast lying between the chorionic membrane and basal plate. Note further that the syncytiotrophoblast lines the labyrinthine intervillous space and conversely covers the chorionic villi. Section 12-1-3, × 100. Previously published by Hertig.[37] (Courtesy of *Yale Journal of Biology and Medicine,* and Carnegie Institution of Washington.)

FIGURE 39. *(Lower)* A low-power view of entire ovum, in mid-cross section to show "Schlusscoagulum" or "scab" of hemorrhagic exudate, actual hemorrhage beneath the "scab," primitive unbranched villi about the entire surface of the chorion, the hemorrhage into the underlying gland(s) and the early decidua now infiltrated by placental site giant cells of trophoblastic origin. Section 12-1-1, × 35. Previously published by Hertig *et al.*[55] (Courtesy of the C. V. Mosby Company, and Carnegie Institution of Washington.)

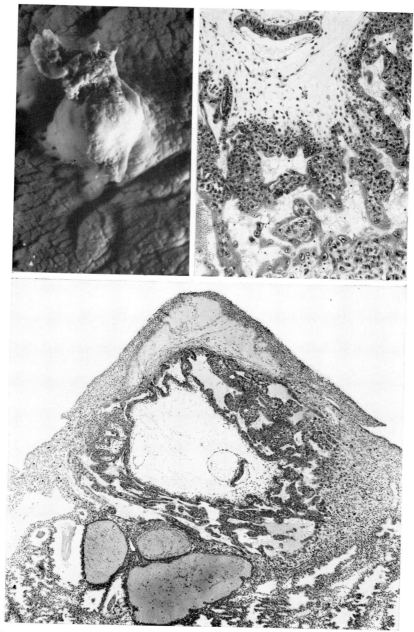

FIGURES 37 to 39 illustrate various aspects of a human 13-day early villous ovum, Carnegie No. 7801, F.H.W. S-40-1461.

villous space is now flooded but not packed with blood containing all cellular elements. Numerous connections are present between the maternal vessels (capillaries) and the primitive or potential intervillous space.

The groundwork for the uteroplacental circulation is now well established. The miniature chorion, now surrounding the entire surface of the ovum, begins to form villi. At first these are simple columnar structures which soon branch, in tree or bush-like fashion, to become the highly vascularized units of the functioning chorion. This phase, occurring during the four to five days after the missed period, will be considered in the next section of this chapter.

Villous Trophoblast

This stage of development begins in the thirteen-day ovum (Figs. 37-39), just before the first missed menstrual period. This is Horizon VI of Streeter's classification, "Primitive villi, distinct yolk sac." This primitive villous period lasts for about two days, at which time the chorionic villi begin to branch and the germ disk has a well-defined axis—Streeter's Horizon VII, as illustrated in Figures 40 to 42. Then begins a period of about five weeks in which both the embryo forms and the chorion is gradually evolving into its definitive organ, the placenta. By the end of this period of rapid growth and development, the embryo is a well-formed little fetus of about 30 mm in length and the chorion has reached a maximum diameter of 80 mm. The beginning of this period of rapid embryonic and chorionic growth and development is seen in Figures 43 to 47. Selected examples of these older stages will be discussed and illustrated later.

The early villous ovum has already increased appreciably in size over the previllous one. During this transitional period of twenty-four to thirty-six hours, the ovum of about one millimeter has increased to approximately 2.5 mm in its greatest diameter. The implantation site is conical and covered with a "scab" of fibrinous and leukocytic exudate, the original "Schlusscoagulum" of Peters, who first saw this stage of human development in 1899.[109] From beneath this "closing coagulum" a small recent blood clot forms (Fig. 37). This is the frequent if not invariable anatomical counterpart and the source of the infrequent clinial bleeding interpreted by the patient as menstrual flow. It is somewhat comparable to the invariable vaginal bleeding described by Hartman in the early pregnant macaque monkey during implantation even though the anatomical details of this process differ in monkey and in man. (It is of interest that this patient had a small amount of blood in her uterine cavity but no clinical bleeding.)

The endometrium is grossly and microscopically characteristic of early decidua measuring up to 6 mm in thickness. The decidual reaction about the ovum is slightly more prominent than elsewhere and, for the first time, shows invasion by placental site giant cells of trophoblastic origin. Although these are often multinucleated in form, they appear to arise from both cytotrophoblast and syncytiotrophoblast as shown by McKay and associates in 1958 and by Bur and associates in 1962. Others of my colleagues including the late Dr. George L. Streeter, Dr. Hugh Grady, and Dr. William B. Ober believe that decidual cells play some role in the formation of these giant cells pathognomonic of pregnancy. This matter will be discussed more fully in the section on histochemistry.

The most striking endometrial change is the presence of recent hemorrhage within the lumina of glands in juxtaposition to the invading trophoblast. At first glance these appear to be dilated congested vessels, but the remnants of flattened epithelium reveal their true nature. This hemorrhage is analogous to, and identical in origin to, the hemorrhage from the "scab"-covered surface of the ovum. The intervillous space is now full of blood. The miniature placenta has its "ceiling" and "floor" supported by the tiny, short, stubby primitive villi of 0.25 mm in length. The explanation of the leaking blood is the defective placental "floor," whether it be at the abembryonic or embryonic pole. The "floor" of the young placenta, untested by the developing blood pressure within the intervillous space, leaks as does a plumbing job when done by an amateur. Unlike the latter, however, nature (or The Lord) soon fixes the leak via blood clotting, and regenerative and repair mechanisms. (The author envisages this period of the blood bath as critical for the early villous ovum. Spontaneous abortions disguised as a menstrual period may take place at this time although there is no evidence as to whether this does or does not happen.) These two sites of hemorrhage are readily appreciated microscopically in Figure 39 and grossly from the surface in Figure 37.

The chorion around the entire surface of the ovum has already formed simple unbranched primitive or primordial villi. These are about one quarter of a millimeter in length and reach from the chorionic membrane to the basal plate of this miniature chorion ("ceiling" and "floor"); although the villi support these two elements of the chorion, as do columns in a room, they are somewhat irregular in shape and diameter. A fortunate plane of section will pass through the villus vertically, as at the top of Figure 39. This villus is quite characteristic of the primordial stage. Its base now has the central mesenchymal core containing a few early, vacuolated discontinuous angioblastic strands, of which more appear later. The trophoblast now has its inner cytotrophoblastic and outer syncytiotrophoblastic layers. This differentiated base, forming about half of the villous structure, merges into the cell column composed of undifferentiated cytotrophoblast, still

→

FIGURE 40. *(Upper left)* The well-implanted villous ovum, 3.75 mm in its greater diameter, shows blood clot attached to its abembryonic pole and decidua capsularis. Note enormous plasma-filled vascular spaces beneath the ovum and the secretory endometrium, now early decidual in type. Section 44-3-5, × 10. Previously published by Heuser *et al.*[69] (Courtesy of Carnegie Institution of Washington.)

FIGURE 41. *(Upper right)* A higher-power detail of the chorion to emphasize the branching nature of the chorionic villi and the general features of the germ disk at the implantation pole. Section 44-3-5, × 30. Previously published by Hertig and Rock.[55] (Courtesy of the C. V. Mosby Company, and Carnegie Institution of Washington.)

FIGURE 42. *(Lower)* A high-power detail of the germ disk cut in cross section to show the ectoderm, endoderm, early mesoderm, and the double-layered definitive yolk sac above and the amnion below. Section 44-3-5, × 250. Previously published by Hertig.[37] (Courtesy of *Yale Journal of Biology and Medicine*, and Carnegie Institution of Washington.)

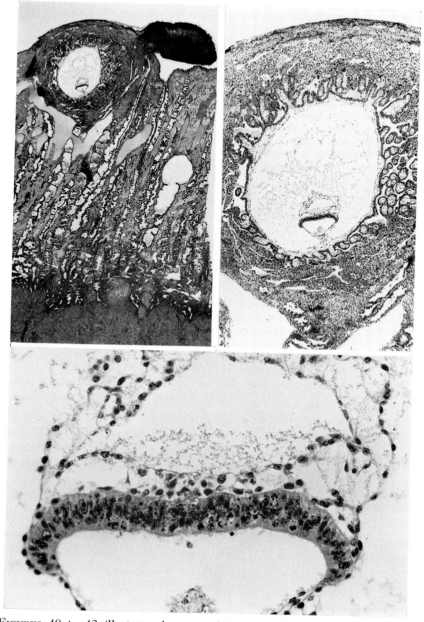

FIGURES 40 to 42 illustrate the general features of the implantation, the branching chorionic villi, and the germ disk of a 16-day human ovum, Carnegie No. 7802, F.H.W. S-40-1524.

covered by syncytiotrophoblast from which the majority of the placental site giant cells arise.

The author has observed in an ovum of this stage, not illustrated, the actual "desquamation" or casting off of the remnants of syncytiotrophoblast penetrating the decidua as the basal plate is forming. Therefore, although the cytotrophoblast does contribute to the giant cells and the decidual cells may contribute, which he doubts, he is sure that the first shower of these large multinucleated cells arises largely from syncytiotrophoblast. (Like all evanescent stages of a biological process, it is hard to catch the process in the act.) The details of villous differentiation are well appreciated in Figure 38. The pathologist-reader will notice the striking similarity of this immature trophoblast to choriocarcinoma. Small wonder that trophoblast frightens pathologists and causes us to make diagnostic mistakes, even those of us who have studied it for years.

Speaking of evanescent processes, the end stage of the metamorphosis of the primary yolk sac into the definitive one is reasonably well shown in Figure 39. The reader will recall the relatively enormous vesicle bounded by Heuser's or the exocoelomic membrane constituting the primary yolk sac of the previllous ovum (Figs. 29, 35, and 36). Apparently during the stage of early villous formation, this membrane fragments, ruptures, or just plain blows up. Its actual disintegration, however, has never been seen by anyone interested in the problem such as the professional embryologists Drs. Corner, Streeter, and Heuser, and the amateur embryologist, the author. The process seems to be analogous to a large soap bubble dividing to form several smaller ones. Within the chorionic cavity, at "9 o'clock" is the presumed remnant of the primitive yolk sac, the definitive one being the remnant of the original one which is still attached to the margin of the endodermal disk. This whole process and a review of the pertinent literature on this and the sixteen-day specimen appears in the monograph written by Heuser, Rock, and Hertig in 1945.

The germ disk measures 0.224×0.253 cm. It is oval in outline, possessing two well-defined germ layers (the ectoderm and endoderm) and the first beginnings of the mesoderm. An embryonic axis or primitive streak is just appearing. The amnion, also of mesoblastic origin, is well formed but possesses only a single layer of cells in contrast to the yolk sac which is already bilaminar. The details of the embryonic disk are seen in Figure 38.

During the four to five days after the first missed menstrual period, the chorion develops branching villi (Figs. 40, 41, and 47). This process begins in a simple fashion by foci of mesoblast differentiating within the trophoblastic cell columns. This process results in the formations of the main branches of the villus. Because of the nature of the attachment of the primitive villus, to both the "ceiling" and "floor" of the placenta, the tips of these main branches are necessarily attached to the decidua. Upon this simple anatomic fact hangs the reason for the shape of the mature placental cotyledon. (When gently teased out of a mature placenta, the cotyledon has a single trunk attached to the chorionic membrane and gives rise to many main branches attached to the *decidua basalis.* Thus, the unit of the placenta strikingly resembles a miniature tree whose branches are covered by canvas, the decidua basalis.)

This primary branching of the primitive villus probably goes on well into the second month of gestation, judging from observations made by the author on routine material. He has, however, no scientific data on this matter beyond his data on angiogenesis up to the nineteen-day specimens to be described later.

Secondary villous formation, however, soon begins to appear within this third week of chorionic development. Secondary villi or secondary branches of primary villi have been seen and/or reconstructed in the seventeen-day Mateer-Streeter ovum (Carnegie No. 1399) and in a comparable specimen, the Heuser presomite specimen (Carnegie No. 6950). A secondary villous structure is defined as one branching or arising secondarily from a villus or the chorionic membrane itself. It does not go through the developmental process of differentiating *in situ* out of a continuous trophoblastic column, the primordial villus. Its process of formation is analogous to a budding yeast; all elements of *previously formed* chorion participate: the trophoblast, the stroma, and the blood vessels. These secondary structures thus are anchored only to a chorionic villus. They have no maternal attachment and thus are moved, within limits, by the blood flow through the placenta. (To the author they are like the gently moving or waving seaweed in a sheltered tidal pool at half tide.)

Aside from the branching of primary villi and the formation of secondary villous structures, many other things happen to the conceptus and its implantation site during its third week of development. These changes may be briefly summarized as follows:

1. The decidual reaction becomes full blown, the endometrium reaching a thickness of 10 mm. Its characteristic pale lavender color and irregularly wrinkled surface (Fig. 43) are familiar to all pathologists, if not to all clinicians.

2. Its chorion leaks blood at fourteen and sixteen days, but the defect is soon healed.

3. The chorionic villi have four to five branches and many secondary ones as well.

4. The ovisac is enlarging rapidly to about 10 mm in diameter.

5. The chorionic cavity is relatively enormous and acts as a tissue culture chamber for the embryo which is just beginning to join its feeble vascular system to that of the independently formed placental vasculature.

These various features are adequately represented by the illustrations of the specimens of sixteen, eighteen, and nineteen days respectively (Figs. 40-42, 43-44, and 45-47).

→

FIGURE 43. *(Upper)* The anterior wall has been incised revealing typical decidua and the interstitially implanted ovum on the posterior wall. The darkness of the decidua capsularis over the ovum is due to blood within the intervillous space. See Fig. 44 for somewhat higher magnification of implantation site. × 1.4.

FIGURE 44. *(Lower)* Implantation site showing characteristic pattern of decidua after fixation. The hemorrhagic smooth elevation of ovoid shape is characteristic of this stage of gestation. See Figs. 45 to 47 for details of another specimen of the same stage of development dissected by Dr. Heuser to show gross details of the embryo, chorionic cavity, and chorionic villi. × 3.

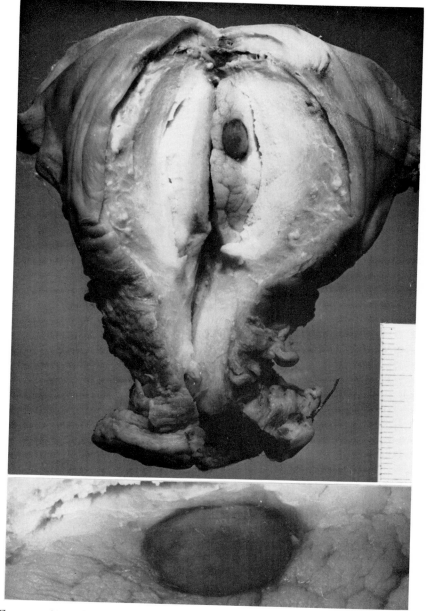

FIGURES 43 and 44 illustrate a pregnant uterus containing a villous ovum of about 18 to 19 days of age, sent the author by Dr. George Elliott, Calgary, Alberta, Canada. H.M.S., CS-63-166.

FIGURE 45. *(Upper left)* A slab of chorion dissected at right angles to the hemisected chorion seen in Fig. 46. The embryo, with prominent yolk sac, is attached at the equatorial pole of the chorion. This will result in the marginal insertion of the umbilical cord at term. The mid-sagittal microscopic section of this embryo and its attached chorion is seen in Fig. 47. Sequence 4, × 5.

FIGURE 46. *(Upper right)* A hemisection of the chorion with its surrounding decidua and underlying myometrium. The magma reticulare of the chorionic cavity has been dissected away to reveal relationships of embryo to chorion. Note uniform development of chorionic villi about ovum, the thin decidua capsularis above, the thick basalis below, and the vera on each side. The dark material is blood within the intervillous space and underlying maternal vessels. The myometrium is the whorled tissue at the bottom. Sequence 2, × 4.

FIGURE 47. *(Lower)* A microscopic section through the axis of the embryonic disk to show the large yolk sac with hematopoiesis, the trilaminar germ disk, the small amniotic cavity, and the body stalk containing the allantois. The decidua capsularis is at the right and the basalis at the left. The multibranched primary villi are readily appreciated especially at "3 o'clock." Section 10-4-2, × 15.

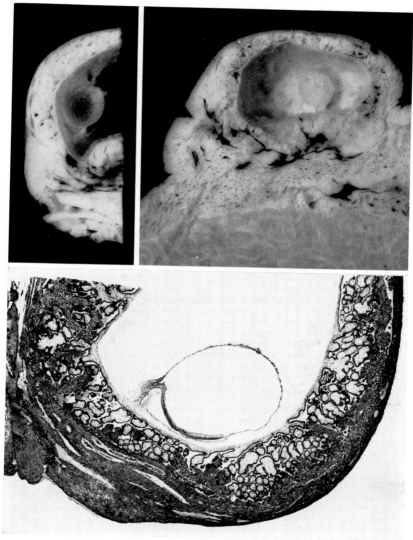

FIGURES 45 to 47 illustrate a human pregnancy of about 19 days' developmental age, comparable to the specimen seen in Figs. 43 and 44. This specimen was meticulously dissected by the late Dr. Chester H. Heuser. It is the best example of this stage of gestation known to the author to show gross relationships of the embryo and body stalk to the chorion and the position of the latter relative to the uterus. Carnegie No. 8671. Originally published by Hertig and Gore.[50] (Courtesy of the C. V. Mosby Company.)

B. FORMATION OF AUXILIARY
PLACENTAL STRUCTURES

This section of the chapter will describe the formation of auxiliary placental structures, the connective tissue, blood vessels, yolk sacs, and amnion.

Much of this subsection will draw upon the author's work on angiogenesis thirty years ago, done under the direction of the late Dr. George L. Streeter.[36] Some of the illustrations are from that monograph and include observations on both the monkey and the human. In addition, corroborative and additional observations will be cited from a few pertinent specimens of the Hertig-Rock series of early human embryos.

The formation of auxiliary placental structures from the trophoblast, aside from its intrinsic biologic importance, is of interest to the pathologist who may look at the trophoblast in one of its various forms. The following few examples will suffice to show the pathological importance of a biologic principle:

1. The common spontaneous abortus, the blighted or pathological ovum of the Carnegie Classification Group II, chorion only, can be explained only on this principle. The absence of an embryo does not prevent the trophoblast from making a chorion, complete with cavity and villi with empty vessels. The absence of an amnion, however, although normally derived from the trophoblast, is due to the lack of an embryonic disk and its inductive powers prior to implantation.

2. If, on the other hand, the blighted ovum contains an empty amniotic cavity, remnants of a yolk sac, or the stump of an umbilical cord, the embryo had been present. However, it had disintegrated some time prior to the spontaneous abortion but after the second and third weeks of development when these structures are forming in response to, but not from, the embryo.

3. The focal or general hydatidiform swelling of chorionic villi in the presence of a normal living embryo is undoubtedly based upon the pattern of vascular development. As the normal villus develops, whether it be of primary or secondary type, the trophoblast and stroma grow faster than the vas-

cular anlagen. The latter thus become isolated. Normally such discontinuous primordial vessels rejoin their fellows to complete a functioning placental circulation. The failure to do so in the abnormality cited above results in stromal swelling of the involved villus and/or its branches. This is not a hydatidiform mole in the classic sense but a congenital anomaly of the chorionic vessels within an otherwise normal villus.

4. Aside from either the biologic or practical aspects of this problem, it illustrates the principle that pathologists using the tools of other disciplines, in this case embryology, can add to the knowledge of human biology. It is generally recognized that pathologists, by using many varied techniques and having a unique overall morphologic approach with access to human material, have solved and can continue to solve problems in human biology.

Mention has been made in section A of this chapter that the uteroplacental circulation begins when the trophoblast erodes maternal blood vessels and thus allows blood to flow into a preformed labyrinthine space within the syncytiotrophoblast. The concept that the placental intervillous space is a variety of arteriovenous aneurysm seems hard to grasp, at least for medical students. Figure 48 is an almost diagrammatic section of a primary placenta (13+ days) of the macaque monkey. The specimen, but not this picture, was originally published by Heuser and Streeter in their 1941 monograph.[71] The author used it in 1933-34 in his studies on chorionic angiogenesis.

Many observers, in describing human chorionic angiogenesis, have noted that the vascular primordia were discontinuous and lay within the mesenchyme of that organ. This led them to conclude that the angioblasts arose from chorionic mesenchyme. Others noted that although the primordia were continuous, they lay within the mesenchyme. It was also concluded that they arose in or from that tissue. Most of these individual opinions were based upon observations of limited material. Since the author had an opportunity to study a series of early human embryos as well as those of the macaque, the morphologic sequence of events, namely, the independent *in situ* origin of angioblasts and mesoblasts from trophoblast, became clear.

The reader is referred to the author's 1935 monograph[36] for a detailed review of the various complicated and somewhat different concepts about both embryonic and chorionic angiogenesis. Suffice it to say that many famous embryologists, going back to His about a hundred years ago, have thought and written about how blood vessels arise and differentiate to become a circulatory system.

As with most problems involving a sequence of events, it becomes easier to work from a well-established stage to one not as well-established. Hence, the author began with the reconstruction of a single primordial chorionic villus from the late nineteen-day, presomite ovum (Carnegie No. 6950) described by Heuser in 1932.[67] After several months of labor, the vascular pattern was indeed shown to be discontinuous and lying within the mesenchyme of the villus (Fig. 67). It was interpreted, erroneously, that the angioblasts arose from the mesenchyme.

Going back to the slightly younger Mateer specimens of seventeen days (Carnegie No. 1399), already carefully studied for angiogenesis by Streeter in 1920,[130] the same general pattern of discontinuous vessels became evident as seen in Figures 61 through 65. It was only when the fifteen-day specimen (the Wharton embryo, Carnegie No. 6706) was studied and its serial

→

FIGURE 48. *(Upper)* The primary placenta with the remainder of the chorionic wall removed to show the nearly diagrammatic relationships of the dilated maternal veins to the intervillous space. The large dark plaque of cells is the maternal epithelial reaction to the presence of invading trophoblast and contrasts with the decidual reaction of uterine stroma in the human. The edge of the embryo is barely represented. Section 2-6-2, × 55.

FIGURE 49. *(Lower)* The earliest recognizable angioblastic mass differentiating in the base of a primary villus is seen at top center as a triangular mass of three cells still attached by its apex to the cytotrophoblast from which it arose. The perfect vertical plane of section allows details of the differentiation of Langhans' epithelium from cytotrophoblast to be appreciated. The large spaces on either side of the primitive villus are lined by syncytiotrophoblast and contain maternal blood. At the bottom, the junction of the trophoblast and maternal tissue shows the flowing proliferative process by which the basal plate or placental "floor" is formed. Section 2-2-5, × 600. Previously published by Hertig.[36]

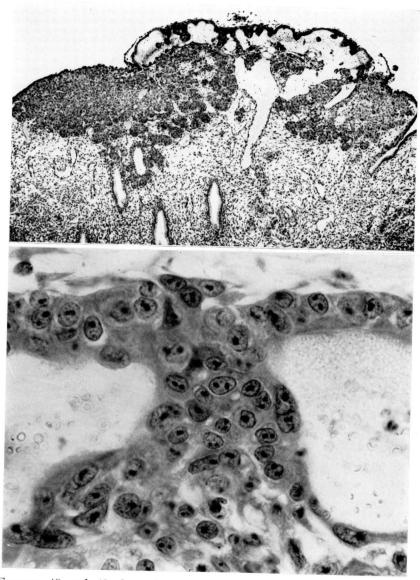

FIGURES 48 and 49 show the general features and a high-power detail of the 13-day macaque monkey chorion. Carnegie No. C-467. (Courtesy of Carnegie Institution of Washington.)

sections reconstructed that the true origin of angioblasts and mesoblasts from trophoblast began to dawn on the author. Figure 59 shows convincing morphologic evidence of a solid angioblastic strand delaminating *in situ* from the chorionic cytotrophoblast at the base of a primordial villus. Other evidence of a similar nature was present elsewhere, especially at the tips of differentiating primitive villi. It was noted that the cytotrophoblast appeared to give rise to two types of cells: the solid strands destined to become blood vessels and the isolated ones destined to become the supporting connective tissue cells of the chorion and its villi (Fig. 60).

From these observations, based on a methodical but basically simple perusal of a graded series of human chorions, the explanation for the discrepant observations in the literature emerged. It soon became evident that the period of primordial villus formation from roughly the eleven- to the fifteen-day stage was critical and that chorionic angiogenesis coincided with the period of trophoblastic development. *Before* that there was only the formation of early primary mesoderm (the term applied by the author to trophoblastic mesoderm to distinguish it from the embryonic third germ layer variety) and angiogenesis. *After* the primordial villi had been formed, the vascular anlagen appeared as discontinuous masses within primary mesoderm in both the chorion and developing villi.

These anlagen then coalesce and combine as a single vascular unit with those of the cord, yolk sac, and embryo in the early somite stage of embryonic development. This corresponds roughly with the beginning of the fourth week of development when the embryo has seven to seventeen somites, varies from approximately 2 to 3 mm in length, and has a chorion from 8 to 18 mm in diameter. (Incidentally, the clinically useful tests for chorionic gonadotropin become positive about that time.)

Following the discovery of trophoblastic pluripotentiality, the author studied younger and older human chorions and a small but significant series of monkey chorions from ten to seventeen days of age. These and later observations will now be summarized. They will be arranged as though the observations were made in an orderly developmental sequence, even though the older stages were studied first. The essential stages of the formation of chorionic auxiliary structures are seen in Figures 49 to 70. The observations concern connective tissue, blood vessels, amnion, and to a lesser extent the yolk sac(s). The latter structures have been described before (Figs. 26-42).

Mesogenesis

This term, coined by the author, is the process of formation of the chorionic or primary mesoderm. Heuser and Streeter, in their classic 1941 monograph on the macaque, designate this tissue as mesoblast.[71] So far as he is aware, the author was the first to show that this tissue arose *in situ* from the primate trophoblast by a process of differentiation and delamination.[36] This was clearly seen in the well-implanted macaque ovum of ten days (Carnegie C-496, not illustrated here) and was confirmed in the human ovum as shown in the Figures 57 and 60. Heuser and Streeter,[71] in their superb summary on page 49 discussing the early stages of trophoblastic differentiation and function during implantation, say:

> It is also accompanied by differentiation of an additional tissue, the primitive mesoblastic reticulum, which is delaminated from the inner surface of the trophoblastic shell. It is suggested that this reticulum serves the purpose of altering the fluid of the blastocyst cavity and that it tends to wall off secondary spaces. During this period the formative cells grouped at the embryonic pole are nourished after the manner of a tissue culture; the culture medium is provided by the trophoblastic shell from the adjacent maternal tissues and is further conditioned by its reticular lining. The latter, known as extraembryonic mesoblast, appears to vary in amount in different species, in direct proportion to the completeness with which the ovum penetrates the endometrium. This appears to be an index of the amount of service it is required to perform.

In the later Hertig-Rock material, the formation of mesoblast from the trophoblast was evident in the earliest stages of implantation available for study (Figs. 14 and 68). In the latter specimen (Carnegie 8225), the process is more advanced than in the former (Carnegie No. 8020). The loose reticulum of primitive mesoblastic cells, widely separated from the embryonic endoderm (thought by some to form this tissue), still shows undoubted attachment to the trophoblastic tissue of its origin. This slight variation in the advancement or retardation of an embryologic process in comparable stages of development has been noted by all observers who have studied a given process in a graded series of embryos. Such variations are undoubtedly responsible for diverse interpretations and indeed errors of interpretation when made from isolated observations or on limited stages of a process. This is true whether a disease or an embryologic process is being interpreted. This misinterpretation of an isolated observation is reminiscent of the interpretation by the three blind men and their evaluation of the gross morphology of an elephant by simple palpation of the trunk, lateral abdominal wall, and tail. The reader will recall that the elephant resembled a tree trunk, the wall of a building, and a rope, respectively, based upon these isolated conclusions from accurate but insufficiently correlated data. (The realization of these biologic variations, with their built-in interpretive and diagnostic pitfalls, has stood the author in good stead. It has taught him to avoid dogmatic statements about the pathogenesis of the few diseases in which he has become personally interested during the past 35 years.)

Mesogenesis in the implanted human ovum continues apace. It may be observed from the time of implantation to the completion of primitive villus formation, namely, from the six- to the fifteen-day stage. These primitive mesenchymal cells form the connective tissue of the chorionic membrane as well as its villi. They also form the primitive yolk sac or Heuser's exocoelomic membrane. The beginning of this temporary, but undoubtedly physiologically important structure, is seen in the youngest of the nine-day specimens (Carnegie No. 8215), not here illustrated but well seen in the Corner Festschrift summary of all the Hertig-Rock specimens.[60] This membrane forms throughout this tenth day of development but at a variable rate. Thus it is only beginning in the oldest of these three specimens (Carnegie No. 8215) as shown in Figures 25 (low power) and 69 (high power). In any event, this primitive yolk sac is beautifully developed in all of the eleven- and twelve-day specimens of which Hertig and Rock found a total of five. Two are illustrated in Figures 26 to 36,

54 and 70. It reaches its peak of development in the twelve-day stage only to become converted suddenly into the smaller definitive yolk sac of the thirteen-day stage. The reader can best appreciate its early but distinctive appearance in Figure 29 (the 11-day specimen). Its mature form is superbly illustrated in the reconstruction of the twelve-day specimen seen in Figure 34. Its histological details are evident in Figures 35, 36, 54 and 70, although none of these illustrations was specifically chosen to illustrate this particular structure.

It is evident that the definitive yolk sac is derived from the primary one by a disintegrative or destructive process. The ragged torn edge of that portion remaining attached to the endoderm coalesces to form the smaller single-layered structure seen in all three of the thirteen-day specimens. That the primary yolk sac "blows up" or "pops" is clearly seen in Figure 39 since the definitive sac has formed and there are distal remnants of the primary one still present. This has been observed in other comparable specimens not in the Hertig-Rock series.

Probably the most authoritative statement about the origins of the yolk sac is to be found in the 1941 classic of Heuser and Streeter.[71] It speaks of the monkey, but your author considers it apropos for the human being. They say:

The yolk sac is also a nonformative or auxiliary structure. From the start it is discrete from the gut primordium. The latter either is induced by the overlying germ disk or receives migrated cells from it, whereas the yolk sac appears to arise from fibroblastic cells like those of the extraembryonic mesoblast and is closely related to the exocoelomic membrane. With them it belongs to the group of auxiliary structures. It does not become a part of the embryo and is unable to produce actual embryo tissues. It does, however, appear to perform an essential function during a specific period of development, as a highly vascular membrane exposed to the fluid contained in the exocoelomic cavity. Whatever physiological requirement it meets terminates with the development of the chorionic villi and the establishment of fetal blood circulation through them. The yolk sac then remains a discarded organ adherent to the placenta near the attachment of the umbilical cord, i.e., body stalk.

The definitive human yolk sac soon takes on a second or inner layer of epithelial nature. The author is convinced that it is de-

rived from the yolk sac wall, although his colleague Heuser[66] interpreted it as being of endodermal origin. The interested reader
is referred to the monograph on the two villous specimens in
Figures 37 to 42 for a thorough review of all the world literature
available at that time.[69] For some reason or other, Heuser, Streeter, and the author never discussed the yolk sac very much in
concert. Dr. Streeter probably wrote the part on the monkey
yolk sac, and Dr. Heuser definitely wrote the part about the
human yolk sac. Your author is a disciple of Dr. Streeter but has
great respect for Heuser's opinions.

This difference of opinion between the amateur, whether gifted
or not, and the professional is universal. The author has been well
aware of it for over thirty years, since his excursions into human
embryology and clinical obstetrics while nominally considered as
and acting like a pathologist. (He has always felt a little like a
portal space whose anatomic and functional loyalties belong to
several contiguous liver lobules.)

Whether the hematopoietic foci of the yolk sac arise from endoderm or embryonic mesoderm the author honestly does not
know. Suffice it to say, his impression from the 1935 work is that
angioblastic foci are definitely seen in the vicinity of the definitive yolk sac wall only after they are successively seen in the
chorion and body stalk. He says, in his 1935 paper, "Angiogenic
foci appear successively in the future body-stalk region and
around the yolk-sac of older macaque specimens possessing primitive villi. This is brought about by what appears to be a process
of growth and migration of elements derived from angiogenic
foci arising from trophoblastic cells. This probably also occurs in
comparable human ova judging from a survey of the previously
reported specimens."

Be that as it may, blood cells do not appear in the fetal-chori-
onic circulation until it is a functional unit. The author never
found any evidence of chorionic hematopoiesis. That the first
blood cells arise in the yolk sac is well established, but whether
those hematopoietic foci arise from migrating embryonic or chorionic cells is unknown, at least to the author. Similarly it has
never been proven in the erythroblastotic placenta, associated
with hydrops of the fetus, whether the hematopoietic foci are

"metatastic" or whether they arise in the perpetually adolescent placenta seen in that disease.

Angiogenesis

Although the author spent a year working out the details of this process, it can be told simply with few words and representative illustrations. The almost diagrammatic "inevitable histologic sequence of events" (a phrase lovingly and frequently used by the late Professor S. Burt Wolbach) is seen for the monkey in Figures 49 to 53. Comparable human material is illustrated in Figures 54 to 60. In both primate forms, the process occurs during the evolution of the primitive villus from differentiating trophoblast. In the monkey ovum, due perhaps to its later implantation, primary angiogenesis takes place from the thirteen- to the seventeen-day stages. In the human ovum, implanting at six days, primary angiogenesis takes place during the eleven- to fifteen-day stages.

The earliest or at least most easily recognized angiogenesis is seen in the base of the primordial villus when its cytotrophoblast is just beginning to differentiate into the primitive unbranched villi. Such a stage is well illustrated from the monkey in Figure 49 and from the human being in Figure 57. The process of chorionic membrane angiogenesis begins a few hours earlier than the twelve- to thirteen-day stage in the human being since it is absent in all three of the nine-day specimens but is occasionally seen within the mesoblast in the eleven- and twelve-day specimens. Thus, the main stimulus for chorionic angiogenesis seems to reside in the primordial villi themselves. This would seem logical (or teleological) since these are the main vascular units of the placenta. The initial stage of angiogenesis appears as a triangular or T-shaped solid mass of cells still attached to or lying within their trophoblastic cells of origin. In no way do early angioblastic foci resemble already differentiated mesoblasts, from which some authors had previously derived them.

Associated with further differentiation of the primary villus, the basal cytotrophoblast becomes the single-layered Langhans' type (Figs. 50 and 54). It forms a cone-shaped invagination in which lie the already differentiated and still differentiating mesoblasts and angioblasts. The latter may be still attached to the tip of cell column trophoblast (Fig. 52) or may be free (Fig. 58).

Reconstructions of primary villi nearing the end of their period of differentiation and growth show clearly that the main vascular unit of the chorion, whether it be monkey or man, lies within and is associated with the villus. Figure 53 shows this beautifully for the monkey; Figure 63 shows this for man. Incidentally, it was the reconstruction of Figure 53 that convinced the late Dr. Warren Lewis, an eminent and hard-to-convince anatomist and former editor of *Gray's Anatomy*, that what I had been talking about for nearly a year was really so. His comment, "I never did believe that chorionic blood vessels originated in the embryo and grew out from the primitive streak. They seem to be separate from mesenchyme from the beginning!" This was indeed balm to the ears of a neophyte in embryology and an only recently trained pathologist who had no preconceptions about embryology in general or angiogenesis in particular. It was my brother Marshall who once reminded me that "the specimen is always right," even though the interpreter thereof might be wrong.

→

FIGURES 50 and 52. *(Upper and lower left, respectively)* This pair shows a differentiating primordial villus. Its base is formed by Langhans' epithelium and contains two typical solid angioblastic strands in the act of differentiating from, but still attached to, the primitive cytotrophoblast of its origin at the tip of the columnar villus. Note isolated angioblastic mass at upper left which had formed earlier and detached, as is normal during angiogenesis. Note also lumen formation in the form of vacuole within angioblastic strands. Carnegie No. C-467, Histologic section 3-1-7, × 600. Previously published by Hertig.[36] (Courtesy of Carnegie Institution of Washington.)

FIGURES 51 and 53. *(Upper and lower right, respectively)* The histological evidence in Fig. 51 is the only primary angiogenesis ever seen by the author arising in a secondary villus. The mitotic figure gives evidence of growth of the angioblastic strand after its initial origin from the primitive cytotrophoblast. The association of the angioblastic network with its primary villus of origin is well seen in Fig. 53. At this stage, secondary sprouts are growing in all directions, ultimately to join with growing foci of angiogenesis associated with contiguous primary (and secondary) villi. Carnegie No. C-457, Histologic section 4-4-3, × 600. Fig. 53 previously published by Hertig.[36] (Both figures courtesy of Carnegie Institution of Washington.)

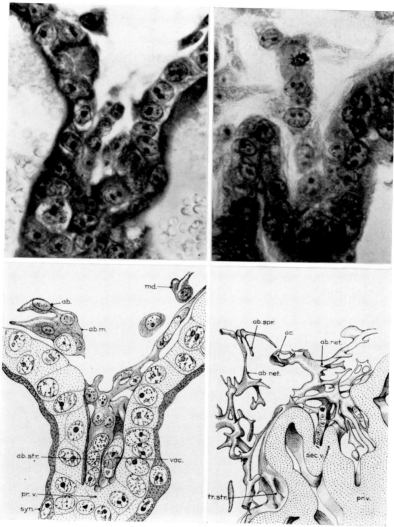

FIGURES 50 to 53 show the histologic details and reconstruction of primary chorionic villi of the 12½- and 17-day macaque monkey respectively. In each instance, the histologic section is the top one used in the plastic reconstruction shown below. The abbreviations used are as follows: ab. = angioblast; ab.m. = angioblastic mass; ab.n. = angioblastic net; ab. spr. = angioblastic sprout; ab. str. = angioblastic strand; ac. = angiocyst; md. = mesoderm; pr. v. = primary villus; sec. v. = secondary villus; syn. = syncytiotrophoblast; tr. str. = trophoblastic strand; vac. = vacuole (primitive lumen within an angioblastic strand).

FIGURE 54. *(Upper)* A primordial villus in the act of metamorphosing into a primary villus. Note Heuser's (exocoelomic) membrane at top, a segment of the primtive yolk sac at its peak of development. Note differentiating Langhans' epithelium about the base of the villus. There are both angioblastic luminated strands and isolated mesoblasts in various stages of differentiation. Note further the active growth of primitive cytotrophoblast growing peripherally into the outer lying syncytiotrophoblast. The potential or early intervillous space now contains appreciable amounts of maternal blood. Note the brush border of the syncytiotrophoblast lining the intervillous space or covering the primordial villus. This stage is just prior to formation of the basal plate or "floor" of the placenta from continued peripheral growth of cytotrophoblast. Carnegie No. 7700, F.H.W. S-38-2655, section 6-4-1, × 400. Previously published by Hertig and Rock.[54]

FIGURE 55. *(Lower)* The implantation (embryonic) pole of the James Merrill ovum to show early differentiation of unbranched primary villi. Even at this magnification, the process of mesogenesis and angiogenesis in the bases of early villi may be appreciated. Developmental age of this ovum lies between the 12- and 13-day stage and represents the best example in the author's collection of formation of early primordial villi, active mesogenesis and angiogenesis, completion of the amnion and the transitional phase between the primary and definitive yolk sac formation. The leukocytic reaction is abnormal, but the trophoblast and embryo are normal. Whether this conceptus was destined to abort is unknown. Carnegie No. 8095, F.H.W. S-51-328, section 6-6-7, × 120.

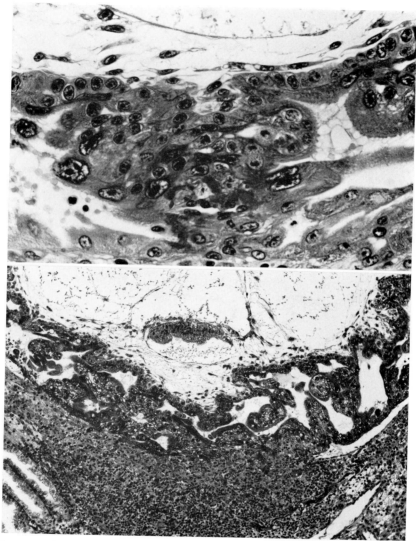

FIGURES 54 and 55 are from early phases of differentiating primitive chorionic villi showing various aspects of mesogenesis and angiogenesis, from two 12-day human specimens of slightly different ages.

Secondary angiogenesis, growth of already formed vasculogenic foci, takes place in the branches of primary villi both in the monkey and in man. The stage in the monkey during which primary angiogenesis is tapering off and secondary growth is beginning is seen in Figures 51 and 53. This is a seventeen-day specimen and is comparable to the Wharton human ovum (Carnegie No. 6706), a fifteen-day specimen shown in Figures 59 and 60.

Figure 51 is a portion of the histologic section representing the top of the reconstruction shown in Figure 53. Most of the isolated angioblastic networks, clustered about the two primary villi, have arisen *de novo* from their respective villi. The tiny secondary villus is still forming its own angioblasts from trophoblast as seen in both the single histological section (Fig. 51) and the reconstruction of the entire region (Fig. 53). How extensive this primary angiogenesis is, as seen in secondary villi and in main branches of primary villi, the author does not know. It probably occurs infrequently based on his own observations. Suffice it to say that it is not present after the fifteen-day human stages. Both are developmentally comparable even though their ages are different, owing to difference in the time of implantation. The monkey blastocyst implants at nine days and the human at six. Paradoxically the monkey gestation lasts only six months as compared to nine months in man.

→

FIGURE 56. (*Upper*) A low-power view which shows slightly better primary villus formation at the implanation pole as compared to that at the opposite (abembryonic) pole. Fig. 58 is from this section; Fig. 57 is from a contiguous one. Sequence 13, No. 4, × 75.

FIGURE 57. (*Lower left*) A high-power detail of the base of an early primary villus whose cytotrophoblast is loosening up to differentiate into a Y- or T-shaped angioblastic strand or mass lying amid early mesoblasts. Section 37-2, × 1000. Previously published by Hertig.[36]

FIGURE 58. (*Lower right*) A somewhat more advanced phase of angiogenesis in the same 13-day early villous ovum as illustrated in Figs. 56 and 57. The T-shaped angioblastic focus has separated from its trophoblastic origin and now constitutes the isolated center of vascular growth which will supply this villus and surrounding chorionic membrane with its blood vessels. Section 37-1, × 1000. Previously published by Hertig.[36]

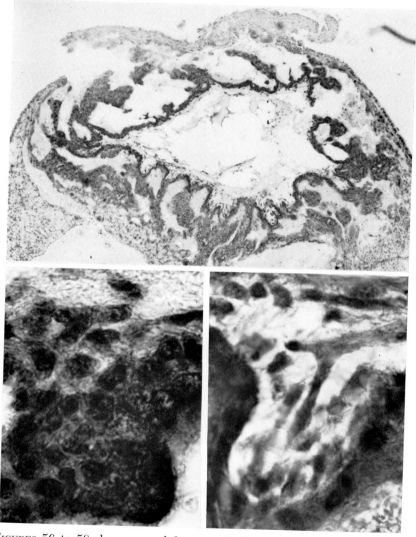

FIGURES 56 to 58 show general features of the famous Linzenmeier ovum originally published in 1914. (*Arch Gynäk, 102*:1-17, 1914) of which there are eight sections of just the chorion in the Carnegie collection as number 6900. Although the tissues are somewhat distorted by the technique of preparation, the specimen represents as good an illustration of angiogenesis in the bases of primary villi as is known to the author. (All figures courtesy of Carnegie Institution of Washington.)

FIGURE 59. *(Upper)* The base of a primary chorionic villus and adjacent chorionic membrane shows delamination of a solid angioblastic strand, demonstrated upon reconstruction, to form a part of the angioblastic network lying within this villus. A mitotic figure is seen at the far right of this strand. (This is the specific section which gave the author the first clue as to *in situ* delamination of angioblasts from trophoblast.) This histological section was originally published by Hertig as Fig. 17; the reconstruction on which it is the top section appeared as text Figures 2 and 2A in the same publication. Section 3-4-10, × 800. Previously published by Hertig.[36] (Courtesy of Carnegie Institution of Washington.)

FIGURE 60. *(Lower)* The differentiating tip and cell column of a primary villus from the same 14-day specimen seen in Fig. 59. Note the loosening of cytotrophoblast with a gradient of mesoblastic differentiation from left to right. Primary angiogenesis and mesogenesis have not been seen after this stage of development in the human chorion. Section 2-4-9, × 1000. (Courtesy of Carnegie Institution of Washington.)

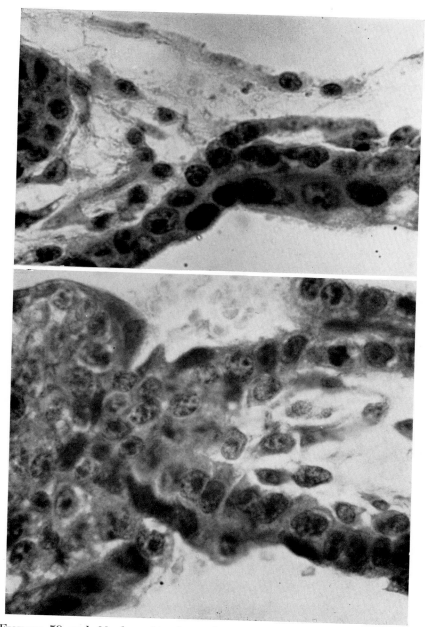

FIGURES 59 and 60 show histologic details of primary angiogenesis and mesogenesis in the base and tip of two different primary villi respectively from a 14-day human ovum (the Wharton). Carnegie No. 6706.

FIGURE 61. *(Upper)* A new secondary branch arising from a primary but multibranched villus to show a solid angioblastic strand connected with its parent in the main stem of the villus. The latter is below; the chorionic membrane is to the right and above. Note that this secondary unit now has all of its components—trophoblastic, stromal, and vascular—still connected to their parent sources. × 600. Previously published by Hertig.[36]

FIGURE 62. *(Lower left)* A secondary branch from another primary, multibranched villus but showing detachment of the angioblastic mass which has now formed a lumen. × 400.

FIGURE 63. *(Lower right)* The reconstruction of a primary, multibranched villus. The three branches at the tip have developed from the original cell column; the six external ones (3 on each side) are of secondary type such as seen in Figs. 61 and 62. Note that much of the vasculature in the main stem of the villus is intact but that within the branches, whether primary or secondary, the angioblastic masses are detached. This results from disproportionate growth of the villus as compared to the blood vessel. The abbreviations are as follows: ab.m. = angioblastic mass; ab. net. = angioblastic network; ch. md. = chorionic mesoderm; ep. = epithelium (trophoblast); and lu. = lumen of blood vessel. × 90. Previously published by Hertig.[36]

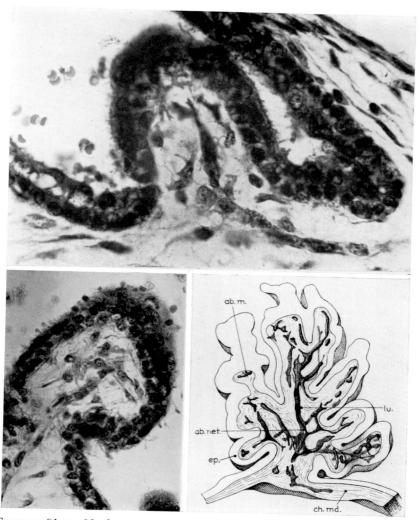

FIGURES 61 to 63 show various aspects of secondary vascular growth in the human chorion of 17 days with respect to secondary villous branches and secondary villi. All from the Mateer Streeter Ovum, Carnegie No. 1399. (All figures courtesy of Carnegie Institution of Washington.)

Once the primary villi have been formed at fifteen days and their associated angiogenesis completed, all vascular growth is secondary in type. The vascular primordium accompanies the secondary structure, whether it be the secondary branch of a primary villus or a new secondary villus. This mechanism of growth is well illustrated in Figures 61 to 67.

The isolated vascular primordium is at first a solid multicellular strand which soon becomes converted to an endothelial tube by coalescence of separate intracytoplasmic vesicles, lacunae, or vacuoles. This process is well illustrated in Figures 61 and 62. They are secondary branches of a primary villus comparable to those from the same seventeen-day specimen in Figure 63. Apparently the secondary villous structures grow more rapidly than their vascular component and thus separate the angioblastic strand from its parent. This process is seen in both the main and secondary branches of the primary villus shown in Figure 63. It is equally well seen in two secondary villi of different stages of growth in Figures 64 and 65 from the same seventeen-day specimen shown in the preceding plate.

This discontinuous nature of the vascular foci in the primary villus (Figs. 66 and 67) of the nineteen-day stage precedes the phase of vascular coalescence. It will be remembered that these isolated foci initially led the author and all of his predecessors to the erroneous conclusion that angioblasts arose from mesoblasts.

$\longrightarrow$

FIGURE 64. (Upper) This histologic section is from the reconstructed villus (V.I.) in Fig. 65. × 400.

FIGURE 65. (Lower) A secondary villus (V.I.) at left arising from the chorionic membrane to show the continuity of all elements: trophoblastic, stromal, and vascular. The angioblastic component may have arisen from the trophoblast of the villus de novo or may merely have come from one lying within the adjacent chorionic mesoderm. The larger more complex secondary villus at right (V. II) has several secondary branches and shows the same discontinuity of its vasculature as do the secondary branches of the larger, multibranched primary villi seen in Fig. 63. Abbreviations are as follows: ab. spr. = angioblastic sprout; ac. = angiocyst; ch. md. = chorionic mesoderm; lu. = lumen; pp. con. = protoplasmic connection; and sec. ab. spr. = secondary angioblastic sprout. × 170. Previously published by Hertig.[36]

FIGURES 64 and 65 are from the same 17-day human ovum (Mateer Streeter) as shown in Figs. 61 to 63, but here they illustrate growth of secondary chorionic villi. Carnegie No. 1399. (Both figures courtesy of Carnegie Institution of Washington.)

Figures 66 and 67 are from the 19-day presomite specimen, the Heuser ovum, Carnegie No. 5960. These illustrations show the discontinuous pattern of the vasculature within a primary villus which now has two main (primary) branches and many secondary ones. Previously published by Hertig.[36] (Courtesy of Carnegie Institution of Washington.)

Figure 66. *(Upper)* The histologic detail of the classic immature chorionic villus, easily recognized by medical students and practitioners, shows the typical inner layer of cytotrophoblast and the outer layer of syncytiotrophoblast. The latter may be designated as syncytium and the former as Langhans' epithelium. The stroma is of characteristic mesenchymal (mesoblastic) type containing immature blood vessels in various stages of growth following their origin and differentiation from trophoblast. In the main portion of this cross section (plane of section A-B from Fig. 67 [29]), the isolated blood vessels are thin walled, empty, and lie beneath the trophoblast. In the tiny secondary branch, at lower center, the solid blood vessels fan out from their parent sources and lie within the central portion of the branch. This illustrates the usual method of vascular growth. At what point it stops during further placental growth is unknown to the author. Section 5-2-1, × 300.

Figure 67. *(Lower)* Parts 29 and 30 represent drawings from a plastic reconstruction of the largest primary villus at the implantation (embryonic) pole. In part 29, the artist has used the conventional anatomic hook in order to draw the entire villus in one plane. Actually, its stem was bent at right angles to the chorionic membrane, as seen in 30. Thus, the line or plane C-D in 29 is seen as the cut surface C-D in 30. The discontinuous nature of vascular primordia is clearly evident except in some of the very smallest secondary branches. The abbreviations used are b.v. = blood vessel, and m.b. = main branch of primary villus. The reconstructions are depicted as having no trophoblastic epithelium since it is no longer germane to the problem of angiogenesis. Both reconstructions × 115.

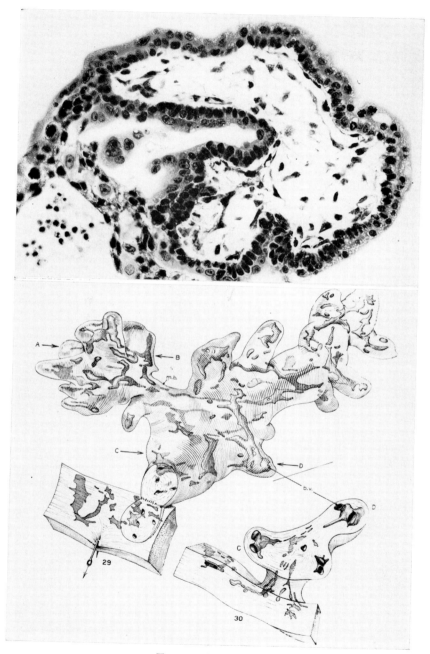

FIGURES 66 and 67

FIGURE 68. *(Upper)* A recently implanted ovum showing solid avillous trophoblast at the implantation (embryonic) pole. Note the single layer of flattened cells lying beneath the germ disk (embryo) but attached to the trophoblast. The amniotic cavity is just beginning to form. Previously published by Hertig.[37] (Courtesy of *Yale Journal of Biology and Medicine,* and Carnegie Institution of Washington.)

FIGURE 69. *(Center)* The bilaminar germ disk has a well-developed chorionic cavity below the ectoderm which is imperfectly enclosed by the veil-like amnion of mesoblastic-appearing cells. The latter are still obviously attached to the trophoblast from which they arose by *in situ* differentiation and delamination. At this stage there is no well-defined exocoelomic (Heuser's) membrane, although an occasional mesoblastic cell is beginning to appear as noted at "2 o'clock" on the inner surface of the chorionic cavity. Previously published by Hertig.[37] (Courtesy of *Yale Journal of Biology and Medicine,* and Carnegie Institution of Washington.)

FIGURE 70. *(Lower)* A still later stage of amniogenesis in which amniogenic cells are growing and being added to by the adjacent trophoblast. Note mitotic figure in telophase within two daughter cells of amniogenic type which are still attached to the trophoblast but obviously part of the amnion. The exocoelomic membrane, the primitive yolk sac, is attached to the margins of the endoderm. Although the membrane is still growing (mitotic figure at right) this structure will soon disintegrate and its phoenix-like remnants will form the definitive yolk sac within the next day or so. The ectoderm of the embryonic disk has become vacuolated (glycogen and glycoprotein), a normal phenomenon during the next few days. Previously published by Hertig and Rock.[54] (Courtesy of Carnegie Institution of Washington.)

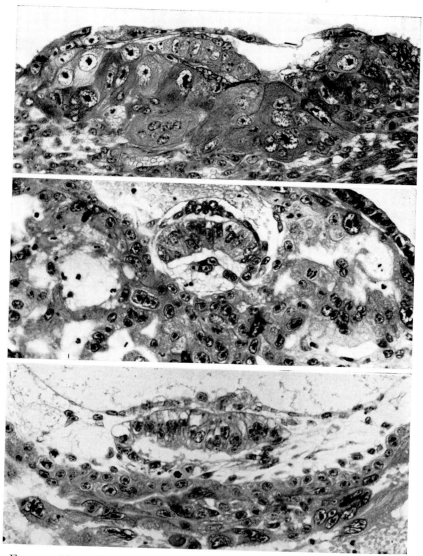

FIGURES 68 to 70 represent the three significant phases of amniogenesis in the human ova of 7, 9, and 12 days. Carnegie No. 8225, section 20-5-5; 8004, 11-4-4; and 7700, 5-7-7 respectively. All magnified × 300.

Within the next few days, the embryonic, yolk sac, body stalk, and chorionic circulations will all coalesce to become a functional unit. This takes place, as indicated previously, at about the beginning of the fourth week of gestation when the early somite embryo of 2-3 mm in length lies within a chorion of 8-18 mm in diameter. A few of these stages will be discussed and illustrated later.

Amniogenesis

This phase begins soon after implantation and is complete by the twelve-day stage as seen in Figures 68 to 70. The author can do no better than to summarize the masterful statement of Heuser and Streeter[71] who say, when writing about the monkey:

> At about the time the formative cells arrange themselves as a germ disk, an adjacent group of cells, derived from the trophoblast, becomes specialized as the amnion. The relative precocity of amniogenesis and of germ-disk development modifies the early relationships of these two discrete structures. The fluid-filled space that constitutes the amniotic cavity follows the development of the germ disk more closely than that of the amnion, and a fairly large cavity may be present before the latter can be recognized. The amnion, like the extraembryonic mesoblast and the trophoblast itself, is an extraembryonic auxiliary specialized structure that is restricted in its potential functions to a need that remains constant throughout fetal life. Judging from its poverty in blood supply and its unchanging character, one must assume for it a simple and probably mechanical role.

In the postimplantation specimen (Fig. 68), the flattened cells of the trophoblast adjacent to the germ disk are clearly seen. The amniotic cavity is not yet present, although it is readily seen in the other seven-day specimen (Fig. 14). Here again is evidence of the biologic variation. The eight-day specimen (Fig. 22) shows a prominent amniotic cavity but little if any amniogenesis. It is of interest that in the monkey ovum the cavity begins first as an indentation of the germ disk before amniogenesis. In the human ovum, however, either the cavity or the amnion may be the first to form.

By the nine-day stage, both the cavity and the amnion are evident. The latter is still attached to the trophoblast from which it arose. It looks, however, neither like the trophoblast nor the embryonic ectodermal cells which it is beginning to enclose. The primitive amniotic cells look like a wispy imperfect veil of mesenchymal or mesoblastic cells (Fig. 69).

At the twelve-day stage, the process is not yet complete. The amniogenic cells are partly epithelial and partly mesenchymal in type but are still being added to by the adjacent trophoblast (Fig. 70). The cavity is more or less imperfectly walled off from the chorionic cavity by the still-forming membrane. Mitoses are still seen in the amniogenic cells.

By the thirteen-day stage, the amnion seems to be fully formed and is "fluid tight," so to speak. It is single layered and composed of cells that appear to be stretched out mesoblastic cells (Figs. 38 and 39). It is during this stage that the surrounding mesoblast is beginning to form a second layer. Incidentally, the mesoblast is doing the same thing to the yolk sac, which is why the author believes that even in the human being the yolk sac is a truly auxiliary structure, except for the obvious embryonic endoderm!

In summary, it may be said that by day 15, just after the first missed menstrual period, the human ovum has its potential placenta well organized and potentially vascularized so that it may begin to support a bilaminar germ disk with a good amnion, yolk sac, and early mesoderm. A lot has happened during the second week of development, mostly due to the feverish growth and development of the chorion and its auxiliary structures!

It is of more than sentimental importance to the author that he helped to establish what Dr. Streeter had long believed and expressed when he said to the author, "Hertig, nature doesn't waste the precious embryonic material in making auxiliary structures."

C. TROPHOBLAST IN ORGAN CULTURE

This aspect of trophoblastic differentiation represents the work done by the author's graduate student, Tien-Wen Tao, Ph.D., in partial fulfillment of her doctoral thesis requirement. The several other parts of this thesis having to do with the tissue or organ culture of human trophoblast have been published.[140, 141, 142] The material which applies to the differentiation of trophoblast was published in 1965.

It has long been argued among anatomists precisely where and how the syncytiotrophoblast arose. It was generally agreed that primitive cytotrophoblast and syncytiotrophoblast were both present in the primate ovum soon after implantation. No one was able to agree, however, as to whether the blastocyst wall trophoblast differentiated into an intermediate form from which the two definitive cell types originated separately or whether the primitive cytotrophoblast gave rise to the primitive syncytiotrophoblast. The author has looked for many hours at serial sections of differentiating human trophoblast in ova of seven to twelve days of age. He could convince neither himself nor his colleagues just what did happen with respect to syncytiotrophoblastic differentiation.

Certain facts were clear. The first element to form after the monkey blastocyst implants is syncytiotrophoblast. It appears to arise directly from the polar trophoblastic cells, judging from the illustrations in Heuser and Streeter's 1941 Monograph.[71] The earliest stage (Carnegie No. C-522), shown in Figure 13 of the present monograph, already has two kinds of trophoblast. Heuser and Streeter, in speaking about a slightly later stage on page 26, have this to say, ". . . the trophoblast on the right side of the section, where attachment has not yet been secured, shows a differentiation into two layers, of which the outer is taking on the character of syncytium (plasmoditrophoblast)." These authors did not discuss the morphogenesis of trophoblast, per se, beyond the above statement. Thus, even in the earliest known implanted primate ova available for study, the histologic sequence of differentiation is not quite clear.

Other points generally agreed upon were that cytotrophoblast grew in the usual fashion by mitosis. Syncytiotrophoblast was, however, never seen to undergo this sort of growth. (The author used to say to his residents and students that perhaps the syncytium grew by budding or that mitosis occurred only at night. Both of these seem ridiculous in the light of later knowledge!)

It was generally agreed, even though based on circumstantial evidence, that the human chorionic gonadotropic hormone (HCG) arose in the cytotrophoblast. This was assumed largely because its peak of excretion coincided with the known peak of cytotrophoblastic growth. It was only when Tao's morphologic observations on young human trophoblast grown in organ culture were available that Midgley and Pierce's immunofluorescent conclusions were understandable. They showed that the placental hormone, human chorionic gonadotropin, was localized to syncytiotrophoblastic cells of immature placenta, hydatidiform mole, chorioadenoma destruens, and choriocarcinoma. In later electron microscopic studies on choriocarcinoma, Pierce and Midgley concluded that syncytiotrophoblast has as a principal function the secretion of chorionic gonadotropin.

It now seems clear that cytotrophoblast is the germinal bed of trophoblast, and its mature, differentiated form, syncytiotrophoblast, arises therefrom. The analogy of these two types of trophoblast to basal and squamous cells of epidermis is quite reasonable. We have long since ceased to expect mitosis in mature differentiated functional cells of any sort. Why then did it take anatomists and trophoblastologists so long to reason out the facts by simple analogy? It is just another example of the fact that the placenta, although complicated, is not quite as complicated or unique as it has been pictured. It follows the same general law of growth, differentiation, maturity, and senility as do other somatic tissues.

In any event, the morphologic details of trophoblastic differentiation in organ culture are really quite simple. The significant phases are shown in Figures 71 to 74 taken from Tao's work.[142] She cultured young normal human chorionic villi obtained at therapeutic abortion from patients in the Boston Lying-in Hospital. There were fifteen specimens in her study ranging from five to twenty-two weeks' gestational age. These villi were cultured on filter paper lying on glass beads within a Petri dish containing horse serum (20%), NCTC medium #109 (15%), and balanced salt solution (65%). Penicillin was added, 100 units per ml. The preparations were incubated at 35 to 36° in a 5% CO_2 and 95% O_2 mixture. Simple morphologic observations on paraffin sections were made at daily intervals during the first week of cultivation and at intervals of three to four days thereafter. The cultures remained viable for four to six weeks. Two examples of these straightforward morphologic studies are seen in Figures 71 and 72.

The cytotrophoblastic cells began to aggregate within twenty-

FIGURE 71. *(Upper left)* This 5-week villous trophoblast has been organ cultured for three days. The original syncytiotrophoblast is at upper right and the villous stroma at lower left. Note alteration of cytotrophoblast in the form of aggregation, chromophilia, and vacuolization of cytoplasm. Note that little remains of the original Langhans' layer which was normally prominent prior to culture. PAS-diastase. × 450.

FIGURE 72. *(Upper right)* This 11- to 12-week villous trophoblast had been cultured for four days. Note incorporation of "altered" chromophilic cytotrophoblast into the cytoplasm of the original syncytium at far right. Note further the position of this new syncytiotrophoblast ("altered cytotrophoblast") between the original syncytiotrophoblast and the remaining original cytotrophoblast. PAS-diastase. × 550.

FIGURE 73. *(Lower left)* A 6-week villus incubated for 24 hours in the usual medium to which had been added 1.5 μc of H^3-thymidine per ml. Isotopic labeling is to be noted only in the nuclei of occasional stromal cell and in many, but by no means all, of the cytotrophoblast. None of the syncytial nuclei are so labeled. Feulgen and light green stain. × 280.

FIGURE 74. *(Lower right)* A culture treated similarly to that in Fig. 73 but cultured for five additional days in a medium free from isotope. Note that isotopically labeled nuclei are scattered throughout the entire trophoblastic layer, including the original syncytiotrophoblast. Feulgen and light green stain. × 450.

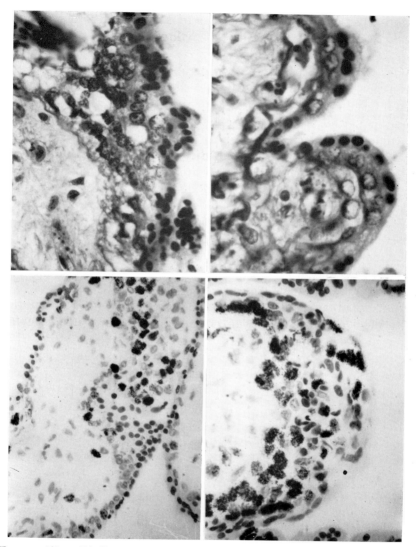

FIGURES 71 to 74 illustrate the differentiation of human syncytiotrophoblast from cytotrophoblast as shown by Tao and Hertig in 1965. Previously published by Tao and Hertig.[142] (Courtesy of the Wistar Institute of Anatomy and Biology.)

four to forty-eight hours, but this process became clearly and uniformly evident only after five to six days. Coincident with such trophoblastic aggregation (analogous to the first event in monkey implantation) there appeared intracellular vacuoles. Such structures are quite comparable to the lacunae of the nine-day human ovum (Fig. 24) during the development of the intervillous space within syncytiotrophoblast. These vacuoles contain neither fat, glycogen, nor mucopolysaccharides. (Such vacuoles or lacunae also appear in the syncytiotrophoblast of hydatidiform moles as will be discussed later.) Together with aggregation and vacuolization, there appeared an increasing basophilia in this new syncytiotrophoblast or "altered cytotrophoblast." Aside from these morphologic evidences of transformation (Fig. 71), the geographic location of the "altered cytotrophoblast," between cytotrophoblast and syncytiotrophoblast, lent convincing evidence that cytotrophoblast was indeed transforming into syncytiotrophoblast (Fig. 72).

Another approach taken by Tao to prove the origin of syncytiotrophoblast was to incubate villi in methyl-H^3-thymidine at a concentration of 1-2 μc per ml of medium. Such preparations were incubated for one hour to two weeks. Some, after six to twenty-four hours of cultivation in the isotopic medium, were removed, washed, and further cultivated in the usual medium. The initial and subsequent appearance of two comparable cultures are seen in Figures 73 and 74 respectively. Briefly these experiments showed that cytotrophoblastic nuclei took up the isotope, whereas those of the sycytiotrophoblast did not (Fig. 73). This was to have been expected since mitoses are known to occur in the former and not the latter. As the specimen was further cultured in nonisotope-containing medium, the previously labeled cytotrophoblastic nuclei appeared among those of the original syncytiotrophoblast (Fig. 74).

That this process of trophoblastic differentiation occurs *in vivo* in other primate forms (rhesus monkey) has been clearly shown by Midgley and associates in 1963.[104] Their *in vivo*-labeled Langhans' cytotrophoblast made its way into the syncytiotrophoblast, presumably in the same way as has been shown to occur *in vitro* in the human by Tao.

Tao showed, in 1964, that trophoblast will disaggregate and reaggregate as do other embryonic tissues.[141] Trophoblastic cells aggregate in the absence of mesenchymal cells but do not resemble chorionic villi. Only occasionally do they group themselves into a villus-like structure about a core of tissue resembling mesenchyme. The ability of trophoblast to reaggregate after dissociation is proportional to its degree of immaturity. At term, the maturity of the organ appears to preclude such embryonic behavior of trophoblast.

When trophoblastic and autologous liver cells (from same conceptus) are reaggregated and grown together, they appear to be incompatible; both types undergo necrosis. Similar admixtures of autologous lung and trophoblast are, however, compatible. One wonders, parenthetically, whether this has some relationship to the frequency of metastatic growth of choriocarcinoma in the lung as against its infrequency in the liver. Certainly the cells of choriocarcinoma once in the lung have little difficulty in getting to other parts of the body! Nevertheless, they seem to thrive best in the vagina, lung, and brain.

D. HISTOCHEMISTRY OF DEVELOPING TROPHOBLAST

The author and his colleagues over the years have studied the various histochemical reactions in early trophoblast.[13, 47, 97] The observations to be recorded here briefly and illustrated concern the alkaline phosphatases, glycogen, and glycoprotein in the trophoblast of the thirteen-day early villous ovum.[47] The illustrations are in Figures 75 to 87.

This specimen (F.H.W. S-54-3305) has never been assigned a Carnegie number, even though it was part of the Hertig-Rock series of ova. (The material was not prepared in Baltimore.) The ovum was comparable grossly with, and is microscopically the same as, the early thirteen-day specimen illustrated in Figure 55. It was fixed in ice cold acetone within five minutes of receipt of the uterus. Miss Eleanor C. Adams serially sectioned the specimen after paraffin embedding. The details of how this unique specimen was handled are to be found in the original publication.[47] Since it represented the only thirteen-day specimen

Alkaline phosphatase pH 9.4 | Hematoxylin-Eosin | Phosphotungstic acid hematoxylin | Acid phosphatase control | Acid phosphatase pH 5.8 | Glycogen | Glycoprotein | Ribonucleoprotein | Ribonuclease digestion | Alkaline phosphatase pH 9.4 | Alkaline phosphatase control | 5-Nucleotidase pH 7.5 | Glycerophosphatase pH 7.5 | 5-Nucleotidase water blank | 5-Nucleotidase | Alkaline phosphatase pH 9.4 | Alkaline phosphatase pH 9.4 | Alkaline phosphatase pH 9.4 | Hematoxylin-Eosin | Hematoxylin-Eosin

1	2	3	4	5	6	7	8	9	10	11	12	13	14	15	16	17	18	19	20
21	22	23	24	25	26	27	28	29	30	31	32	33	34	35	36	37	38	39	40
41	42
61
81
101
121
141
161
181
201
221
241
261																			280

Legend:
- ☐ – Endometrium only
- ⧄ – Trophoblast
- ⊠ – Trophoblast and chorionic cavity
- ⊠ (filled) – Trophoblast and chorionic cavity and germ disk

FIGURE 75. The distribution of the 280 serial sections mounted *ad seriatum* on 20 separate sets of microscopic slides. The various stains or enzymatic reactions are indicated at the top of the chart. At a glance, one may see what particular part of the implantation site or ovum is present on any specific slide and how that slide was stained or reacted. Previously published by Hertig *et al.*[47] (Courtesy of the C. V. Mosby Company.)

likely to be available for histochemical study, Miss Adams planned the seriation of the sections so that every twentieth one was placed in proper order on the same microscope slide. In this way, all parts of the endometrium, trophoblast, chorionic cavity, and embryo could be reacted or stained in any desired manner. Figure 75 (Fig. 1 in original publication[47]) shows the master plan whereby the maximum use was made of this single specimen. It will be seen at a glance that all parts of the specimen were stained or reacted by all the techniques used. Actually this ingenious technique of Miss Adams is applicable to the study of any single piece of tissue to which a variety of stains or histochemical reactions may be applied. It is the technique she has used in sectioning the many small embryos studied histochemically and reported by McKay and associates in 1953 and 1955.

The histochemical findings may be briefly summarized as follows:

1. Adenosine-5-Phosphatase

Adenosine-5-phosphatase (Figs. 76-79) is confined to the peripheral invading syncytiotrophoblast and to the stroma and glands *except* the general zone around the ovum. The few maternal cells *immediately* in contact with the syncytiotrophoblast do, however, contain the enzyme. It suggests that the trophoblast obtained the enzyme from the endometrium rather than producing it within its own cytoplasm. Actually, its function is unknown but presumably has to do with ingestion and digestion of maternal tissue.

2. Alkaline Phosphatase

This nonspecific phosphatase (Figs. 80-82), active in the alkaline range, is present throughout the syncytiotrophoblast but most strikingly in the brush border. It is also present within the bilaminar germ disk and in the maternal capillary endothelium.

3. Acid Phosphatase

This nonspecific enzyme (not illustrated) is absent from the ovum and implantation site but is strikingly present in the "Schlusscoagulum" or "scab" covering the ovum.

FIGURE 76. *(Upper left)* The ovum and surrounding implantation site. Note presence of enzyme in syncytiotrophoblast and endometrium away from but *not* near the ovum. Section 15B-1-1, × 40.

FIGURE 77. *(Upper right)* An endometrial gland which should contain the enzyme being ingested and digested by the enzyme-rich syncytiotrophoblast. The latter appears to be surrounding and engulfing the glandular secretion known to be rich in glycogen and glycoprotein. Section 15B-1-2, × 200.

FIGURE 78. *(Lower left)* The junction of endometrium on left with trophoblast on right. Note marked concentration of enzyme in syncytiotrophoblast *and* the immediately adjacent maternal stromal cells. Note also lesser concentration or absence of enzyme in stromal cells elsewhere (left), in cytoplasm of syncytiotrophoblast in center, and in cytotrophoblast at upper right. See maternal-trophoblastic junction for higher-power detail in Fig. 79. Section 1 5B-1-2, × 200.

FIGURE 79. *(Lower right)* The maternal-syncytiotrophoblastic junction to show intense concentration of enzyme in both tissues at the junction thereof but none, or greatly reduced amounts, elsewhere. Section 15B-1-2, × 400.

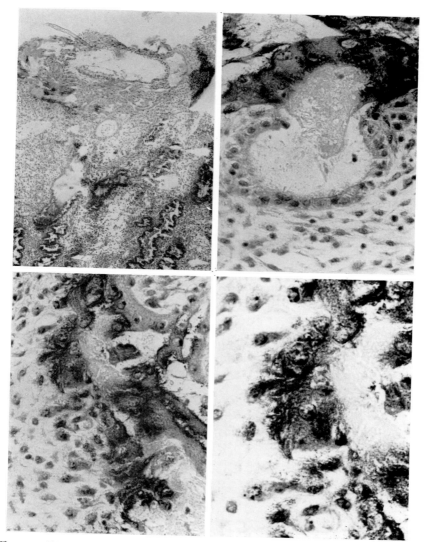

FIGURES 76 to 79 represent one section at low power and three details from another at higher power to show the distribution of the specific enzyme, adenosine-5-phosphatase, in a 13-day human ovum. F.H.W. S-54-3305, Harvard Embryo Series No. 55. Figs. 78 and 79 previously published by Hertig *et al.*[47] (Courtesy of the C. V. Mosby Company.)

FIGURE 80. *(Upper)* The enzyme is concentrated in the embryonic disk, the syncytiotrophoblast, and the maternal capillary endothelium. Section 10B-1-1, × 67.

FIGURE 81. *(Lower left)* From the equatorial region of the trophoblast of the ovum in same section as shown in Fig. 80. Note the maternal blood within the intervillous space, the strong concentration of enzyme in the brush border of the syncytiotrophoblast and in capillary endothelium. There are lesser amounts of enzyme in the cytoplasm of the syncytiotrophoblast; None is within the cytotrophoblast itself or in the endometrial stroma. Section 10B-1-1, × 150.

FIGURE 82. *(Lower right)* Another detail, from another section, to show the great concentration of the enzyme in the brush border of the syncytio-trophoblastic lacunae which will form the intervillous space by coalescence. Thus, the enzyme is present prior to the completion of that space. The enzyme is present in maternal capillary endothelium and cytoplasm of the syncytiotrophoblast but is strikingly absent in the maternal stroma and cytotrophoblast. Note junction of these latter two tissues at upper right corner. Section 1B-1-3, × 150.

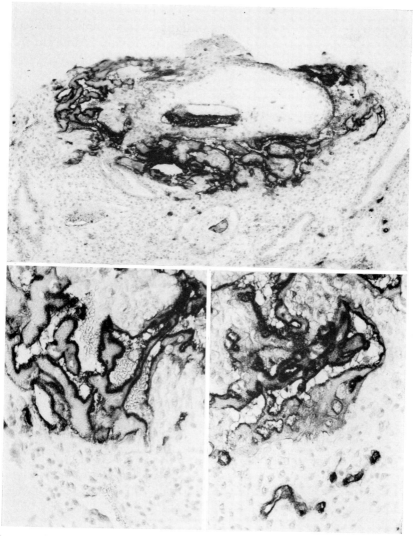

FIGURES 80 to 82 show the general and detailed distribution of the non-specific alkaline phosphatase (pH 9.4) in the 13-day ovum and its implantation site. F.H.W. S-54-3305, Harvard Embryo Series No. 55. Previously published by Hertig *et al.*[47] (Courtesy of the C. V. Mosby Company.)

4. Glycogen

Glycogen (Figs. 83-87) is abundant in the ovum and surrounding endometrium, most prominently in the endoderm and cytotrophoblast. This is thought to be of primary or indigenous type, whereas that in the syncytiotrophoblast is secondary due to ingestion of maternal tissues. Glycogen is abundant in endometrial stroma and glands.

5. Glycoprotein

This complex of carbohydrate and protein (not illustrated as digested PAS sections) is found within both the ovum and endometrium. In the former, it is within the mesenchyme or mesoblast of the chorionic cavity nearest the germ disk and in the yolk sac nearest the endoderm. Possibly the concentrations are the result of fixation artifact. It delineates beautifully, as might be expected, the basement membrane between ectoderm and endoderm. It is present within the intervillous space at one point, having been derived from the one endometrial gland in that area eroded by trophoblast (Fig. 85). The normal endometrial glands contain glycoprotein and glycogen within the glandular epithelium, and the luminal secretion.

6. Ribonucleic Acid

This precursor of protein (not illustrated in this section) is found most abundantly in the cytoplasm of the syncytiotrophoblast except for its brush border. Since it is believed to be asso-

$\rightarrow$

FIGURE 83. *(Upper)* The PAS-positive material within the embryo, cytotrophoblast, syncytiotrophoblast, and maternal glands is largely glycogen since it disappeared on diastase digestion (not illustrated). See Fig. 84 for greater detail of embryo and implantation pole of ovum. Section 6B-1-1, × 50.

FIGURE 84. *(Lower)* The germ disk and trophoblast at the implantation pole of the ovum. Note heavy concentration of glycogen in endoderm and mesoblast of chorion but lesser amounts in ectoderm. The glycogen within the cytotrophoblast is coarse and irregular but is finely rounded within the syncytiotrophoblast. For specific details of glycogen distribution within trophoblast, refer to Figs. 85 to 87. Section 6B-1-1, × 200.

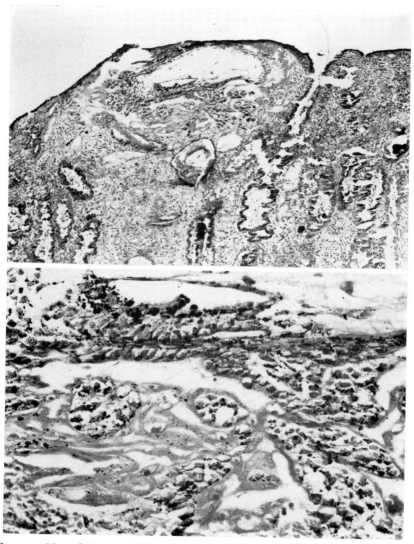

FIGURES 83 and 84 are PAS-undigested sections of a 13-day human ovum to show general and detailed distribution of glycogen *and* glycoprotein throughout the ovum and implantation site. F.H.W. S-54-3305, Harvard Embryo Series No. 55. Previously published by Hertig *et al.*[47] (Courtesy of the C. V. Mosby Company.)

FIGURE 85. *(Upper)* A detailed view of the junction between the syncytiotrophoblast and cytotrophoblast, diagonally upper right, and the maternal gland and stroma, diagonally lower left. The luminal contents of the gland, now being incorporated into the syncytiotrophoblast as well as into the intervillous space, contain both glycogen and glycoprotein. Note particularly the fusion of syncytiotrophoblast with glandular epithelial nuclei and the definite, easily seen, rounded masses of glycogen derived from the ingested glandular cytoplasm. This picture illustrates well the difference in appearance between granules of indigenous glycogen in maternal cells and in ovular cytotrophoblast and the ingested rounded masses of glycogen, "lollipops," within the syncytiotrophoblast. Section 6B-1-1, × 400.

FIGURE 86. *(Lower left)* The junction of trophoblast with maternal stroma. At left middle center is a stromal cell in the act of being surrounded by the invading syncytiotrophoblast. Note rounded masses of ingested glycogen, "lollipops," in cytoplasm of latter (upper part of picture) and coarse blocks or granules of indigenous glycogen in cytotrophoblast (right center). The maternal stroma at lower left also contains some glycogen within its cytoplasm. Section 6B-1-1, × 400.

FIGURE 87. *(Lower right)* The syncytiotrophoblast at the equatorial pole of the ovum seen in Fig. 83. This picture shows particularly well the difference between the indigenous glycogen of the cytotrophoblast at bottom and right center and the ingested glycogen, "lollipops," of the syncytiotrophoblast. Section 6B-1-1, × 400.

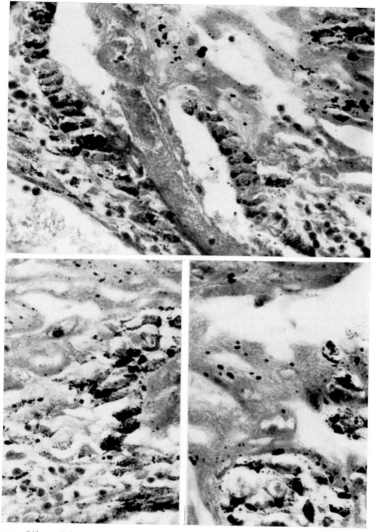

FIGURES 85 to 87 are other PAS-undigested, histologic details of the same 13-day human ovum shown in the previous nine figures. In the original paper, Figs. 86 and 87 are in color and show the glycogen very well. F.H.W. S-54-3305, Harvard Embryo Series No. 55. Previously published by Hertig *et al.*[47] (Courtesy of the C. V. Mosby Company.)

ciated with protein synthesis and is found in rapidly growing tissues, it is expectedly found in the cytotrophoblast, chorionic mesoblast, and ectoderm. Within the endometrium it is confined to the basal third, in keeping with its absence during the secretory phase of the cycle as shown by McKay and associates in 1956.[98]

E. PHYSIOLOGIC SIGNIFICANCE OF THESE HISTOCHEMICAL FINDINGS

It is clear that the invading syncytiotrophoblast is enzymatically the more active of the two trophoblastic elements. It contains striking amounts of adenosine-5-phosphatase. This specific phosphatase hydrolyzes the nucleotide to a nucleoside. The fact that the invading trophoblast, the few contiguous stromal cells, and the endometrial glands and stroma *elsewhere* all contain large amounts of the enzyme must have some significance (Figs. 76-79). It suggests that the trophoblast obtains the enzyme from the maternal tissue during the process of ingestion and digestion of the latter. It is as though a "wave" of the enzyme flows or is sucked into the ovum, leaving a "trough" or low concentration of the enzyme between the main maternal source and the ovum itself. Unlike the nonspecific alkaline phosphatase (Figs. 80-82), this enzyme is strongly concentrated within the cytoplasm of the syncytiotrophoblast and not in the brush border.

Although the nonspecific alkaline phosphatase (Fig. 82) is present in the cytoplasm of the syncytiotrophoblast, its tremendous concentration in the brush border is striking. The brush border lines the intervillous space and its precursors, the syncytiotrophoblastic lacunae. That this concentration of enzyme must play a role in transfer of materials across the so-called placental barrier is suggested by the very localization of the enzyme, if for no other reason. In this regard, it is well to note that another site of known exchange, the capillary endothelium, possesses this same enzyme (Fig. 82). It is strikingly absent in the endothelium of the veins and spiral arterioles of the endometrium where little or no exchange takes place.

The indigenous glycogen is concentrated within the cytotrophoblast, the chorionic mesoblast, and particularly the endoderm and germ cells of the embryonic disk. This suggests an active carbohydrate metabolism. The endometrial stromal and glandular cells also contain abundant amounts of glycogen, appearing within the cytoplasm as coarse irregular masses or granules. This general distribution is appreciated in Figure 83, the details of which are in Figure 84.

Although the actively invading syncytiotrophoblast contains large rounded masses of glycogen, "lollipops," an obvious metaphor, these are clearly from ingested maternal tissue rather than from indigenous metabolic sources. The details of this process are to be seen in Figures 85 to 87. Whether the synctiotrophoblast obtains all of its own nutritional requirements as well as those for the rest of the ovum by the processes of ingestion and digestion is not known. Since the syncytiotrophoblast, by its relatively large surface, has much more maternal contact, blood, and tissue than the rest of the ovum, this concept is probably so. At least it makes logical and teleological, if not biological, sense.

It was the study of this critical phase of implantation by special techniques that prompted the author to regard trophoblast as nature's first experiment with cancer and man's first cure (choriocarcinoma). This concept was used as the title for the George H. Whipple Lecture (not published) given at Rochester, New York, during September of 1965.

FIGURE 88. *(Upper left)* A 16-day ovum to show the "scab" or Schlusscoagulum with recent hemorrhage of maternal origin escaping from beneath its edge. Note early decidual transformation of endometrial surface. Carnegie No. 7802, F.H.W. S-40-1524, sequence 4, × 6. Previously published by Hertig and Rock.[55] (Courtesy of the C. V. Mosby Company, and Carnegie Institution of Washington.)

FIGURE 89. *(Upper right)* A 17-day implantation site at left margin of posterior uterine wall (right side of photograph); the fundus is at the top. Note fully developed decidua and small amount of hemorrhage from the edge of the ovum. The latter shows the characteristic beading as a dark dotted circle owing to maternal blood within the intervillous space. Carnegie No. 8602, F.H.W. S-48-2088, sequence 1, × 1.5. Previously published by Hertig *et al.*[60] (Courtesy of the Wistar Institute of Anatomy and Biology, and Carnegie Institution of Washington.)

FIGURE 90. *(Lower left)* An 18- to 19-day ovum seen as rounded mass at top center. Note intact mucosal surface over the ovum. Other details of this specimen are seen in Figs. 45 to 47, and 93. Carnegie No. 8671 (from Free Hospital for Women) sequence 1, × 1.5. (Courtesy of Carnegie Institution of Washington.)

FIGURE 91. *(Lower right)* A 19-day ovum originally described by Heuser in 1932. Note mottling of decidua over the ovum due to necrosis and hemorrhage. Carnegie No. 5960, sequence 1, × 2. Previously published by Heuser.[67] (Courtesy of Carnegie Institution of Washington.)

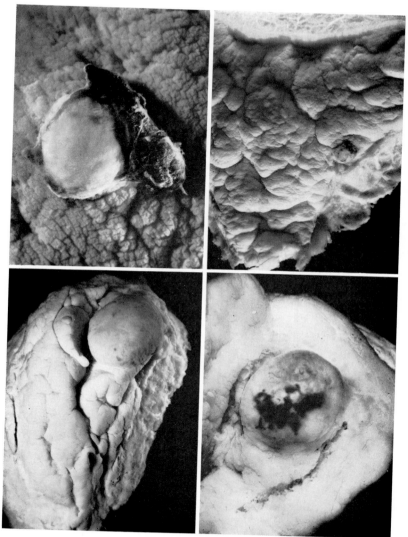

FIGURES 88 to 91 show the significant gross features of implantation sites of villous ova during the third week of development.

CHAPTER V

CHORION-EMBRYO RELATIONSHIPS

OVER the years, the author has attempted to teach medical students and residents the essential gross relationships between the growing uterus, chorion, amnion, umbilical cord, and embryo during the first two and one-half months of gestation. It is during this critical period of early development that all of these anatomic relationships are being established in their definitive form. In point of time, this occupies the first eight weeks of actual development of the conceptus, or ten weeks in terms of the menstrual age of the pregnancy. By the end of this period, the uterus has begun to assume its globular shape and soft consistency. The chorion now fills but does not yet obliterate the uterine cavity. The definitive placenta is beginning to assume its thick discoid form by transformation of the *chorion frondosum*. The thin membranous portion, the *chorion laeve,* is becoming thinner, and the villi are becoming ischemic with subsequent atrophy. The amnion is now beginning to fill the chorion but is attached only to the umbilical cord. The embryo has become a fetus.

Most of the pregnancies destined to abort will have aborted. All of the congenital anomalies, whether the patient aborts or not, are either grossly or microscopically visible. It is during this time that maternal viral infections damage the embryo. The illustrations used here show some of these relationships. These figures have been gathered from the author's own material, from the files of the Carnegie embryological collections, and from Patten's text book on embryology.[108]

The first four illustrations (Figs. 88-91) give the practicing pathologist the changing gross appearances of the implantation site during the third week of gestation. The microscopic details of villus formation from two of these specimens, the sixteen- and nineteen-day specimens shown grossly in Figures 88 and 90,

120

have already been illustrated microscopically in Figures 40, 41, and 47 respectively. Since pathologists are the first persons who are likely to see this stage of implantation and since only isolated stages have been reported even in the anatomic literature, the author believes that these normal developmental changes in the pregnant uterus should be made available in the pathologic literature.

It is during this third week of development that uteroplacental circulation is well established, the decidua well formed, the *decidua capsularis* over the embryo healed, and the early villous ovum transformed into a rapidly expanding chorion. The elevation of the endometrium by the interstitially implanted ovum is at first flattened and then rounded, increasing in size from approximately 5 to 20 mm in greatest diameter. The early villous ovum bleeds from beneath the "scab" at or just after the first missed period (Figs. 37 and 88).

As the reparative process of the *decidua capsularis* proceeds, the red-beaded appearance of the underlying intervillous blood (Fig. 89) is lost. The decidua overlying the chorion, although thin and intact (Fig. 90), soon takes on a mottled appearance (Fig. 91). This is due to variable degrees of congestion, hemorrhage, and actual tissue necrosis. In the author's experience, such alterations are universally present to some degree or other until the middle of pregnancy. At this time, the *decidua capsularis* fuses with the contiguous *decidua vera* and obliterates the uterine cavity. Such obliteration is analogous to the obliteration of serous cavities by the organization of exudate.

The importance of this alteration of the *decidua capsularis* lies in the fact that this tissue may give rise to clinical bleeding. How frequently this occurs is impossible to state. It is important to realize, however, that the potential for uterine bleeding is present in all normal pregnancies without inevitable jeopardy to the conceptus. When such clinical bleeding occurs, it may be interpreted as a "threatened abortion" but without subsequent abortion. Since the probable incidence of spontaneous abortion is about 12 to 15 per cent, it may give some clue as to how frequently normal patients may bleed from necrotic *decidua capsularis* without subsequently aborting. All patients prior to

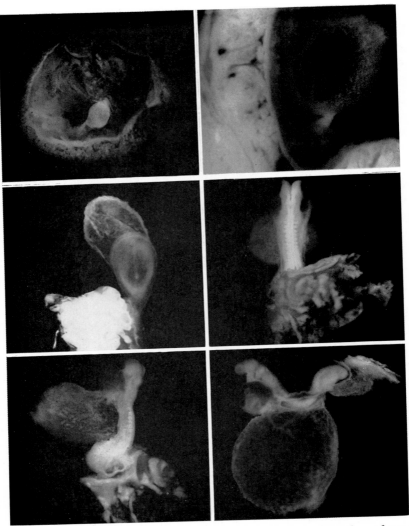

FIGURES 92 to 97 show a series of human chorions or portions thereof ranging in developmental ages from about 18 to 24 days. All were dissected by
the late Dr. Chester H. Heuser and show clearly the development of the
body stalk at the caudal end of the embryo with its subsequent shift to a
ventral position.

FIGURE 92. *(Upper left)* An 18-day chorion, hemisected with removal of
gelatinous magma so as to show the embryo attached by its body stalk to
the implantation pole of the chorion. (This specimen, one of twins, aborted
within 24 hrs after the surgical removal of the corpus luteum owing to
an ovarian tumor. From Boston Lying-in Hospital.) Carnegie 7170A,
sequence 1, × 5. (Courtesy of Carnegie Institution of Washington.)

FIGURE 93. *(Upper right)* A high-power view of an embryo (18 to 19 days) seen at lower power in Fig. 45. Note simple, early, branching chorionic villi at left. The embryo, consisting largely of a distended yolk sac with blood islands, occupies the center. The germ disk is seen on edge as a shadowy curved line parallel to the chorionic membrane. The body stalk is plainly seen as an opaque mass at the caudal end of the embryo merging into the mesenchyme of the chorion from which it arose. Carnegie 8671, sequence 6, × 12. Previously published by Hertig and Gore.[50] (Courtesy of the C. V. Mosby Company, and Carnegie Institution of Washington.)

FIGURE 94. *(Center left)* The embryonic disk of the Heuser embryo as viewed from above. The closely applied amnion covers the pear-shaped, trilaminar, presomite embryo which contains a primitive streak and Hensen's node. The yolk sac is collapsed artifactitiously (top center). Note the body stalk attaching the caudal end of the embryo to the white opaque chorionic mass. The gross implantation site is seen in Fig. 91; various aspects of angiogenesis and villus development are seen in Figs. 66 and 67. Carnegie No. 5960, sequence 4, × 12. Previously published by Heuser.[67] (Courtesy of Carnegie Institution of Washington.)

FIGURE 95. *(Center right)* A 10-somite embryo viewed from above. The amnion has been dissected off to reveal details of somite, heart, and nervous system formation. The distended yolk sac is ventral (or in the background). The caudal end of the embryo is attached to the chorion by its body stalk, better seen in Fig. 96. Carnegie No. 5074, × 10. Previously published by Heuser and Corner.[68] (Courtesy of Carnegie Institution of Washington.)

FIGURE 96. *(Lower left)* A lateral view of the same specimen as seen in Fig. 95. Note broad attachment of embryo, with some amnion still present, to chorion by broad mass of body stalk. The attachment is both caudal and dorsal. Contrast this with specimen in Fig. 97 in which the attachment of the body stalk has shifted ventrally owing to caudal growth of embryo. Carnegie No. 5074, × 10. Previously published by Heuser and Corner.[68] (Courtesy of Carnegie Institution of Washington.)

FIGURE 97. *(Lower right)* A 19-somite Horizon XI embryo, with amnion partially removed, to show caudo-ventral attachment of body stalk. Note that the body stalk mass, adherent to the ventral aspect of the embryo, is separated from the caudal aspect of the embryo by the remnant of the amnion. This illustrates clearly the mechanism through caudal growth of the embryo by which the body stalk assumes its ultimate ventral position. Note further the oval opening, resembling a cut edge, connecting the coelomic tract of the embryo and the exocoelomic or chorionic cavity. It is through this wide portal that nutrient fluid pulsates synchronously with the heart beat. The heart is ventral and to the left. The large yolk sac is ventral and below. Carnegie No. 6050, sequence 9, × 10. Previously published by Streeter.[132] (Courtesy of Carnegie Institution of Washington.)

abortion threaten to abort (i.e. they bleed). It is generally agreed by experienced clinicians that approximately 50 per cent of patients who threaten to abort do not carry out the threat but go on to term. Hence, innocuous bleeding from the top of a normal ovum may occur in approximately 10 per cent of normally pregnant patients.

This clinico-anatomic-pathologic fact is of great practical importance. It emphasizes that all patients who bleed are not necessarily going to abort. Therefore, the enthusiastic clinician who vigorously treats his threatening aborters would do well to realize that nature would have cured about half of them without his administrations.

Moreover, let the medicolegal expert be aware of this simple basis for bleeding in early normal pregnancy. The patient who is in an automobile accident and happens to bleed coincidentally or shortly thereafter probably bleeds from the top of a normal ovum. If she subsequently gives rise to a congenitally defective infant, such bleeding could in no possible manner have caused the defect. The author once had the satisfaction of preventing a group of plaintiffs from collecting outrageously large damages for such alleged causal relationship as cited above. The medical expert who testifies in court that trauma causes abortion or congenital defects is usually wrong—embryologically. More will be said on this matter in the chapter on spontaneous abortion.

The evolution of the umbilical cord always seems to baffle the medical student and young obstetrician. A typical question is, "How does the body stalk at the caudal end of the embryonic disk come eventually to be ventrally attached to the center of the abdominal wall?" The illustrations (Figs. 92-97) show the critical stages in this transformation and migration.

The body stalk is clearly evident soon after "the axis of the germ disk has been defined," as stated by Streeter for his Horizon VII.[137] The chorionic villi are branching, and the ovum is about sixteen days of age. The beginning of body stalk formation, condensation of chorionic mesoblast caudal to the primitive streak, is seen, however, when the villi are still simple (Horizon VI). Thus the two specimens, the thirteen- and sixteen-day ova (Carnegie No. 7801 and 7802) described by Heuser, Rock, and the author[69] cover these early stages of body stalk formation. The gross appearance of these specimens is to be seen in Figures 37 and 88, and the microscopic features in Figures 38 to 42. The gross appearance of the early body stalk, dissected free of the surrounding *magma reticulare* and viewed from various aspects, may be seen in Figures 92 to 94.

As the embryo reaches the early somite stage of Horizon X with four to twelve pairs of body segments, it measures about 1.5 to 2 mm in length. The chorion is 8 to 15 mm in diameter, and the embryonic-chorionic circulation is beginning to become a functioning vascular unit. (The ovum is developmentally 22 ± 1 days of age.) The body stalk is very prominent, especially when viewed laterally, and is still essentially a caudal structure as illustrated in Figures 95 and 96.

The critical shift of the body stalk from its caudal to ventral position begins soon after the above stage or horizon. This change in position of body stalk coincides with the rapid growth of the embryo, probably associated with completion of the embry-onic-chorionic circulation. Although the body stalk appears to have shifted ventrally, this relationship is actually due to caudal growth of the embryo. Close examination of Figure 97 will show that the increasing mass of the body stalk is literally being "invaded" by the growing caudal end of the embryo, thus displacing the main mass of the body stalk ventrally. The embryo is protected, of course, by its amnion.

This stage is also significant since it shows the mechanism by which the amnion first becomes applied to the surface of the body stalk, ultimately to cover completely the umbilical cord. Thus, the beginning of this shift in the relationship of the embryo to its body stalk begins in Horizon XI. The twenty-four-day embryo is now 2.5 to 3 mm in length and possesses a heart which is just beginning to beat or flutter. There are thirteen to twenty pairs of somites, a primitive foregut and hindgut communicating broadly with the yolk sac cavity, a feature readily seen in Figure 97. This very tiny embryo lies in a relatively enormous chorionic cavity of 15 to 18 mm in diameter. The gentle ebb and flow of fluid from the intraembryonic coelomic tract to the extraembryonic coelomic cavity (chorionic) is the main source

FIGURE 98. *(Upper)* A hemisected human chorion, 21 mm in diameter, containing a normal 14-somite embryo, 2.4 mm in length, Horizon XI, whose developmental age is about 24 days. This perfect example of a stage of human development, of which there are not too many well-preserved and studied examples, was originally published in monograph form by Heuser in 1930, although this gross photograph was not used. It is illustrated here to emphasize the small embryo with its closely applied amnion, the large yolk sac, the short (not visible) body stalk, and the relatively enormous size of the chorionic cavity. The latter functions as a tissue culture-like chamber. Carnegie No. 4529, sequence 1, × 3. (Courtesy of Carnegie Institution of Washington.)

FIGURE 99. *(Lower)* A pathological condition, namely an ectopic pregnancy containing a normal 26-somite embryo, 3 mm long, Horizon XII, of 26 days' developmental age. Although the embryo is not a particularly good example of this phase of human development and the intervillous space is greatly distended by recent blood clot, the picture of the chorionic villi gives the observer a clear idea of what a human chorion is like in three dimensions. The chorionic membrane, the intervillous space, and the tree-like villi attached to the "floor" of the placenta are easily identified. Carnegie No. 6937, × 2. (Courtesy of Carnegie Institution of Washington.)

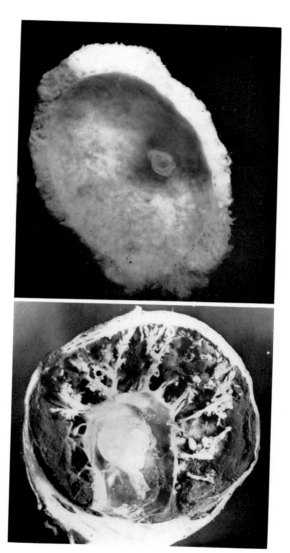

FIGURES 98 and 99

FIGURE 100. *(Upper left)* Note relatively large chorionic cavity and the small embryo, better seen in Fig. 101. Note also the hemorrhagic polyp which may be a source of a threatened but not completed abortion. Carnegie No. 7999, F.H.W. S-42-429, sequence 1, × 2.

FIGURE 101. *(Upper right)* The 28-somite embryo from the previous specimen. The picture was used to show the short ventral cord (passing under the embryo) and the constricted yolk sac. The developing nervous system, the otic vesicle, and the branchial arches are clearly visible. Carnegie No. 7999, sequence 9, × 13.

FIGURE 102. *(Lower left)* This chorion was used to illustrate the very important anatomic fact that the tips of immature chorionic villi may be easily torn owing to the trophoblastic cell columns at their periphery. Note that the placental "floor" or basal plate is still attached to the uterus, although the tips of the villi have been artifactitously torn. Carnegie No. 8306 (from Johns Hopkins Hospital, No. 62610) sequence 1, × 2.

FIGURE 103. *(Lower right)* The normal embryo from the previous figure. Note the proximity of the embryo to its chorion owing to the normally short cord whose ventral insertion is not visible. The yolk sac is on the right. The curvature and twist in the embryonic axis are normal. The simply branched villi are normal except that their trophoblastic tips or cell columns, together with the placental "floor," are missing. The amnion has been dissected off for photographic purposes; however, it was closely applied to the embryo. Carnegie 8306, sequence 3, × 5.

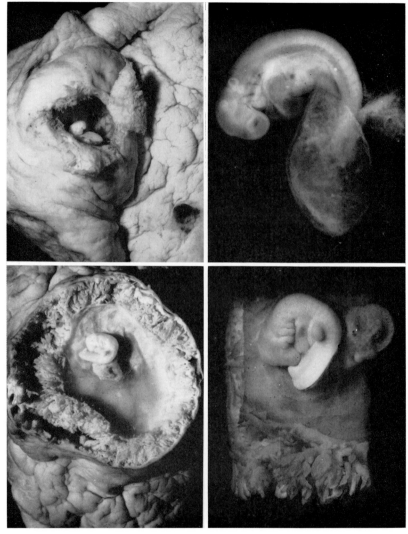

FIGURES 100 to 103 show two human chorions of 28 days' developmental age in their normal relation to the uterus. The author dissected the upper one which reveals the thick *chorion laeve* and the late somite embryo within. Dr. Heuser dissected the other in the equatorial plane revealing the expected large chorion and the small normal embryo of about 6 mm with characteristic three branchial arches, the head at right angles to the body, and the beginning limb buds. (All figures courtesy of Carnegie Institution of Washington.)

FIGURE 104. *(Upper)* A hemisected human chorion containing an embryo of about 18.5 mm, Horizon XIX. The chorion measured approximately $45 \times 40 \times 25$ mm. Clearly evident is the amnion which is closely applied to the embryo but is unattached to the chorion except by the umbilical cord. The yolk sac is at the right, still distended but probably waning in its function. Note luxuriant, finely branched villi which have been entirely removed from the basal plate of the placenta, probably at hysterotomy. Carnegie No. 8537A, sequence 1, × 1.5. Previously published by McKay *et al.*[102] (Courtesy of the C. V. Mosby Company, and Carnegie Institution of Washington.)

FIGURE 105. *(Lower)* A slightly older embryo than seen in Fig. 104 but removed from its chorionic sac. The amnion is still intact except at the stump of the cord. The latter is covered by amnion owing to the "prolapse" of the embryo into its own amniotic sac during its growth and development. The embryo is about 22 mm in length and lies within Streeter's Horizon XXI. Its chorion was approximately $54 \times 45 \times 30$ mm in its various diameters. This relationship of amnion to chorion explains the uncommon variety of incomplete abortion consisting of a normal embryo inside an intact amnion. Carnegie No. 7554, × 1.6. (Courtesy of Carnegie Institution of Washington.)

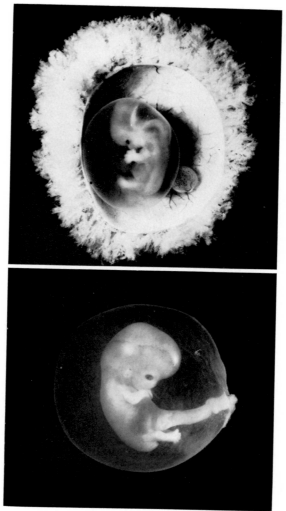

Figures 104 and 105 are probably the best illustrations in existence to show the relationship of the amnion to the chorion at 39 days and the ease with which it may be removed at 43 days. Mr. Chester Reather, now chief of photography at the Johns Hopkins Hospital, won a first prize in medical photography for Fig. 104.

of nutrition for the embryo at this time.[132] Thus, the embryo lives in a large tissue culture chamber whose fluid is a thixotropic gel, as shown by McKay and associates in 1955 and 1958.

This disparity in embryonic and chorionic size, well-seen in Figure 98, becomes gradually less, but it is still present in Horizon XXIII just beyond the stage shown in Figure 104. Horizon XXIII includes embryos of 28 to 30 mm in length with a chorion measuring up to 80 mm in diameter. (The developmental age is 47 ± 1 days).

As the embryo develops, the connection between the gut and yolk stalk becomes progressively constricted, as seen in Figures 98 and 101. Meanwhile the body stalk mass increases in length and breadth and becomes increasingly covered by the expanding amnion. It is as though the embryo progressively prolapses into its own amniotic cavity and pulls its cord behind it. In so doing, the cord becomes increasingly covered by the amnion since the latter has, from the beginning, been attached to the embryo. The tenuous nature of the attachment of the umbilical cord to the chorion is illustrated in Figure 105. This embryo (43 ± 1 days of age) of approximately 22 mm in length lay within a chorion of about 65 mm in maximum diameter. The amnion at this stage has not yet attached itself to the chorion as illustrated in Figure 104. Indeed the amnion does not fuse with the chorion until about midterm. At this time the *chorion laeve,* covered by *decidua capsularis,* fuses with the *decidua vera* as stated before. Thus, the chorionic and the uterine cavities become obliterated at about the same time (i.e. at midterm).

It is hoped that this brief description of the changes in the chorionic-embryonic relationship during the eight weeks of development will be helpful to the pathologist. The few basic principles touched upon are necessary to the pathologist if he wishes to examine with interest and understanding the material from a spontaneous abortion or, indeed, any placenta. Should the reader be interested in the gradual and detailed stages of umbilical cord formation illustrated by the late great medical artist Max Brödel, reference may be made to Cullen's classic book on diseases of the umbilicus published in 1916.[19] This is the only publication to date known to the author in which the various complicated structures that lie within the umbilical cord are illustrated during its complicated growth and development.

Figure 106, though diagrammatic, is the best representation of the several stages of pregnancy up to eight weeks' developmental age known to the author. These diagrams, in conjunction with the actual specimens shown in Figures 88 to 105, should make the overall gross development of the pregnant uterus and its passenger clear to the pathologist.

The author, in his practice of obstetrical pathology, has found the various charts or tables prepared by the late Dr. Streeter invaluable.[131, 137] Since these are either out of print and hard for the pathologist to secure, or have not even been published at all, their inclusion in this chapter seems worthwhile. They are listed in order of their probable use in the pathology laboratory.

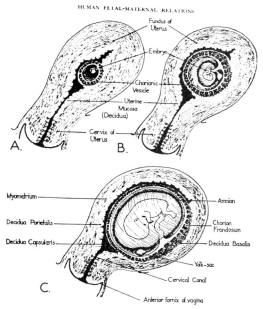

FIGURE 106. Pregnant uteri at 3, 5, and 8 weeks' developmental age to show the relationship of embryos and their membranes to the uterus. Embryos and their membranes are drawn to actual size. Uterus is within actual size range—about correct for a small primipara: A. at 3 weeks; B. at 5 weeks; C. at 8 weeks' fertilization age. Previously published by Patten.[108] (Courtesy of Dr. B. M. Patten, and the Blakiston Company.)

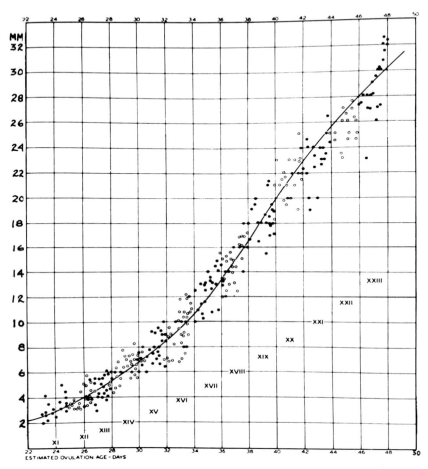

FIGURE 107. "Graphic plot of specimens in the Carnegie Embryological Collection which have been surveyed and assigned to Horizons XI to XXIII. Embryos belonging to odd-numbered horizons are represented by black dots, and those of even-numbered horizons by white circles." The embryological or ovulation age in increments of two days is along the top and bottom of the graph, and the crown rump (CR) length of the embryo in increments of 2 mm is at the side. Previously published by Streeter.[136] (Courtesy of Carnegie Institution of Washington.)

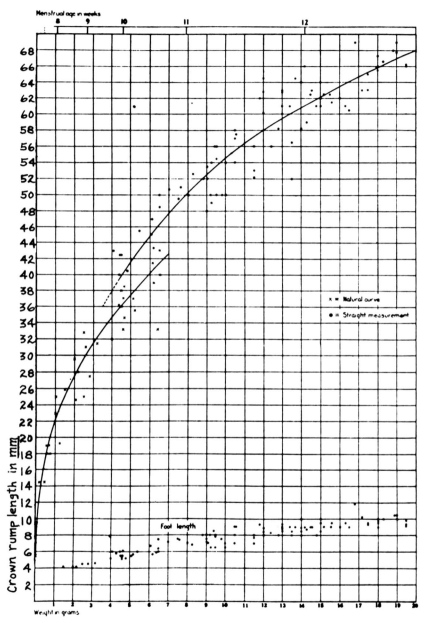

FIGURE 108. A graph showing the correlation of sitting height or crown rump length of human embryos from approximately 7 to 13 weeks' *menstrual* age. Note that the corresponding weight and foot length are also correlated with the stage of pregnancy. Published originally by Streeter.[131] (Courtesy of Carnegie Institution of Washington.)

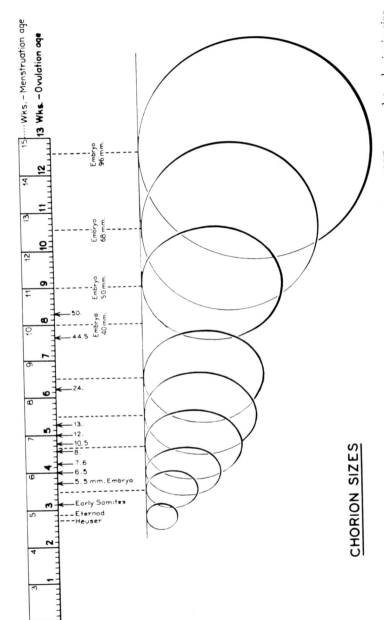

CHORION SIZES

FIGURE 109. An unpublished chart drawn for Dr. Streeter by Mr. Didusch in 1937 to correlate chorionic size with that of the embryo during the first thirteen weeks of development. (Courtesy of Carnegie Institution of Washington.) This is reduced to approximately two-thirds natural size.

TABLE II

MEAN SITTING HEIGHT AND WEIGHT, CORRELATED WITH MENSTRUAL AGE FROM 8 WEEKS TO TERM.[131]

Based on 704 specimens of the Carnegie Embryological Collection, distributed as follows: white males 252; white females 241; negro males 66; negro females 60; other races, males 15, females 11; unidentified as to race or sex, 59.

Menstrual Age weeks	Sitting Height at end of Week mm	Increment in Height mm	Increment in Height %	Formalin Weight* grams	Increment in Weight grams	Increment in Weight %
8	23			1.1		
9	31	8	26	2.7	1.6	59.3
10	40	9	22.5	4.6	1.9	41.3
11	50	10	20	7.9	3.3	41.8
12	61	11	18	14.2	6.3	44.4
13	74	13	17.6	26	11.8	45.4
14	87	13	15	45	19	42.2
15	101	14	14	72	27	37.5
16	116	15	13	108	36	33.3
17	130	14	10.8	150	42	28
18	142	12	8.4	198	48	24.2
19	153	11	7.2	253	55	21.7
20	164	11	6.7	316	63	20
21	175	11	6.3	385	69	18
22	186	11	6	460	75	16.3
23	197	11	5.6	542	82	15
24	208	11	5.3	630	88	14
25	218	10	4.6	723	93	13
26	228	10	4.4	823	100	12.2
27	238	10	4.2	930	107	11.5
28	247	9	3.6	1,045	115	11
29	256	9	3.5	1,174	129	11
30	265	9	3.4	1,323	149	11.3
31	274	9	3.3	1,492	169	11.3
32	283	9	3.4	1,680	188	11.2
33	293	10	3.1	1,876	196	10.4
34	302	9	3	2,074	198	9.5
35	311	9	3	2,274	200	8.8
36	321	10	3.1	2,478	204	8.2
37	331	10	3	2,690	212	8
38	341	10	3	2,914	224	7.7
39	352	11	3.1	3,150	236	7.5
40	362	10	2.8	3,405	255	7.5

* Many of the specimens between the twenty-eighth and fortieth weeks were embalmed, and in these cases the weight given is the fresh weight plus 5 per cent.

In Figure 107, the crown rump length or sitting height of the human embryo of 2 to 32 mm has been correlated with developmental ages in days and placed within Streeter's "Developmental Horizons in Human Embryos." The horizons are in roman numerals.[137]

In Figure 108, the sitting height or crown rump length of the human embryo has been correlated with its foot length, its weight in grams, and its *menstrual age* from approximately seven to thirteen weeks.[131] The pathologist is expected by the clinician to give the *menstrual age* of the conceptus. Developmental ages and menstrual ages can be confusing unless definitely stated since the latter ages are actually two weeks longer than the former.

In Figure 109, the size of the normal human chorion has been correlated with the age and size of the embryo. This chart was never published by Dr. Streeter, but the author and other pathologists have found it invaluable in evaluating normal and abnormal conceptuses.

CHAPTER VI

PATHOLOGICAL TROPHOBLAST—EARLY

INTRODUCTION

THE material to be presented in *this* chapter is largely from the early ova found by Hertig and Rock at the Free Hospital for Women.[60] The specimens are all less than two weeks of age. Although all are abnormal in one way or another, they were found in uteri removed surgically for various indications from women of proven normal fertility.

These specimens may well be potential abortuses. It is not surprising that normally fertile women produce defective conceptuses as do all other living creatures. The interested reader is referred to the classic article by Corner who showed that the domestic pig (as do all mammals) has a predictable fetal loss which is greatest during the early stages of gestation.[16] The author and his colleagues have similarly shown the same sort of fertility or infertility rates for the human being.[61] The graph at the end of this chapter (Fig. 139) is a résumé of the fertility rate in this series of 210 patients of known fertility.

Aside from the determination of fertility rate in the human being, the series of thirty-four ova—good, bad and indifferent—gives definitive data on the time of human ovulation. Figure 138 shows the distribution of presumed times of ovulation of the thirty-four specimens based on all parameters available to Hertig and Rock. It will be seen at a glance that the "bad eggs" tend to ovulate relatively late, after the fourteenth day. It suggests that the unfertilized ovum becomes "stale" while awaiting the completion of the enormously complex process of oocytic maturation and ovulation. It seems unlikely that an intrinsically "bad egg" delays ovulation, per se. Otherwise, why would Gemzell and others be getting such a rash of multiple births by the artificial, hormonal stimulation of ovulation in the human

female?[28] Many of the oocytes, thus therapeutically ovulated,
were normally destined to languish in the graafian follicle. It
has been known for ages that the human being tends to produce
but one baby at a time. It has been known for many years by
anatomists and pathologists that nonovulated oocytes undergo
involution or degeneration. The interested reader is referred to
the transcript of a conference held on human ovulation in
September 1962.[80] The author's chapter goes into some detail
on the data summarized in Figure 138.[45, 46]

SEGMENTING EGGS

In this series of thirty-four fertilized eggs, there were eight
found during the segmenting, preimplantation state.[62] Of these,
four were found to be normal, and four were abnormal. The
three normal ones (one was lost prior to microscopic sectioning)
are to be seen in Figures 7 to 11. Only one of the four abnormal
ones is illustrated here (Figs. 110-115). When this specimen was
found in the laboratory, the Boston Red Sox and the St. Louis
Cardinals were engaged in the 1946 World Series in Boston at
Fenway Park. The baseball fan will remember that during the
critical seventh game, in the ninth inning, Dominic DiMaggio
hit his timely double which tied the game and the Series, up
to that time. The avid baseball fan will also remember that
Johnny Pesky, later to become the Red Sox manager, neglected
to throw a fielded ball to home plate and thus the Series was lost.
If memory serves the author, that was the last time the Sox
played in a World Series.* Since this specimen was literally found
in the laboratory at the moment of DiMaggio's double, the segmenting morula has been known, at least to the author, as the
"DiMaggio Ovum." Although the author and his colleagues were
hopeful of its value when first found, the value of the egg was
comparable to the outcome of the Series, both bad. When this
specimen, along with other segmenting ova, was discussed in

---

* Since this manuscript was written, the Boston Red Sox and the St. Louis
Cardinals have again clashed in the World Series (1967). Alas the result was
the same, even to the Boston team losing the seventh and critical game. The only
difference in these series, twenty-one years apart, was the fact that no human eggs
were being searched for at the time of the second.

the 1954 *Contributions to Embryology,*[62] Dr. George W. Corner, then editor, deleted the above account of when the specimen was found as being "too temporal." My apologies to my friend, Dr. Corner, and to any reader who so agrees. This is, however, a Weller Lecture Monograph and the author has related in lectures this same story many times. The audience always seems to like it. It makes human embryology even more "human."

All defective segmenting eggs seem to have certain features in common: necrotic blastomeres, multinucleated blastomeres, and distortion of embryonic and trophoblastic blastomeres. Moreover, there is a tendency for them to grow slowly. It must be emphasized, however, that even in obviously defective segmenting stages there is mitotic activity present so that the eggs are not merely dead or dying. Thus, they are "stunted" in the sense used in the Carnegie Classification of abortuses according to Mall and Meyer.[93] A stunted ovum or stunted embryo is not merely a small *but* normal structure; it is both a small *and* abnormal one.

Of the many biologic problems about early defective fertilized ova, the question here is, What proportion of them completely disappears prior to implantation, and what proportion implants only to abort later? The data from the author's material suggest that some may degenerate while some may implant but eventually disappear or abort. Limited though this series of eight segmenting human ova is, it is the only one in existence. Since 50 per cent of the segmenting series are defective but only 28 per cent (6 of 21) are obviously defective when well-implanted (Fig. 139), this suggests that some defective eggs disappear prior to implantation and some implant. Of course this entire series of human ova is not extensive enough to give all of the statistical answers to the entire problem of early human development, but Dr. Stephen M. Shea[122] of our department assures me that the data on the time of ovulation, gleaned from this series, are just barely statistically significant.

Another unanswered question about human fertility is, What percentage of mature secondary oocytes normally ovulated and exposed to spermatozoa are fertilized? According to Corner[16] about 10 per cent of pig eggs are unfertilized. He also shows

FIGURE 110. *(Upper left)* The specimen was photographed after fixation by surface illumination only. Sequence 5, × 250. Previously published by Hertig and Rock.[59] (Courtesy of Carnegie Institution of Washington, and Charles C Thomas.)

FIGURE 111. *(Upper right)* The same specimen photographed in the same position but by transillumination. Note, moth-eaten defect at "8 o'clock" shown later in serial sections to be due to necrotic blastomeres. Sequence 8, × 300. (Courtesy of Carnegie Institution of Washington.)

FIGURES 112 to 115 *(Center and lower left and right)* show microscopic details of multinucleation, necrosis with pyknosis, remnant of polar body, normal blastomeres, and a still intact zona pellucida. The flat discoid shape of this obviously abnormal morula is evident from these sections as was suspected from the gross appearance. Sections 5, 6, 7, and 8, respectively, all × 500. Figs. 112 to 114 previously published by Hertig *et al.*[62] (Courtesy of Carnegie Institution of Washington.) Fig. 115 previously published by Hertig and Rock.[58] (Courtesy of the C. V. Mosby Company, and Carnegie Institution of Washington.)

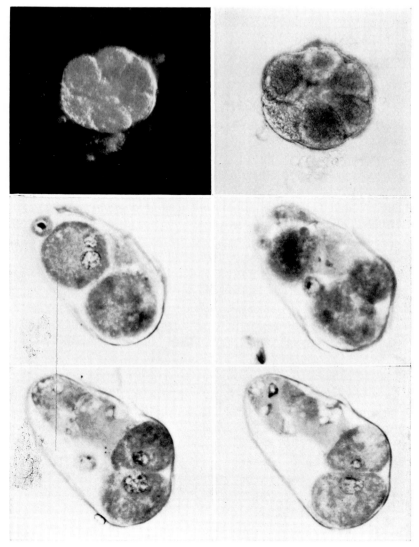

FIGURES 110 to 115 show the gross and microscopic aspects of a typical abnormal segmenting human morula. This 8-cell segmenting ovum (Carnegie No. 8450, F.H.W. S-46-3352) was recovered from the uterine cavity of a 30-year-old gravida 8, Para 6 with a history of psychic disturbance and stress incontinence since her fifth baby, two years prior to surgery. She subsequently had a spontaneous abortion and was delivered of her sixth child four and one-half months previously. She stated that she had induced the abortion of a 60-day pregnancy twenty-four days prior to admission.

that, with advancing pregnancy, the proportion of "bad eggs" decreases. In summary, his data reveal that of about 5,000 pig eggs exposed to spermatozoa, based on corpora lutea, ova, and embryo counts, 10 per cent fail to become fertilized, 10 per cent segment but degenerate, and 10 per cent implant but fail to go to term. The remaining 70 per cent deliver normally at term. The last datum is comparable to the clinical human abortion rate. The other data seem reasonably comparable to our data in man.

It need not be emphasized that the pig ovulates many ova, whereas man usually only one. This fact in itself, however, may contribute to the conclusions of Hertig, Rock, Adams, and Menkin[61] that the proven fertile patient *in any one month* when conditions for pregnancy are optimal, has only a 42 per cent chance of missing her menstrual period owing to a normal ovum, a 16 per cent chance owing to a defective ovum, and a 42 per cent chance of never missing her period at all (Fig. 139). This conclusion is based on the twenty-one implanted specimens (6 abnormal and 15 normal) whose endometria were twenty-five days or older and which were found in a group of seventy-eight women whose coital and menstrual data were perfect, who were shown to have ovulated, and whose uterus, tubes, and ovaries were demonstrably normal both grossly and microscopically. Thus, we see that the human fertility rate, although lower than that of the domestic pig, has a curve which is quite comparable and probably coincides with fertility rates in animals that normally ovulate but one oocyte. Certainly once the human female has become pregnant, her chance of having a clinical abortion, about 10 per cent,[52] is comparable to fetal loss in the sow once her ova became implanted.

The critical observer can question, and rightly so, the validity of comparing fertility rates in young domestic animals coming to slaughter with those rates of women who are ten years past their statistical peak of fertility coming to hysterectomy for a variety of clinical indications. Nevertheless, the data referred to are the only ones in existence for man. Dr. Rock has personally told me that these morphologic data, obtained by finding the implanted egg, are quite comparable to his clinical experience. It is common knowledge that not all young normal nullipara become pregnant immediately, even though conditions are optimal for conception.

Another discrepancy must be explained. If a patient *misses* her period, she has a 28 per cent chance of a defective ovum (6 out of 21) rather than the 10 per cent infertility rate. How can this be rationalized with the known human spontaneous clinical abortion rate of about 10 per cent or perhaps 15 per cent? The answer lies in the fact that some of these defective ova are bound to abort undetected prior to the classic tenth week when most spontaneous abortions occur. This follows unless the patient and/or her physician is interested *and* the passed tissue is examined by a pathologist. Even if examined, a tiny implantation site comparable to the one in Figure 116 may go undetected unless carefully searched for under the binocular dissecting microscope. Moreover, some truly abortive ova are disguised in a prolonged and/or only slightly delayed menstrual period. No obvious tissue is passed.

IMPLANTED OVA

The degree of abnormality in these specimens is as varied as that found in clinical abortion. The obvious and questionable defects in the specimens here illustrated may be simply enumerated and described:

1. The most abnormal is an implanted ovum consisting entirely of syncytiotrophoblast (Figs. 116 and 117). It contains no cytotrophoblast, and there is neither chorionic cavity nor embryo. The corpus luteum, endometrium, and remainder of the internal genital tract were normal. This has an ovulation age of about eleven days. Aside from its obvious defects, it is much too small. Moreover it has some features of maturity beyond its apparent age, namely, the hemorrhage within glands seen only in the thirteen-day stage or beyond. That this ovum would have aborted is beyond question. Whether the patient would have missed her menstrual period is unknown. It probably would have been somewhat delayed in onset, judging from the good gestationally hyperplastic corpus luteum, and probably would have been more profuse when it did occur. It is dubious whether the patient

FIGURE 116. *(Upper left)* Gross view of surface of implantation site; the cross section of the ovum is to be seen in Fig. 117. Note depressed ulcer with radiating lines or furrows in overlying endometrium owing to distortion from lack of chorionic cavity and general lack of growth of ovum. Carnegie No. 8329, F.H.W. S-45-1809, sequence 2, × 22. Previously published by Hertig and Rock.[58] (Courtesy of the C. V. Mosby Company, and Carnegie Institution of Washington.)

FIGURE 117. *(Lower)* A mid-cross section of the specimen shown grossly in Fig. 116. Note depressed ulcer seen grossly and the pure syncytiotrophoblastic nature of the ovum without cytotrophoblast, chorionic cavity, or embryo. Carnegie No. 8329, section 13-2-3, × 100. Previously published by Hertig and Rock.[58] (Courtesy of the C. V. Mosby Company, and Carnegie Institution of Washington.)

FIGURE 118. *(Upper right)* A gross surface view of a normal 11-day previllous specimen, comparable in developmental age to that seen in Fig. 116. This same specimen has been shown in Figs. 26 to 29 and 30, and has been discussed in Chapter IV-A. Carnegie No. 7699, sequence 8, × 22. Previously published by Hertig and Rock.[54] (Courtesy of Carnegie Institution of Washington.)

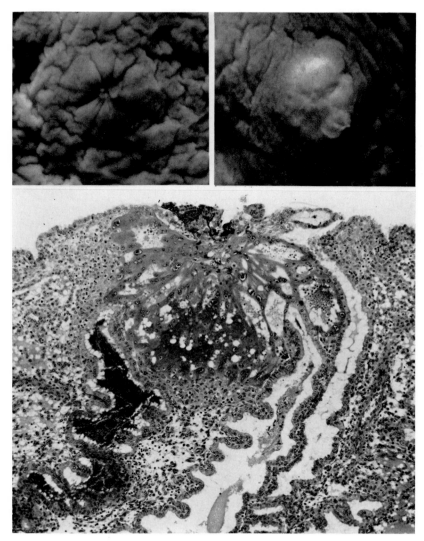

FIGURES 116 and 117 show the most abnormal implanted human ovum in the author's series. A comparable normal specimen is seen grossly in Fig. 118; its microscopic details are to be seen in Fig. 29.

FIGURE 119. (*Upper left*) Surface view of implantation site showing flattened rather than the normally expected rounded appearance such as seen in Fig. 23. Sequence 6, × 46.5. (Courtesy of Carnegie Institution of Washington.)

FIGURE 120. (*Upper right*) A low power mid-cross section showing the absence of a chorionic cavity, the malorientation of trophoblast, and the normal gestationally hyperplastic endometrium. Section 6-3-5, × 100. Previously published by Hertig and Rock.[58] (Courtesy of the C. V. Mosby Company, and Carnegie Institution of Washington.)

FIGURE 121. (*Lower*) A higher-power photomicrograph of the upper part of the ovum seen in Fig. 120. Note horizontal stratification of cytotrophoblast (upper) and syncytiotrophoblast (lower). The embryonic (germ) disk is barely visible with its early amniotic cavity below the ectoderm. The multinucleated mass at top is proliferating maternal epithelium which has been affected by the adjacent trophoblast, a normal phenomenon so well-seen in Fig. 135. Section 6-3-5, × 300. Previously published by Hertig and Rock.[58] (Courtesy of the C. V. Mosby Company, and Carnegie Institution of Washington.)

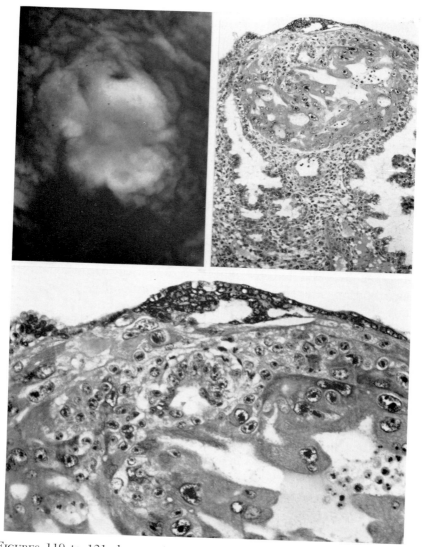

FIGURES 119 to 121 show various aspects of an abnormal 9-day specimen whose gross implantation site is flattened, whose chorionic cavity is absent, and whose trophoblast is horizontally laminated rather than being circumferentially oriented. Carnegie No. 8370, F.H.W. S-46-676.

would have considered herself pregnant unless she had passed
a decidual cast and the physician had found the implantation
site. (The author has spent many hours, some of them fruitless,
in searching for just such an implantation site as this from
patients with just such a history.)

That other primates, specifically the chimpanzee, have "bad
eggs" of this type is shown in Figure 136. It is to be contrasted,
in Figure 137, to a normal specimen of ten and one-half days
described by Elder, Hartman, and Heuser[26] in 1938. (At the
time this specimen was found—the first chimpanzee ovum to be
seen—Dr. Streeter estimated its value at a half million dollars,
based on the cost of running the Orange Park Laboratory in
Florida. The director was Dr. Robert M. Yerkes, the specimen
being named in his honor.)

2. That the chorionic cavity is absent is clearly evident in the
specimen shown in Figures 120 and 121. (With experience, the
observer may be led to expect a defective ovum when the
implantation site shows some gross abnormality. In Fig. 116
it is shrunken; in Fig. 119 it is flattened; in Fig. 124 it is too
hemorrhagic; and in Fig. 127 it is much too polypoid.) The cause
of the absence of the chorionic cavity must lie in the failure of
formation of its precursor, the segmentation cavity of the blastocyst. This structure is a function of the trophoblastic wall of the
blastocyst. It will be noted in both Figures 120 and 121 that the
trophoblast is horizontally laminated rather than having an outer
syncytiotrophoblastic and an inner cytotrophoblastic orientation.
It further suggests that the implanting ovum was a flattened
disklike object such as seen in Figures 110 and 111, rather than
a beautiful balloonlike object such as seen in Figure 11. The
ultimate cause of such early "congenital anomalies" is unknown.

$\rightarrow$

FIGURE 122. *(Upper)* Surface view showing slightly flattened appearance of
an otherwise somewhat polypoid implantation. Sequence 4, × 22.

FIGURE 123. *(Lower)* A mid-cross section to show slightly polypoid nature
of implantation site of a previllous ovum whose trophoblast is slightly hypoplastic; intervillous space congested and implantation site more advanced
than expected owing to hemorrhage within an endometrial gland. The
embryo and its primordial yolk sac are normal. Section 12-3-5, × 100.

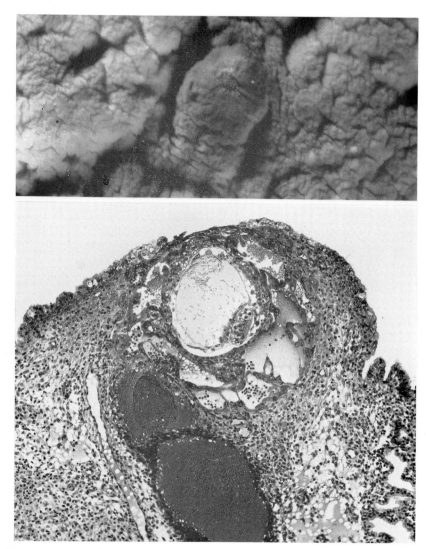

FIGURES 122 and 123 show the gross and microscopic features of 12-day previllous ovum whose trophoblast is slightly hypoplastic and whose intervillous space is congested with maternal blood which has flooded the underlying endometrial gland. Carnegie No. 7770, F.H.W. S-40-749. Previously published by Hertig and Rock.[55] (Courtesy of the C. V. Mosby Company, and Carnegie Institution of Washington.)

FIGURE 124. *(Upper left)* A lateral view of implantation site to show massive hemorrhage which, although normal in time of appearance, is excessive in amount, probably owing to structural deficiency in the trophoblastic shell of the ovum. Sequence 3, × 8.

FIGURE 125. *(Upper right)* Dorsal view of implantation site; the hemorrhage largely obscuring the underlying endometrium. Sequence 2, × 8.

FIGURE 126. *(Lower)* A mid-cross section to show virtual absence of villous trophoblast except for a thin shell of peripheral syncytiotrophoblast of varying thickness. Note thin inner layer of cytotrophoblast and only a single primordial villous anlage. The remainder of the implantation site is within normal limits. Compare with Figs. 38 and 39 for normal morphology at this state of development. Section 15-1-3, × 35.

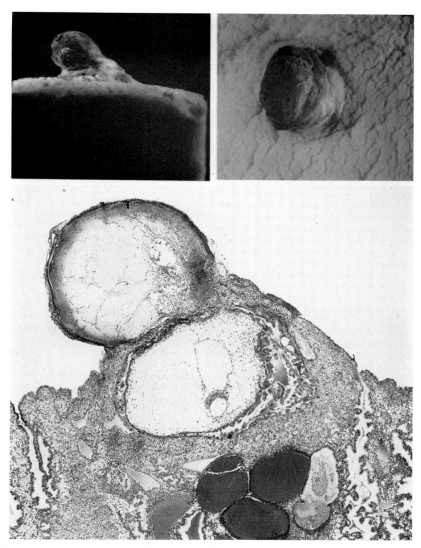

FIGURES 124 to 126 are from a 13-day ovum with marked trophoblastic hypoplasia, but the clinical age and embryonic development indicate that early chorionic villi should have been present. Carnegie No. 7800, F.H.W. S-40-1327. Previously published by Hertig and Rock.[55] (Courtesy of the C. V. Mosby Company, and Carnegie Institution of Washington.)

FIGURE 127. *(Upper left)* Lateral view of implantation site to show its polypoid nature but the normal hemorrhage from its surface. Sequence 7, × 5. Previously published by Hertig *et al.*[60] (Courtesy of the Wistar Institute of Anatomy and Biology, and Carnegie Institution of Washington.)

FIGURE 128. *(Upper right)* A low-power photomicrograph of the implantation site to confirm its polypoid nature and the normality of the surrounding endometrium. Section 25-2-4, × 12. Previously published by Hertig and Rock.[59] (Courtesy of Charles C Thomas, and Carnegie Institution of Washington.)

FIGURE 129. *(Lower)* A detailed view of the ovum to show its defective trophoblast at implantation pole but its normality elsewhere. The buckling or "subluxation" of the germ disk may, in some way, be related to this deficient trophoblast. In any event, the latter is probably not responsible for the shallow implantation. Compare with Fig. 155. Section 25-2-4, × 60. Previously published by Hertig and Rock.[58] (Courtesy of the C. V. Mosby Company, and Carnegie Institution of Washington.)

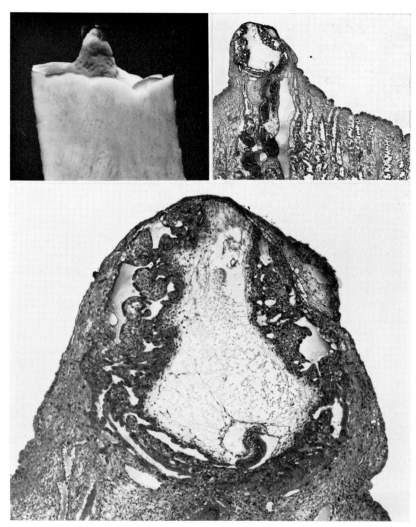

FIGURES 127 to 129 show the essential gross and microscopic details of a polypoid implantation site of a 13-day ovum whose polar trophoblast is deficient and whose germ disk is buckled. (Its similarity to a sea horse is amusing but coincidental.) Carnegie No. 8290, F.H.W. S-44-2785.

Figure 130. *(Upper left)* Posterior uterine wall to show details of uterine cavity, ostia of fallopian tubes, lower uterine segment, upper cervical canal, and position of the ovum. (It reminds the author of a dress shirt containing a single luminous pearl stud.) This also illustrates the end result of a uterus bivalved to expose the posterior endometrial surface. Sequence 1, × 1.5.

Figure 131. *(Upper right)* A higher-powered view of what is typical of a normal 12-day implantation site. Note defect in endometrium and expanding globular ovum beneath. Sequence 4, × 22.

Figure 132. *(Lower)* A mid-cross section of the ovum to show the expected 12-day morphology except for the malpositioned embryonic disk. Note that it seems to have become unfastened or loosened from its mesoblastic attachments to the trophoblast with subsequent distortion of the primordial yolk sac. Section 11-5-4, × 100. Previously published by Hertig *et al.*[60] (Courtesy of the Wistar Institute of Anatomy and Biology, and Carnegie Institution of Washington.)

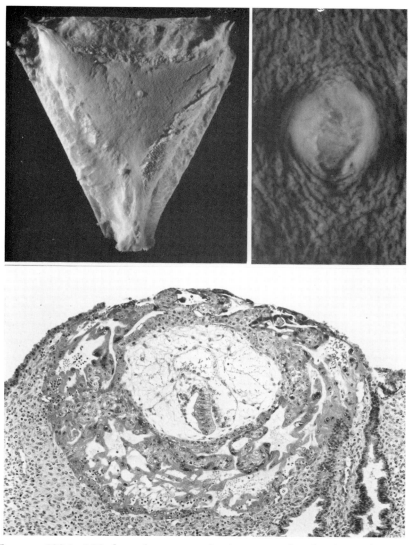

FIGURES 130 to 132 show the gross and microscopic details of an otherwise normal 12-day ovum whose germ disk is rotated or tipped 90° upon its horizontal axis with respect to the adjacent trophoblast. Carnegie No. 8299, F.H.W. S-45-1220. Figs. 130 and 131 previously published by Hertig and Rock.[58] (Courtesy of the C. V. Mosby Company, and Carnegie Institution of Washington.)

Figure 133. *(Upper left)* The slight elevation made by such a small, recently implanted ovum is characteristic of the late 8- or early 9-day stage. This specimen was missed for some days, in spite of multiple careful searches. Sequence 3, × 36.

Figure 134. *(Upper right)* A comparable microscopic view to show tiny ovum at top and normal, slightly gestationally hyperplastic endometrium below. Section 3-2-11, × 36.

Figure 135. *(Lower)* A higher-power view to show details of the early stage of lacuna formation within the syncytiotrophoblast (see Chapter IV-A), the communication of lacunae with maternal blood vessels, and the intense abnormal leukocytic infiltration around the ovum. The author would have a guarded prognosis about the future of this ovum even though it is beautifully normal. The endometrium is *not* otherwise inflamed or infected. Section 3-2-11, × 175.

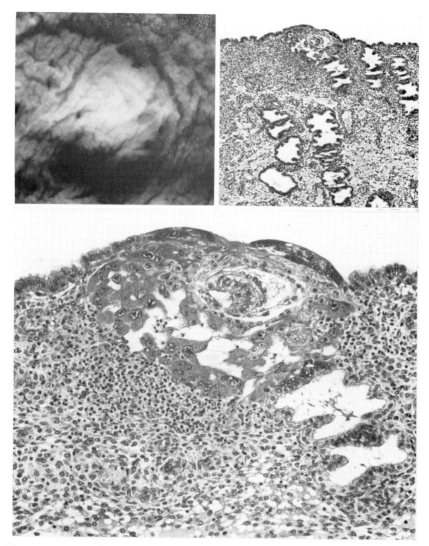

Figures 133-135 show the gross and microscopic features of a normal 9-day ovum whose adjacent endometrium is infiltrated by leukocytes, an abnormal finding. Carnegie No. 8171, F.H.W. S-43-1098. Previously published by Hertig and Rock.[57] (Courtesy of Carnegie Institution of Washington.)

Nevertheless about one third of abortuses whose amnions are grown in tissue culture have been shown by Szulman[139] to yield abnormal chromosomes.

3. Several ova of the series had varying degrees of trophoblastic hypoplasia. Figures 122 and 123 show this to a mild degree, perhaps within essentially normal limits. Figures 124 to 126 show a marked degree of this failure to form an adequate trophoblastic shell for the ovum. In the first of these two specimens, the overall growth and orientation of the several parts are not quite normal. For instance, the embryonic disk and primitive yolk sac are like the twelve-day specimens (Fig. 34), whereas the glandular hemorrhage ordinarily comes a day later (Fig. 39). Moreover, the trophoblast, although normal as far as it goes, does not have as many primordial trophoblastic masses which will form chorionic villi. Perhaps the overdistention of the intervillous space resulted from a chance erosion of a small arteriolar branch with subsequent hemorrhage through the "floor" of the primitive chorion into a gland. Obviously, since it is not quite clear as to the normality of the ovum, it is impossible to say whether the conceptus would have aborted or not. Certainly the pathologist sees as maturing placentas all degrees of trophoblastic hypoplasia. Such variations range from the slightly irregular and multilobular term placenta to the so-called bald chorion of the spontaneous abortion. Figure 126 is undoubtedly the precursor of such an inadequate placenta or chorion. Although this thirteen-day specimen has a beautifully normal embryo, it is destined to die at some stage of development with

→

FIGURE 136. *(Upper)* A pathologic chimpanzee ovum consisting only of syncytiotrophoblast. It is quite comparable in age and morphology to the human ovum in Fig. 117. Note normal lacunae in ovum and normal decidual transformation in endometrium. Carnegie No. C-462, section 4-2-3, × 500.

FIGURE 137. *(Lower)* A chimpanzee ovum (10½ days). This stage in the human being lies between the author's 9- and 11-day stages (Figs. 23 to 25 and Figs. 26 to 29, respectively). Note that the chimpanzee reacts to its interstitially implanting ovum as does the human being, by decidual response of stroma. The monkey, however, stimulates endometrial epithelium at its implantation site(s) as seen in Fig. 48. Carnegie No. C-620, section 4-1-5, × 100.

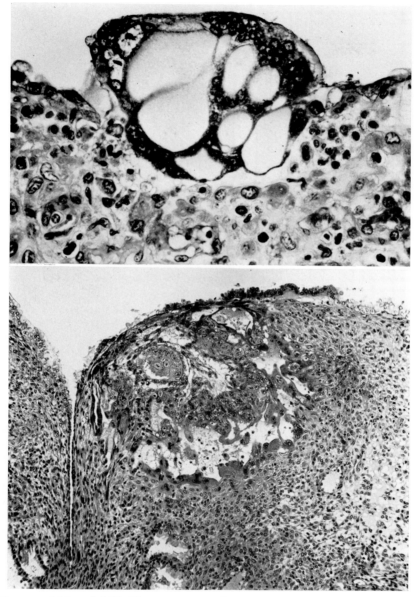

FIGURES 136 and 137. There are two chimpanzee ova of about the same age (10½ days). The top one is very abnormal; the bottom one is normal. Such specimens are rarely available for study. These are the only ones known to the author. (Courtesy of Carnegie Institution of Washington.)

HUMAN OVULATION

Distribution of Presumed Day of Ovulation Based on Endometrial Histology and
Ovular Development of 34 Fertilized Ova; 21 Normal and 13 Abnormal

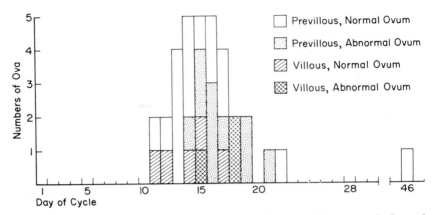

FIGURE 138. A bar graph showing the distribution of presumed day of ovulation of the thirty-four human ova recovered by Hertig and Rock from 210 patients of proven fertility. Note that the majority of the abnormal ova ovulated on or after the fifteenth day of the cycle, whereas more than half (12 out of 21) of the normal ones ovulated on or prior to the fourteenth day of the menstrual cycle. Previously published by Hertig.[45] (Courtesy of Dr. C. S. Keefer, and Little, Brown and Company, Inc.)

consequent spontaneous abortion. The principle for the pathologist to remember as he looks at placental tissue is that the chorionic villus arises from these little trophoblastic foci during the nine-, ten-, eleven-, and twelve-day stages of the ovum. If there are few foci, there are few villi maturing as cotyledons.

4. The depth of implantation of the ovum is also variable. All normal ones seem to be well below the surface of the endometrium by the nine- to eleven-day stages. The polypoid type of implantation, the cause of which is unknown, is to be seen in Figures 127 to 129, Figures 149 to 152, and Figures 153 to 155. Such protruding chorions may be associated with poor polar trophoblast and a poor embryo (Figs. 127-129), or good polar trophoblast and a good embryo (Figs. 153-155). Therefore the quality of the tissues at the implantation-embryonic pole is not

at fault, although it would be tempting so to conclude. The importance of a shallowly implanted, good but small ovum (Figs. 153-155) lies in the fact that it probably is the early stage of the circumvallate placenta. This will be discussed in the next chapter on abortion. Suffice it to say here that the circumvallate placenta causes most of the uncommon mid-trimester abortions. It is also a significant cause of last trimester premature

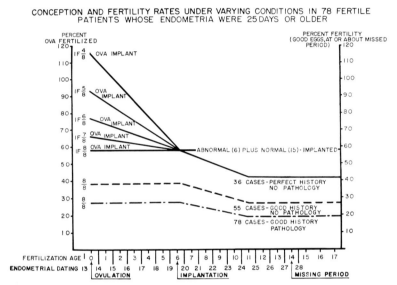

CONCEPTION AND FERTILITY RATES UNDER VARYING CONDITIONS IN 78 FERTILE PATIENTS WHOSE ENDOMETRIA WERE 25 DAYS OR OLDER

FIGURE 139. This shows an attempt to construct a curve or index of physiologic human fertility-infertility-sterility *during any one* menstrual cycle when conditions were optimal for conception in seventy-eight patients of proven fertility. The last part of the curve is constructed from these patients whose endometria were 25 days or older. The thirty-six perfect patients are a part of the 55 series, which is in turn a part of the 78 series. The preimplantation curve(s) are problematical since it is not known how many of the eight segmenting ova (4 normal and 4 abnormal) *would* have implanted had the uterus not been surgically removed. (These data were from the whole optimal series of 107 patients, of which the 78 were merely a part). It is likely that the curve starts at 80 or 90 per cent and certainly finishes at 42 per cent. The latter figure is that of normal human fertility at the first missed period. The 16 per cent is physiologic infertility; the other 42 per cent represents physiologic sterility in any one menstrual cycle. Previously published by Hertig *et al.*[61] (Courtesy of Charles C Thomas.)

labor, placental separation, or rupture of the membranes—all potential bad news for the patient, her baby, and her obstetrician.

5. In any series of specimens, even such a small one as this, there are bound to be slightly queer or "offbeat" ones just as with people; Figures 130 to 132 show such an example. The uterus, suggesting a tendency toward the bicornuate form, was THE MOST HANDSOME and technically the most perfect one ever dissected by the author in his seventeen years of ovum searching. Moreover, the ovum was where all anatomists think the ovum *should* be, but seldom is, in the middle of the upper posterior uterine wall. The high-power view of the ovum was also normal (Fig. 131). Imagine the disappointment when the flawless series of serial sections revealed a germ disk tipped on its side! It will be seen in Figure 132 that such malposition is nontraumatic. Actually this specimen was treated with the same care, operatively, and postoperatively, as the other 209 of the series. The author suspects that this malposition might well interfere with proper umbilical cord formation, but who can tell?

6. And finally, there is the good ovum with inflammatory cell infiltration of its implantation site. This process has been commented on before as being strikingly absent in the usual implantation sites. The failure of leukocytes to appear has been taken to mean that the trophoblast does not provoke a homograft rejection response. The cause of this infiltration, so clearly seen in Figure 135, is unknown. Equally unclear is the ultimate fate of such an otherwise beautifully normal nine-day specimen. Even the low-power histology of the endometrium as seen in Figure 134 shows that the endometrium itself is normal.

CHAPTER VII

SPONTANEOUS ABORTION

THIS phenomenon is usually defined medically as the premature expulsion of a nonviable conceptus. In terms of medical experience and practice, this coincides with the twenty-eighth week of gestation. The legal profession often regards medical problems somewhat differently than does the medical profession. Certainly this is true with respect to the time when an abortion becomes a premature delivery; twenty weeks is the time set by the law. Prior to this time, the delivery of a legally nonviable conceptus is not reportable either as a birth or as a death but is regarded as a spontaneous abortion or miscarriage. After that time, both the birth and frequently the death of such a conceptus during this eight-week legal-medical period of discrepancy must be reported. Between twenty and twenty-eight weeks, the fetus has only a slight chance of survival, even when it is over 500 grams in weight (23 weeks' menstrual age). If memory serves the author, one pound and six ounces or about 640 grams (24 plus weeks) was the long-time record at the Boston Lying-in Hospital for survival of a premature infant. The practical pediatrician and obstetrician both clinically and statistically regard 1000 grams as the lower limit of optimism as far as the survival of a premature baby is concerned. This coincides with the *end* of the twenty-eighth week, menstrual age, of the fetus or with the beginning of the eighth lunar month. The sitting height of the fetus is then 24.7 cm. Dr. Streeter's data in Table II may be helpful to the pathologist in correlating the size of the baby and its menstrual age.

Perhaps it is not necessary to emphasize to this audience that the medical profession divides the term abortion into two categories: induced and spontaneous. The lay public, however, almost universally equates the term abortion with one which is induced, either self or criminal, whereas the term miscarriage means spontaneous abortion. This fact may be of more value to medical

165

students and resident or practicing physicians than to pathologists. The author is sure that statistics on abortion, both spontaneous and induced, are inaccurate because the takers of medical histories do not appreciate this simple problem of medical nomenclature.

In this regard, the author is reminded of an incident with amusing overtones associated with his medical exhibit held in Springfield, Massachusetts during the early forties. The material was on spontaneous abortion, and it attempted to demonstrate to the members of the Massachusetts Medical Society the pathogenesis of this most common complication of pregnancy. The lay public, however, was also welcome to the exhibits held in the Springfield Armory. Many of them, especially the women, were obviously disappointed with the context of the material exhibited. They thought, on seeing the word ABORTION on the very large prominent sign, that here was a place where they could learn how to perform abortions!

Speaking of exhibits at the Massachusetts Medical Society reminds the author of the time that the Hertig-Rock ova were first unveiled to the public, medical and otherwise. One lady, apparently a high school teacher of biology, was fascinated with the gross pictures of the implantation sites photographed under fluid and at fairly high magnifications. She said, "Aren't these beautiful pictures, but *how* did you get inside the uterus to take them?" Such are the trials, tribulations, and amusements of medical contact with the lay public. The latter also includes the fainting of an adult during a wintry Sunday afternoon lecture at the Harvard Medical School, also on spontaneous abortion. The time was during the Depression of the mid-thirties, the room was warm, and perhaps the man was hungry and had come in to warm himself.

In any event, the subject of the pathogenesis of spontaneous abortion has interested the author for over thirty years since his contact in 1933-34 with the personnel at the Carnegie Department of Embryology and the material in its collection. If the reader has read the introduction, he may remember that the late Dr. Frederick C. Irving, Chief of the Boston Lying-in Hospital, sent the author to Dr. Streeter in Baltimore to learn how to examine and interpret an abortus.

Over the years, the author has examined pathologically well

over a thousand spontaneously aborted conceptuses. The several papers published in 1943, 1944, and 1954[63, 52, 91] give the author's general experience with this pathologic material.[144] Whether the interested pathologist chooses to follow the time-tested classifications used in the Department of Embryology of the Carnegie Institution of Washington in Baltimore[93] or the author's slight modification[63] is immaterial. Some well-established, sensible, anatomic-pathologic classification, nomenclature, and technique must be used in the pathology laboratory where abortuses are to be examined. Otherwise the examination and reporting of this material is just so much wasted time for the doctor, technician, and secretary, not to mention the physician who hopes to tell the patient why she aborted. In a general vein, the author deplores the vast literature on the treatment of threatened abortion which does not contain much evidence that the clinician or pathologist bothered to examine the tissue from the therapeutic failures. The striking exception seems to be the writings of the author's friend and colleague, Dr. Eleanor Delfs.[20B] Perhaps her original training at Johns Hopkins has something to do with her interest in embryologic pathology. There the laboratory of pathology *in* the department of obstetrics examines the aborted material with painstaking care. The proximity at that time of Johns Hopkins to the Carnegie Laboratory, across the street, probably influenced the late Professor John Whitridge Williams to establish such a laboratory.

The Carnegie classification of abortuses and the author's slight modification are as follows:

Carnegie Classification

Group I	Specimens composed of villi only
Group II	Chorion without amnion or cyema
Group III	Chorion with amnion
Group IV	Chorionic vesicles with nodular cyemata
Group V	Cylindrical cyemata
Group VI	Stunted cyemata
Group VII	Fetus compressus

Hertig's Classification of Pathologic Ova

Group I	Villi only
Group II	Chorion only (empty)
Group III	Chorion containing amnion only
Group IV	Chorion, amnion, and nodular embryo
Group V	Chorion, amnion, and cylindrical embryo
Group VI	Chorion, amnion, and stunted embryo
Group VII	Chorion, amnion, and macerated fetus

The technique of examining an abortus, whether spontaneous or induced, is summarized as follows:

1. The equipment necessary consists of a good binocular dissecting microscope with good oblique illumination. The modern American Optical Company or Zeiss products are more than adequate. A good set of fine dissecting instruments is necessary. This set should include tools such as needles, iris scissors and iris forceps, smooth and mouse-toothed.

2. All material is much better appreciated in three dimensions if floated in fluid. Whether the tissue is fresh or already fixed, physiological saline is the most useful. If there is fresh or fixed blood clot, it must be removed before the examiner can get an adequate look at the material. Several changes of fluid may be necessary.

3. Once the chorion has been identified and is intact, it must be opened carefully, under fluid, to determine the presence of embryo, amnion, yolk sac, and umbilical cord.

4. If the chorion is opened, there usually will be evidence of the nature of the embryo, its accessory membranes, and the umbilical cord. (The author has found that, in a large series of abortuses, chorions, whether ruptured or opened as intact specimens, do not show any significant difference in their contents. In other words the contents usually do not get lost even though the chorion is ruptured.) Presumably the magma reticulare, a thixotropic gel, prevents too much loss or distortion of the chorionic contents.

5. The competent pathologist does not need to be told how to select a block for microscopic section. Nevertheless, a word here might be helpful. An embryo can be better evaluated by a careful gross examination and comparison with the unique illustrations in Streeter's five collected monographs,[137] or with the few selected specimens illustrated here. The embryo in an abortus is usually either malformed, stunted, macerated, or missing. It is infrequently normal *and* unmacerated. Therefore serial sections are not practically feasible unless the specimen is living and the observer and his technician are able and willing to prepare a series of serial sections worth examining. Few pathologists and their staffs are so-equipped. Aside from the embryo, well-selected sections of the *chorion frondosum* (including main portion and

margin), the *chorion laeve*, the *decidua vera*, the stump of the umbilical cord if that alone remains, and the membranes (amnion and yolk sac) will suffice for an intelligent appraisal of material submitted to the pathologist. A word of caution! In the decidua of all abortions, there may be thrombosis, necrosis, and *recent* hemorrhage, whatever the ultimate cause of the abortion. The final casting off of the conceptus and decidua is merely a delayed menstrual period and is caused by the same factor—hormonal withdrawal of endometrial support. As in all pathological diagnosis, the value lies in the training of the pathologist and his interest in the diagnosis. Dr. S. Burt Wolbach, the author's teacher and predecessor, was a mild and gentle person. He seldom said ill of anyone. The most scathing remark ever heard about a fellow pathologist by the author was, "He was content to put a name on it (the tissue) and forget it!"

Unless a pathologist is willing to learn, or relearn a bit of normal human embryology, look at the specimen with tender loving care, and think about what probably took place during the six to seven weeks of development preceding the abortion, he might better throw (or urge the clinician to throw) away the material. As a dismal afterthought of a once-busy and harassed practicing pathologist, now an administrator, "it takes far longer to look at an abortus or a placenta than any other surgical specimen, even a complete set of tubes, ovaries, and uterus!"

The morphologic and/or etiologic diagnoses of one thousand examined abortuses in the laboratory of the Boston Lying-in Hospital are listed:[63]

I. Ovular Factors:
   1. Pathologic ova, with absent or defective embryos   489
   2. Embryos with localized anomalies   32
   3. Placental abnormalities   96

   Total   617   617

II. Maternal Factors:
   1. Criminal abortions   21
   2. Uterine abnormalities   64
   3. Febrile and inflammatory diseases   20
   4. Miscellaneous   12
   5. Anatomically normal ova (classified)   265
   6. Trauma (automobile accident)   1

   Total   383   383
   Grand Total   1000

The more important diagnoses are listed as follows:

I.　3.　Placental Abnormalities
　　　　a.　Circumvallate placenta　　　　　　　　　　　　　　45
　　　　b.　Hypoplasia of the placenta　　　　　　　　　　　20
　　　　c.　Placenta membranacea, partial　　　　　　　　　2
　　　　d.　Velamentous insertion of umbilical cord　　　　1
　　　　e.　Hypoplasis of amnion　　　　　　　　　　　　　1
　　　　f.　Rupture of marginal sinus　　　　　　　　　　　3
　　　　g.　Premature senility of placenta　　　　　　　　　4
　　　　h.　Breus' mole (intraplacental hematomata)　　　19
　　　　i.　Succenturiate lobe with total infarction　　　　1
　　　　　　　　　　　　　　　　　　　　　　　　　　　　—
　　　　　　Total　　　　　　　　　　　　　　　　　　96

II.　2.　Uterine Abnormalities
　　　　a.　Low implantation of placenta　　　　　　　　　56
　　　　b.　Placenta accreta　　　　　　　　　　　　　　　2
　　　　c.　Bicornuate uterus　　　　　　　　　　　　　　2
　　　　d.　Multiple leiomyomata of uterus　　　　　　　　1
　　　　e.　Retroversion of uterus, fixed　　　　　　　　　3
　　　　　　　　　　　　　　　　　　　　　　　　　　　　—
　　　　　　Total　　　　　　　　　　　　　　　　　　64

II.　3.　Febrile and Inflammatory Diseases
　　　　a.　Bacterial inflammation of decidua, acute　　　12
　　　　b.　Small pox　　　　　　　　　　　　　　　　　1
　　　　c.　Pyelitis with horseshoe kidney　　　　　　　　1
　　　　d.　Fever of unknown etiology　　　　　　　　　　5
　　　　e.　Chronic endometritis　　　　　　　　　　　　1
　　　　　　　　　　　　　　　　　　　　　　　　　　　　—
　　　　　　Total　　　　　　　　　　　　　　　　　　20

II.　4.　Miscellaneous
　　　　a.　Radiation effect on ovaries　　　　　　　　　　2
　　　　b.　Erythroblastosis fetalis　　　　　　　　　　　3
　　　　c.　Surgical removal of corpus luteum　　　　　　4
　　　　d.　Blood dyscrasis　　　　　　　　　　　　　　1
　　　　e.　Interference with circulation of cord　　　　　2
　　　　　　　　　　　　　　　　　　　　　　　　　　　　—
　　　　　　Total　　　　　　　　　　　　　　　　　　12

II.　5.　Anatomically Normal Ova (classified)
　　　　a.　Anatomically normal ova without disease　　　227
　　　　　　Fetus, macerated　　　　　　　　146
　　　　　　Fetus, nonmacerated　　　　　　74
　　　　　　Fetus, by history only　　　　　　7
　　　　b.　Acute chorionitis, consistent with spontaneous
　　　　　　premature rupture of membranes (fetus macerated
　　　　　　in 9, and normal in 5)　　　　　　　　　　　14
　　　　c.　Positive Hinton and Wasserman tests (the syphilis
　　　　　　was probably not responsible for the abortion)　3
　　　　d.　Infarction of placenta, extensive (all fetuses were
　　　　　　macerated)　　　　　　　　　　　　　　　　13
　　　　e.　Toxemia of pregnancy (fetus macerated in 3, and
　　　　　　normal in 2 cases)　　　　　　　　　　　　　5

f. Trauma (internal) 3

    Two successive biopsies on sterility patient not
    known to be pregnant 1
    Exploratory celiotomy 1
    Intrauterine lipiodol injection, 7 weeks prior to
    last menstrual period 1

    Total 265

These tabulations, though prosaic at first sight, are an attempt by the author and his personally supervised residents to interpret, from tissue and history submitted, the etiology and pathogenesis of these spontaneous abortions. After all, the pathologist should remember that, as Dr. Irving used to remark wisely, "A woman does not come to the Boston Lying-in Hospital to have a case of childbirth!" She comes to take home a living, normal baby. If she cannot, she and her husband deserve to know why the pregnancy ended unhappily, insofar as any one can give them the answer. Let not the pathologist be guilty of the diagnoses, "products of conception" or "normal placenta." The obstetrician knew at least that, and probably more, before he sent the specimen to the pathologist.

One final word of caution: There is leukocytic infiltration in decidua of all abortions. Most of it is due to the sterile necrosis associated with the terminal sloughing of a dying hemorrhagic thrombosed decidua. Earlier writers such as the famous Drs. Mall and Meyer, both embryologists, considered that the majority of spontaneous abortions were due to infection of the endometrium. Nothing could be further from the truth. Bacterial infection seldom causes abortion, and viral infection causes congenital anomalies that, unfortunately, usually fail to abort. When the experienced pathologist sees true bacterial infection of the decidua or the chorion, he can be reasonably sure that the abortion has been induced rather than having been of spontaneous or "natural" origin. And finally, it is comforting to the patient and her obstetrician to know what the abortus shows. Most patients believe that it is due to moving of furniture, a heavy washing, or some other household chore. The well-attached, normal ovum in a normal uterus survives all manner of psychic and/or traumatic shock, the legal profession to the contrary and notwithstanding. Another Irving aphorism, "An empty house is better than a bad tenant!" is apropos. This has comforted many a patient, but the pathologist has to tell the clinician which "uterine tenant" is bad and which is good.

And while we are on the subject of medicolegal experts and the relationship of external trauma to abortion, the reader is referred to the incidence of bona fide traumatic abortion in the author's experience. It is *one in one thousand!* Nevertheless in this series of one thousand abortuses, there were thirteen with a history of trauma by automobile accident. Only one of these was probably caused by the shock, psychic and/or physical, preceding the abortion. In the other twelve, the conceptus could be shown to have been dead or defective prior to the traumatic incident. Honest, competent clinicians in great numbers have told the author that they have *never* seen a bona fide example of traumatic abortion. Let then the medicolegal expert who thinks just because the patient was pregnant and the insurance company rich, through our premiums, that the slight automobile accident "caused" the abortion; let him reflect on the embryological facts of the matter.

As a final, somewhat wry and ironic slant, let the author relate his own tale. He gave a talk at the Quincy City Hospital about 1937. On the way home late at night, he was run into by a larger car containing four or five people. The pictures showed that the author was well across the intersection when struck, but, no matter, both participants by law are guilty. The bill of complaints filed by the plaintiff (the author was of course the defendant) alleged that the wife of the driver aborted as the result of the accident. Strangely enough, between the morning and afternoon of the trial, and because I had honestly told the court where I had been and what I had been doing, namely, talking about spontaneous abortions, THAT particular complaint about my causing the abortion mysteriously disappeared from the total bill. Even lawyers sometimes can see medical as well as legal logic.

Enough of this discursive talk about abortion. There are some superb pictures of some aspects of this problem which have been collected by the author over the years. Most, if not all, of them were taken or drawn by his friends and colleagues, so that he can admire them along with the audience. It is obviously not within the scope of this lecture-monograph to illustrate all of the many

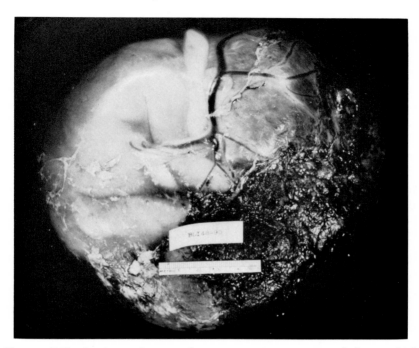

FIGURE 140. An intact human chorion containing a normal fetus which aborted as the result of an incompetent cervix. Note that the maturing placenta is a discoid patch of hypertrophied and hyperplastic tissue which arose from the *chorion frondosum*. The membranous insertion of the cord is seen in the center of the picture and is anatomically abnormal, but it did not cause the abortion. B.L.I.H., S-48-90. Reduced to about one half natural size. Previously published by Hertig and Gore.[49] (Courtesy of the W. F. Prior Company, and Dr. C. H. Davis and Dr. B. Carter.)

varieties and subvarieties of pathologic anatomy seen in spontaneous abortions from the human patient.

The author is admittedly an amateur embryologist, much to the disdain of his professional embryological colleagues. Therefore, he is perforce interested in the embryogenesis of the bad fruit of the womb that falls prematurely. He has chosen several important types of abortion, the "blighted" ovum and the circumvallate placenta, to illustrate his life's philosophy that only the early stages of any condition are truly interesting to him. (His writings seem to bear this out when he peruses his own bibliography.)

That the normal patient may abort a perfectly normal living

FIGURE 141. *(Upper)* The originally intact chorion was opened under saline by the author. In the center is an amnion containing neither embryo nor vestige of umbilical cord, Carnegie Group III. The main stems of the chorionic villi radiate in all directions from the chorionic membrane like the spokes of a wheel. The fundus of the uterus is at the left. Carnegie No. 8664, sequence 1, × 6. From Free Hospital for Women. (Courtesy of Carnegie Institution of Washington.)

FIGURE 142. *(Lower)* A specimen comparable to that in Fig. 141 except that there is an amnion (left) and a yolk sac (right). The chorionic villi, even at this low magnification, show the bulbous swelling of early hydatidiform "degeneration," actually stromal edema. For details of this process, see Figs. 143 to 148. Carnegie No. 8770, sequence 1, × 2.5. From the Boston Lying-in Hospital. Previously published by Hertig and Gore.[49] (Courtesy of Carnegie Institution of Washington, the W. F. Prior Company, and Dr. C. H. Davis and Dr. B. Carter.)

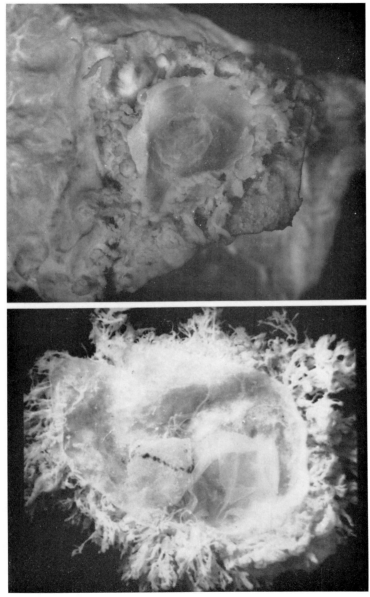

FIGURES 141 and 142 show two pathologic or "blighted" ova: the upper still attached to the uterus, and the lower having spontaneously aborted.

conceptus can happen, as shown in Figure 140. This seldom happens, but it can and does. The specimen illustrates perfectly the principle that, on occasion, the maternal environment may be entirely at fault, as it appeared to be in about 35 to 40 per cent of the author's series (see above). The specimen in question appeared to have aborted because of an incompetent cervix which dilates prematurely and lets an otherwise normal ovum fall out. Shirodkar, a famous Indian obstetrician, has devised a simple operative procedure to stop this sort of thing; he simply ties a string around the cervix to hold it shut until the proper time. He unties the string as term approaches.[123, 124]

The commonest ovular abnormality of all, occurring in about 5 per cent of all pregnancies (50% of all abortions) is the "blighted" or pathologic ovum. Two examples of this are seen in Figures 141 and 142; one is still attached to the uterus, and one has been delivered. There are all degrees of this "blighting." The common denominator lies in the early death or absence of the embryo. What remains of the trophoblastically formed membranes, amnion, and yolk sac, will depend on how far the embryo had developed and when it died and/or was resorbed. Most of these specimens, in the author's experience, consist of an empty chorion or one with, at most, an empty amnion.

The importance of this type of abortus lies in its frequency and in the fact that it is the precursor of the uncommon, though dangerous, hydatidiform mole.* More of this anon. Fortunately most of these potential moles are aborted at nine to ten weeks' menstrual age. The potential hydatidiform mole is retained *in utero* for another five to ten weeks to develop into a full-blown hydatidiform mole. The six illustrations (Figs. 143-148) show some of the curious distortions of the chorionic villi of the majority (66%) of these "blighted" ova before they develop into the typical grape-like swellings of the mole.

Although most of the spontaneous abortions take place well within the first trimester, a few occur during the middle trimester.

---

* It has come to the author's attention since this manuscript was written that "blighted" ova with minimal hydropic change have a different chromosomal constitution from the true mole. (Unpublished data of J. G. and M. A. Boué, Paris, France.)

FIGURES 143 to 148 show isolated chorionic villi dissected (from 1935 to 1937) from the chorionic membranes of pathologic or "blighted" ova comparable to those seen in Figs. 141 and 142. Note irregular, bulbous, hydropic swelling. All were photographed by either Dr. Hugh H. Nuckols, then a resident pathologist at the Boston Lying-in Hospital, or the author. They were photographed under fluid using a Zeiss℗ stereo camera presented by Professor Ernst to Professor S. Burt Wolbach and then to the author. B.L.I.H. No number, S-37-29, S-37-290, S-36-994, S-37-29, and S-35-930C, respectively.

FIGURE 149. *(Upper left)* A polypoid implantation of a 12-day ovum viewed from above. Carnegie No. 7771, sequence 1, × 14, F.H.W. S-40-791.

FIGURE 150. *(Lower left)* A mid-cross section of specimen seen grossly in Fig. 149. Note poor quality of trophoblast, the small size of the chorionic cavity, and the abortive attempts at primordial yolk sac formation—even though the embryonic disc is rudimentary, if indeed even present. Carnegie No. 7771, section 3-4-1, × 100.

FIGURE 151. *(Upper right)* A gross lateral view of an implantation site: the chorion containing an early somite embryo. The polypoid nature of this structure is well illustrated in Fig. 152. Carnegie No. 7701, sequence 3, × 4. From Free Hospital for Women.

FIGURE 152. *(Lower right)* The same implantation site as in Fig. 151, also viewed laterally but rotated 90°. Note relatively narrow pedicle of polypoid implantation site (on left) and relatively broad base (on right). The ovum is superficially implanted and appears, at least on the left, to have "herniated" or "prolapsed" into the uterine cavity owing to chorionic growth. From this picture is apparent the early stage of the mechanism by which the *chorion laeve* with further growth "folds over" the *chorion frondosum* to form the thick, yellow, opaque, peripheral zone of decidua at the margin of a circumvallate placenta (Figs. 156-159). Carnegie No. 7701, sequence 2, × 4. From Free Hospital for Women.

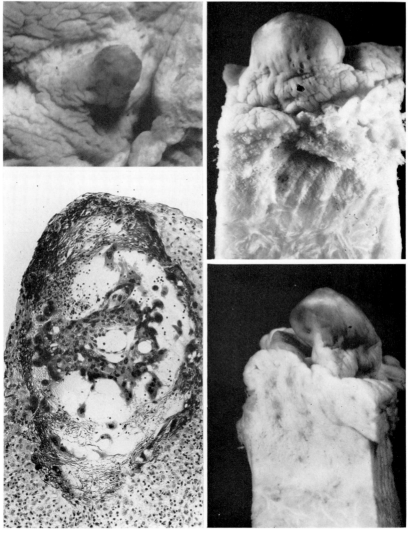

FIGURES 149 to 152 show two different early human ova having various degrees of polypoid implantation. Figs. 149 and 150 on the left represent a potential abortus owing to the absence of an embryo. Previously published by Hertig and Rock.[55] (Courtesy of the C. V. Mosby Company and Carnegie Institution of Washington.) Figs. 151 and 152 represent a potential circumvallate placenta. This specimen contained a normal early somite embryo of 2 to 2.5 mm in length. (Courtesy of Carnegie Institution of Washington.)

Figures 153 to 155 show a normal 12-day previllous human ovum which is small and superficially implanted despite its apparent morphologic normality. Carnegie No. 8000, F.H.W. S-42-217. Previously published by Hertig and Rock.[55] (Courtesy of the C. V. Mosby Company, and Carnegie Institution of Washington.)

Figure 153. *(Upper left)* Lateral view of implantation site showing massive hemorrhage which virtually obscures the implantation site. Sequence 2, × 5.

Figure 154. *(Upper right)* A photomicrograph, at low power, to show the massive hemorrhage from a small superficially implanted but otherwise normal ovum. The histologic details of the ovum may be seen in Fig. 155. Note normality of endometrium with early decidual reaction about the ovum. Section 11-3-3, × 20.

Figure 155. *(Lower)* A normal 12-day previllous ovum whose other features have been seen in Figs. 153 and 154. Note normal embryo with amnion and primordial yolk sac. This ovum, for its stage of development, is almost 25 per cent smaller than normal specimens in comparable stages of trophoblastic and embryonic development. Section 11-3-3, × 100.

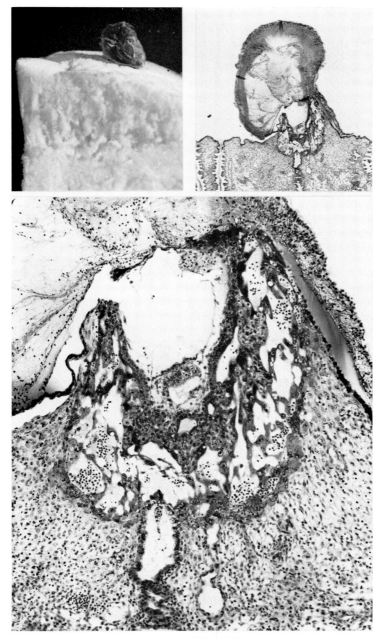

FIGURES 153 to 155

By the end of the tenth or twelfth week, the common denominator of most abortions, death or absence of the embryo, has caused the failing chorion to abort. A striking exception is the vigorous but pathologic chorion designated as the circumvallate placenta. Its immature stage is to be seen *diagrammatically* in Figure 156 and *actually* in Figure 157. Its mature stage can be seen diagrammatically in Figure 158 and the actual specimen in Figure 159. One of the few scholarly articles on the subject was written by the late Professor Whitridge Williams of Johns Hopkins in 1927. The diagrams (Figs. 156, 158, 160, 161, and 162) from the classic article[146] were drawn by the master medical illustrator, Max Brödel. He was the first professor of art as applied to medicine at Hopkins and was succeeded by his pupil, James F. Didusch, who drew all of the reconstructions used by the author in this monograph.

Although no one has very many specimens of the early stage of this interesting and important placental anomaly, it is the author's firm belief that such is caused by a small but normal ovum which is superficially implanted. It would appear from the nature of the anomalous placenta that its placentogenic area is small because it is superficially implanted. Hence, the placenta developing from or at the implantation pole of the chorion is small and thick. Because it is small and thick and hence physiologically insufficient, there is an "unseemly" or disproportionate growth of the placental margin. This results in undermining or

---

→

FIGURE 156. *(Upper)* A mid-sagittal section of a pregnant uterus of about 8 weeks' developmental age. Note the "herniated" appearance of the chorionic sac containing the embryo and its amnion. Note further the double fold of membranes, circumvallate, together with the invasion of the *decidua vera* by the growing placental margin. Previously published by Williams.[146] (Courtesy of the C. V. Mosby Company.)

FIGURE 157. *(Lower)* An early mid-trimester, spontaneously aborted, intact chorion containing a normal but macerated fetus. Note relatively small chorionic sac, which "crowds" the embryo, and the disproportionately large amount of extrachorionic or peripheral growth of the placenta. It is this feature which causes the marginal premature separation resulting in the dark blood clot seen below the rump of the fetus. From the Boston Lying-in Hospital Museum, number unknown. About natural size.

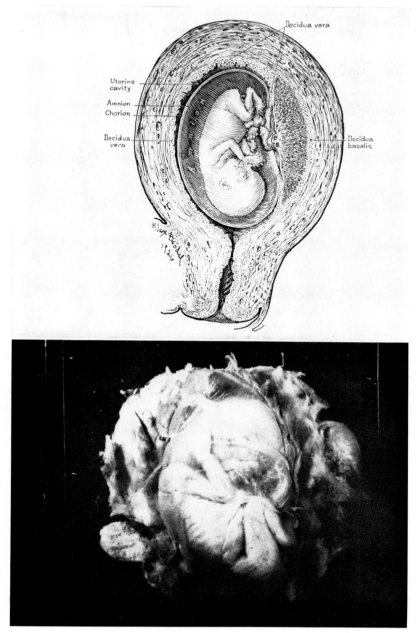

FIGURES 156 and 157 represent the artist's (Max Brödel) concept of the immature circumvallate placenta *in utero* and a comparable mid-trimester abortus which aborted owing to the same anomalous chorionic development.

splitting the *decidua vera* at the placental margin and the appearance of the opaque ring of subchorionic decidua around the circumference of the placenta.

The small size of the ovum or chorionic sac is nearly universal in the author's experience. The smallness of the ovisac, together with the disproportionately large normal embryo, also makes the ovisac prolapse or herniate into the uterine cavity, folding back the *decidua capsularis;* thus, the combination of the small size of the ovum and the undermined *decidua vera* at its margin will account for the typical appearance of the immature form in Figure 157 and the mature form in Figure 159. The opaque circumferential ring of folded membranes and underlying decidua gives the name to this anomaly. The circummarginate placenta is a less serious or marked variety of this same anomaly of the placenta.

Whether this or some other explanation is correct, these facts remain. The circumvallate chorions are smaller than they should be and contain a normal fetus. (The author has *never* seen a defective embryo associated with this anomaly.) The anomaly results in mid-trimester abortion, such as seen in Figure 157, in which the normal embryo may or may not be living. The membranes may or may not be intact, but there is always massive hemorrhage from the margin of the placenta where it had separated or invaded the nearby *decidua vera*. Approaching term, the anomalous placenta appears to be responsible for a triad of disasters, singly or *in toto*: premature labor, premature rupture of membranes, or premature marginal separation of the placenta.

→

FIGURE 158. *(Upper)* This superb drawing shows the same general features as the immature stage seen in Fig. 156. Note, however, that the membranes are now adherent to the uterine wall and that the uterine cavity is obliterated. Previously published by Williams.[146] (Courtesy of the C. V. Mosby Company.)

FIGURE 159. *(Lower)* A mature circumvallate placenta viewed from fetal surface. Note central placentogenic area surrounded by the double fold of amnion and chorion. The remnants of necrotic *decidua vera* are seen at the periphery beyond the circumvallate surface of the placenta. About two thirds natural size. (From the Boston Lying-in Hospital Museum. Previously published by Hertig.[39])

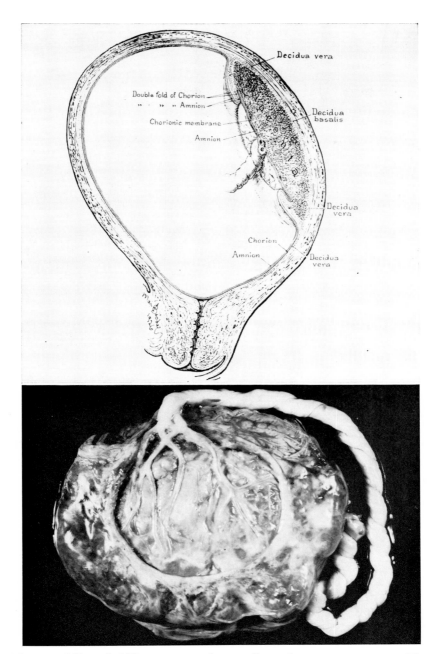

FIGURES 158 and 159 represent circumvallate placentas near term. The drawing by Max Brödel of a circumvillate placenta *in utero* toward the end of pregnancy may be compared to an actual specimen after delivery.

Figure 160. *(Lower left)* A pregnant uterus of about 25 days' ovulation age based upon the development of the 14- to 19-somite embryo (2 to 3 mm) belonging to Streeter Horizon XI. This is quite comparable to the embryo in Fig. 97 and the transected chorion in Fig. 98. The embryo in this drawing is magnified slightly, but the chorion and uterus are slightly reduced. Note that chorionic villi surround the ovisac and that the uterine cavity is prominent. Menstrual age about 39 days or 5½ weeks.

Figure 161. *(Lower right)* A pregnant uterus of about 32 days' ovulation age, based upon the development of the embryo (6 to 7 mm) with well-developed limb buds, Streeter Horizon XV. The embryo is about natural size, but the chorion and uterus are about two thirds natural size.

Figure 162. *(Upper)* A pregnant uterus, at or near term, minus the baby to show the relationships of the placenta and *chorion laeve* to the uterine wall and the amnion to the chorion. Note that the amnion is adherent to the chorion and that the uterine cavity is obliterated, both having occurred during the middle trimester of pregnancy. The *decidua capsularis* and *decidua vera* have fused and become a single tissue, thus obliterating the uterine cavity. The uterus is about one third natural size.

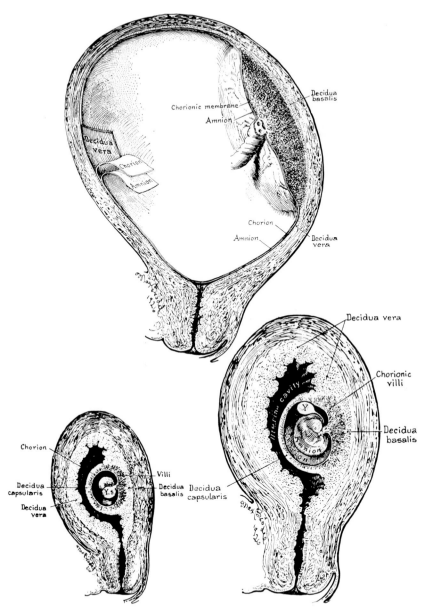

FIGURES 160 to 162 are the superb drawings by Max Brödel from Williams' 1927 article on the circumvallate placenta. They represent successive critical stages of normal placental development as seen in mid-sagittal section of the uterus. The placenta is on the posterior wall as is usual. The attachment of the umbilical cord to the chorion is transected. Previously published by Williams.[146] (Courtesy of the C. V. Mosby Company.)

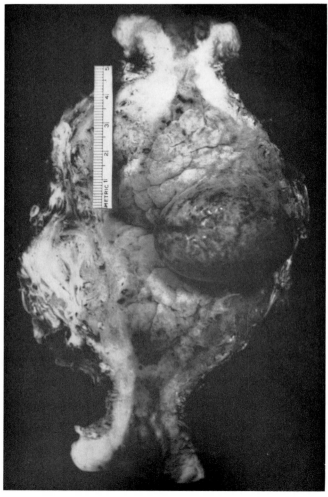

FIGURE 163. This illustrates the proper method of opening a pregnant uterus so as to expose the implantation site and endometrial surface. Note ovisac (right center) covered by congested, hemorrhagic, and focally necrotic *decidua capsularis*. Note hemorrhage in *decidua vera* (lower center) situated near lower uterine segment. Both sites could be sources of intra-uterine bleeding as part of the threatened abortion syndrome. The ovum of about 8 weeks' menstrual age, however, is good and was not destined to abort. It contained a normal embryo (21 mm) of Streeter Horizon XX whose ovulation age was 41 ± 1 days. F.H.W. S-47-1008, Carnegie No. 8553. (Courtesy of Carnegie Institution of Washington.)

The reader is referred to Figures 153 to 155 which illustrate what, in the author's opinion, is a potential early circumvallate placenta. The ovum is small but normal. It is superficially implanted and obviously has a small mass of placentogenic tissue at the site of the future placenta. Hence, unless it aborts, it cannot help but develop into the diagrammatic stage seen in Figure 156, the abortus in Figure 157, or the mature forms seen in Figures 158 and 159.

As a superb resumé of normal placental development, the reader is invited to review the three classic drawings by Brödel in Figures 160 to 162.

The diagram of chorionic and embryonic sizes and their correlations with menstrual and ovulation ages is to be seen in Figure 109. This was prepared by Streeter and was drawn in 1937 by Didusch; however, it was never published. It was originally drawn natural size so that the pathologist or embryologist could see at a glance the age of the chorion and its embryo. The author, his trainees, and his colleagues have found it useful for reference during gross examination of immature chorions.

THREATENED ABORTION

This common phenomenon has been discussed in Chapter V when the subject of the necrotic hemorrhagic *decidua capsularis* covering the growing ovum was described. Figures 164 and 165 show such a specimen. The patient was known to be exactly six weeks pregnant by her menstrual dates, the conceptus thus being twenty-eight days in developmental age. The patient was twenty-eight, married, and happily wanted and expected this baby. She came to autopsy, as a medical examiner's case (Harvard Legal Medicine, 58-43). Her death was due to massive pulmonary edema and hemorrhage interpreted as due to fulminating pneumonia. The uterus contained an implantation site of 2.0 × 2.3 × 1.3 cm on the anterior wall. The cervix contained pink mucus owing to the hemorrhagic decidua seen so clearly in Figure 164. The specimen was intact; the defect seen in the picture is due to a needle inserted by the prosector to distend and preserve the specimen with 10 per cent formalin.

The importance of this specimen, which came to the author's

attention because of the question of normality or abnormality of the *decidua capsularis,* lies in the fact that this specimen *is* perfectly normal. Not only is the chorion normal but also the chance section, showing an embryo of 5.3 mm with developing limb buds all in the same plane of section. There is considerable postmortem autolysis of the embryo and chorion, but there is no gross or microscopic abnormality of this pregnancy.

Whether the patient experienced vaginal bleeding or, if so, to what clinical extent will never be known; but she had obviously bled anatomically from the necrotic hemorrhagic *decidua capsularis,* as seen in the tissue itself and as deduced from the finding of pink mucus in the cervical canal. The great majority of such specimens at this stage of development seen by the author over the years show just such hemorrhage. It is usually slight, as in this case, but it may assume clinical proportions and constitute a "threatened abortion." It is obvious to the thoughtful observer that hemorrhage from necrotic decidua over the ovum does not jeopardize the placental attachment to the uterus.

Such a clinical threat to abort may also involve the *decidua vera* alone or in combination with decidus capsularis. The author well remembers a pregnant uterus (of 3½ months) removed therapeutically for psychiatric reasons at the Free Hospital for Women. The patient had experienced some vaginal bleeding. The *decidua vera* had entirely sloughed off, but the ovisac, covered by more or less viable decidua, contained a normal embryo whose heart continued to beat for many minutes under direct observation after immersion in warm saline.

To return to the material in Figures 164 to 166, it was this case which enabled the author to convince a Georgian jury that the slight automobile accident to the mother at twenty-six days of pregnancy, followed by five minutes of uterine spotting a day or so later, did not cause her daughter to have a toe and a fibula absent at birth. Embryologically the problem was quite simple. The mother-plaintiff for her unborn child knew precisely when she became pregnant. From Dr. Streeter's horizon data, it was easy to show that the trauma occurred when no limb buds were present. The hemorrhage a day or so later, like that in Figure 164, could not in any possible way have caused local anoxia (as the opposing medical expert testified) to a limb that did not exist. Even if it had existed, it seems difficult to see how bleeding from the often necrotic *decidua capsularis* could have affected a local area in one lower limb bud. In any event, Professor Frank C. Fraser of McGill University assured me in writing that the congenital defect in question was of genetic nature even though the parents had no history of such an anomaly in either family tree.

The author cites this obviously anecdotal material to give the reader some idea that normal human embryology and embryologic pathology play an important role in the interface between the law and medicine. More and more cases of the type cited above will be coming to trial. Indeed, it has been told the author by one of William Curran's law students sent to discuss trauma in relationship to congenital anomalies, that the Georgian case cited above had made legal history.[15] Although the plaintiff lost her case, it established that the unborn child (the embryo in this case) has its legal rights and may sue for alleged or actual damage sustained while *in utero.**

---

* In 1960, the Massachusetts law was changed which allowed an unborn child to show cause of action in its own name for injuries sustained *in utero.* This change stemmed from the case of Hornbuckle vs. Plant Pipe Line Co. of Georgia, June 1958. The author testified and the case was lost for the plaintiff. Nevertheless, the case made legal history so that now the unborn child can sue in its own name. Mr. Donald L. Conn, an assistant Attorney General of the Commonwealth of Massachusetts says, "Please be advised that the case reference in Massachusetts law which now allows a viable child to recover in an action of tort is Keyes vs. Construction 1960, advanced sheets of page 507."

CHAPTER VIII

ABNORMALITIES OF IMPLANTATION
AND SEPARATION

ABNORMALITIES OF IMPLANTATION

THE implantation of the normal six-day blastocyst appears to be due to a coincidence of factors. The size and the development must have something to do with this complicated phenomenon as discussed in Chapter IV-A. The predilection of the normal ovum for the posterior upper portion of the corpus endometrium has never been explained. That a normal ovum can implant, however, in nonendometrial tissue is universal knowledge. Therefore, the physiologic and pathologic factors of tubal and uterine motility, laxness of myometrial tone, and actual mechanical obstruction must play a part. The presence of a functioning corpus luteum is taken for granted and is undoubtedly necessary.

In general there are a few clinicopathologic facts known about abnormal sites of blastocyst implantation and subsequent placental attachment. These may be briefly enumerated:

1. Pelvic inflammatory disease of whatever type, but usually of gonorrheal origin, predisposes to tubal ectopic pregnancy. This presupposes that the patency of the tube is such that the spermatozoa can reach the oocyte and that the latter can get into the tube. The usual tubal ectopic pregnancy is associated with follicular salpingitis, a sequel to gonorrheal salpingitis. Paradoxically, the salpingitis of pelvic tuberculosis nearly always results in sterility even though the end to the fallopian tube is patent. The distortion of the lumen prevents the male and female gametes from getting together. Kistner *et al.*[82] have described one of these rare tuberculous complications, an ectopic pregnancy associated with tuberculous salpingitis. It is not understood why the noninflamed tube can occasionally be the seat of an ectopic preg-

192

nancy, but it sometimes happens. Perhaps there is physiologic slowness of tubal contractility. In any event, tubal pregnancies have the tendency to repeat themselves on the other side. Intelligent patients, who have already had one such event, recognize the signs and symptoms and can thus make the diagnosis of another ectopic pregnancy.

2. *Placenta previa* is almost always a complication of multiparity. Since it is unlikely that the blastocyst of a parous patient is biologically any different than that of the primigravid patient, the difference must lie in the uterus or its motility. It is universally recognized that the uterus, once delivered at term with subsequent normal involution, is never the same as it had been as a nulliparous organ. It is larger and less firm. When pregnant again, it has less tone and the head engages later in pregnancy or not until the onset of labor. Of course, the abdominal wall tone plays a factor in engagement of the head. The author has always pictured the low implanted normal ovum within a lax or relaxed multiparous uterus as playing the major role in the etiology of *placenta previa.*

3. When an ovum implants in any location other than one with adequate endometrium, there results a condition designated as *placenta accreta.* This is generally applied to the normal placenta in the usual location. The usual history in such a patient reveals multiparity, many previous curettages, or a cesarean section. Pathologically, the lesion is simple and straightforward. The trophoblast and/or its villous derivatives are adherent to fibrous and/or muscular tissue, as seen in Figures 173 and 174. Thus the ovarian pregnancy (Fig. 167), the tubal pregnancy (Figs. 99 and 168), and the *placenta previa* (Figs. 169, 170, and 171) are histopathologically all variants of the accreta syndrome. The usual cause of this serious complication is the poor quality of endometrium in the normal location owing to infection, trauma or poor regeneration, or the physiologically deficient endometrium in a location not intrinsically suitable for an implantation site. It need not be emphasized that an ovarian, abdominal, tubal, cornual, lower uterine segment, or cervical pregnancy will have little if any decidua and hence will be impossible to separate normally. For comparison of the normal implantation sites at four

FIGURE 164. *(Lower)* The striking feature of this normal specimen is the massive hemorrhage into the necrotic *decidua capsularis,* a feature which always occurs to some extent during this stage of pregnancy. Harvard Department of Legal Medicine, No. 58-43, H + E, × 4.

FIGURE 165. *(Upper left)* The embryo from the specimen in Fig. 164 showing the closely applied amnion, the developing nervous system, gut, coelomic cavity, and all four limb buds. The upper limb buds are normally more advanced in development than the lower limb buds. Harvard Department of Legal Medicine, No. 58-43, H + E, × 15.

FIGURE 166. *(Upper right)* A normal embryo (5.3 mm), identical in its development to the sectioned specimen seen in Fig. 164 and 165. Carnegie No. 8065, sequence 8, × 12. Previously published by Streeter.[133] (Courtesy of Carnegie Institution of Washington.)

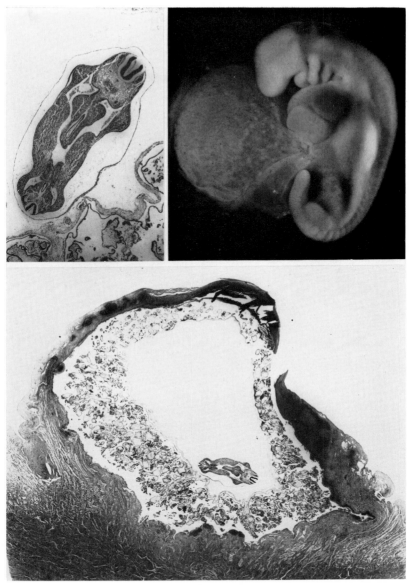

FIGURES 164 to 166 show various aspects of a human conceptus of 28 days' development and 42 days' menstrual age respectively. The vertically sectioned chorion, Fig. 164, was intact; the defect resulted from an injection needle inserted by the medical examiner in order to fix the specimen. The embryo showing development of all four limb buds is at the implantation pole and is seen more highly magnified in Fig. 165. A comparable embryo (5.3 mm) is to be seen in Fig. 166.

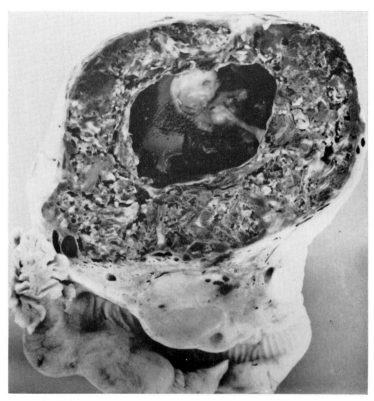

FIGURE 167. An ectopic pregnancy lying entirely within the ovary, presumably owing to the fact that the oocyte never completely left the mature follicle or its environs and that it was there fertilized *in situ*. No one has ever seen the early stage of an ovarian ectopic pregnancy. Therefore the precise site of the oocyte when fertilized is unknown. Thus, such pregnancies may or may not reveal remnants of the corpus luteum arising from the follicle of origin. ("Follicle of the month" in the author's laboratory.) This conceptus was normal, but its abnormal environment caused death of the embryo. Harvard Medical School, Department of Pathology, CS-64-497, about × 2. Previously published by Gibson.[29] (Courtesy of Dr. George B. Gibson and Professor Macafee, Belfast, Northern Ireland, and the Royal College of Obstetricians and Gynaecologists.)

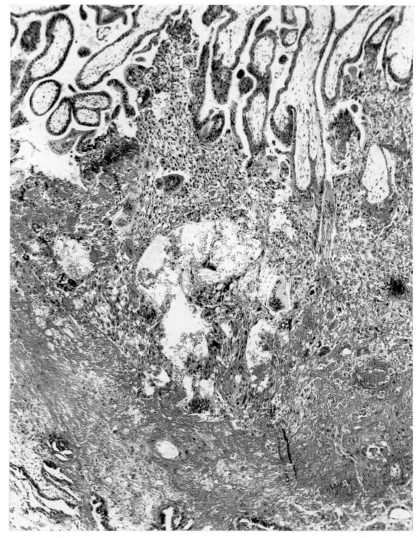

FIGURE 168. The implantation site of a tubal ectopic pregnancy. The normal immature chorionic villi are fused with necrotic tubal wall through the medium of the basal plate or "floor" of this immature placenta. The follicular salpingitis of the tubal wall is seen below and at the left. There is no decidua, as is to be expected, although foci of such may be present coincidentally, as in any fallopian tube associated with any normal intra-uterine pregnancy. A.F.I.P. Acc. No. 218754-358 H + E, × 73. (Courtesy of Armed Forces Institute of Pathology.)

FIGURES 169 and 170 are the photograph and diagram, respectively, of a pregnant uterus of about 15 weeks, removed surgically and showing a complete placenta praevia, from the Boston Lying-in Hospital.

FIGURE 169. *(Upper)* The uterus appears to have been opened posteriorly by a Y-shaped incision. The placenta, completely covering the internal cervical os, is clearly evident just below the sacrum of the fetus. Note that the uterine cavity is not yet obliterated by the growing ovisac. The amniotic sac has been incised, and the amnion is loosely adherent to the chorion. About three fourths natural size.

FIGURE 170. *(Lower)* Diagram of Fig. 169 drawn by Miss Marilyn Costello, Free Hospital for Women. Previously published by Hertig.[43] (Courtesy of Encyclopaedia Britannica, Inc.)

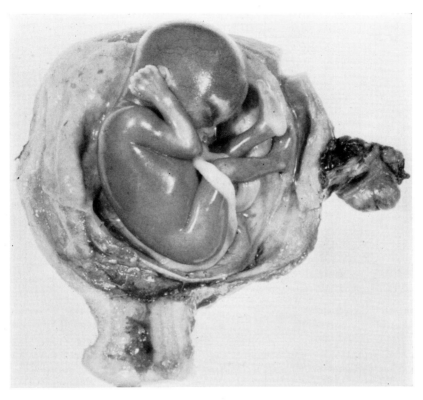

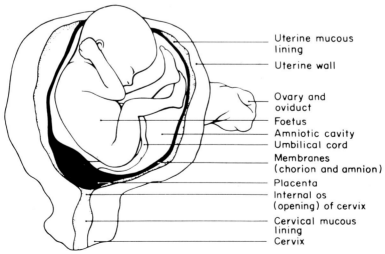

Uterine mucous lining

Uterine wall

Ovary and oviduct

Foetus

Amniotic cavity

Umbilical cord

Membranes (chorion and amnion)

Placenta

Internal os (opening) of cervix

Cervical mucous lining

Cervix

FIGURE 171. *(Upper)* A uterus, at or near term, removed supracervically because of the coincidence of placenta *percreta, accreta, increta, praevia,* and *membranacea.* This is the only specimen ever seen by the author that combines all of these abnormalities of uterine implantation of an otherwise normal conceptus. Note rupture at left, containing cut end of the umbilical cord. Note further the thinned-out placenta in lower uterine segment at lower right. B.L.I.H. S-51-168. About one half natural size. Previously published by Hertig and Gore.[49] (Courtesy of the W. F. Prior Company, and Dr. C. H. Davis and Dr. B. Carter.)

FIGURE 172. *(Lower)* A uterus and placenta, still attached, from a patient dying of eclampsia. The uterine wall, with interstitial portion of the tube at right lower corner, is below; the placenta is above. Note large black retroplacental "concealed" hemorrhage. Neither the clinical history nor the physical status of the patient led the obstetrician to suspect the presence of this "toxic separation" of the placenta. B.L.I.H. A-40-65. Previously published by Hertig and Gore.[49] (Courtesy of the W. F. Prior Company, and Dr. C. H. Davis and Dr. B. Carter.)

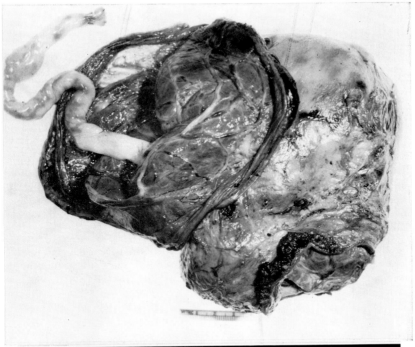

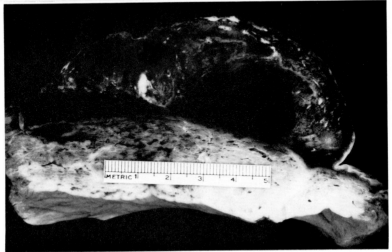

FIGURES 171 and 172

FIGURE 173. *(Upper)* From a full-term, classic, complete *placenta accreta.* The mature villi are above, the basal plate with fusion of Rohr's and Nita-buch's fibrin and fibrinoid striae is in the center, and the general inter-mingling of trophoblast and muscle of the placental site is below. The large sinusoids or veins are normal in size but occur in myometrium rather than in decidua, owing to the absence of the latter. The "prolapsed" chorionic villi are normal and do not "cause" the adherence of the placenta as claimed by some observers. B.L.I.H. S-32-165, P.T.A.H., × 90. Previously published by Irving and Hertig.[78] (Courtesy of Surgical Publishing Company of Chicago.)

FIGURE 174. *(Lower left)* From the same placental site as seen in Fig. 173. Note fibrous core of chorionic villi above and to the left, the intermingling of myometrial fibers and trophoblastic cells on left, and the rather solid mass of trophoblastic cells on the right. There are no decidual cells present. B.L.I.H. S-32-165, E.M.B., × 90. Previously published by Irving and Hertig.[78] (Courtesy of Surgical Publishing Company of Chicago.)

FIGURE 175. *(Lower right)* The implantation site, obtained at curettage sixteen days after the passage of a malignant, Group VI hydatidiform mole, shows trophoblastic giant cells within myometrium. The endometrium is above. This lesion, often previously and sometimes even now, is diagnosed as syncytial endometritis; the latter is an "atypical chorionepithelioma." That this is a normal phenomenon is shown by (a) its similarity to Fig. 174 and (b) the survival of the patient for at least 4 years after the curettage with her uterus still intact. This represents one of the author's many mistakes, he having advised hysterectomy on the basis of this specimen. B.L.I.H. S-39-5 (M-49) H + E, × 85. Previously published by Hertig and Sheldon.[64] (Courtesy of the C. V. Mosby Company.)

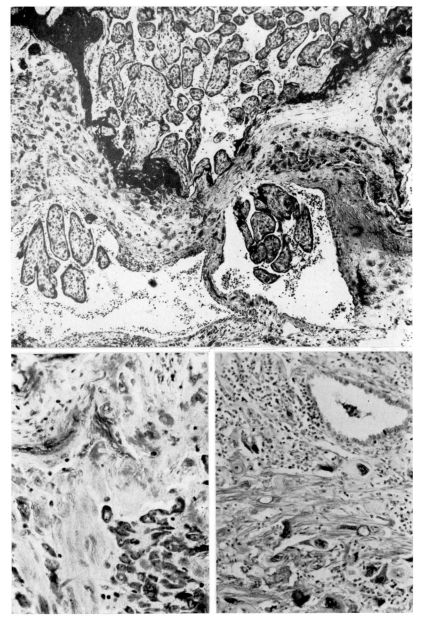

FIGURES 173 to 175 show several aspects of the placental basal plate and/or the infiltration of placental site giant cells of trophoblastic origin.

and one-half, seven, and nine months, the reader is referred to Figures 176, 177, and 178 respectively. This thick, though diminishing *decidua basalis,* the ultimate clevage plane during the third stage of labor, is in sharp contrast with the absence of decidua as seen in the classic, complete *placenta accreta* seen in Figures 173 and 174.

The interested reader is referred to the articles on *placenta accreta* previously published by the author in conjunction with one or another of his colleagues Irving[78] and Kistner.[81] The practical aspects of pathologic diagnosis of *placenta accreta* are very simple. The clinician suspects the disease if the placenta fails to separate and then attempts manual separation. If that fails, a hysterectomy is generally done. Adequate sections through the placental site including both placenta and myometrium confirm the diagnosis: the lack of decidua. If the placenta is removed, it will necessarily be ragged in its maternal surface. It is best to fix the placenta in formalin *in toto* and then to select the thickened tufted areas which appear to be adherent myometrium. The thin torn areas will show only torn placental tissue which is not diagnostic of *placenta accreta.* Only if the microscopic slide reveals the adherence of trophoblast and/or chorionic villi to fibrous tissue and/or myometrium can the definite diagnosis of *placenta accreta* be made. There are all degrees of *placenta accreta,* from focal through partial to total. Very often *placenta previa,* when seen at cesarean section, will show a focal or *partia accreta* owing to the physiologic lack of decidua in the lower uterine segment.

If the clinician elects to leave an adherent placenta *in situ* to involute, as can and does happen, he must not make the definite diagnosis of *placenta accreta.* Such may or may not be the true tissue diagnosis. It is clinically a nondelivered or adherent placenta but not necessarily a *placenta accreta.*

Just as there are degrees of *placenta accreta,* there are variations in the degree of myometrial invasion by otherwise normal trophoblast. The author considers trophoblast to be nature's first experiment with cancer, albeit a physiologic one. The normal trophoblast, for reasons quite unknown, gradually loses its invasive qualities by the end of the first trimester. Although the *decidua basalis* becomes progressively thinner as pregnancy advances, it is the result of uterine growth and stretching rather than invasion by the basal trophoblastic plate or "floor" of the placenta. It cannot be the quality of the implantation site per se, abnormal though it be, since the usual *placenta accreta* is within the myometrium only to the depth normally present in a normal endometrial implantation. The reader may compare Figure 178, the normal placental site at term, with the term *placenta accreta* site in Figures 173 and 174.

Whatever the factor and whether it resides in the trophoblast or maternal tissue, normal appearing trophoblast may penetrate the normal uterus too deeply. This results in *placenta increta,* a partial invasion and in *placenta percreta,* a total invasion with uterine rupture. The latter condition may be seen grossly in Figure 171.

If the ovum penetrates too deeply, it upsets the normal relationship between the *chorion frondosum* and the *chorion laeve.* This results in a so-called *placenta membranacea,* which was also present in the specimen shown grossly in Figure 171. Thus that patient had a *placenta previa, increta, percreta,* and *membranacea.* The cord is still attached to the adherent placenta but lies within the defect created when the uterus and the membranes ruptured.

Paradoxically the placentas adherent to uteri owing to the *accreta, increta,* or *percreta* processes do not tend to bleed. They cannot bleed because they cannot separate. The patient with a partial or focal *accreta* bleeds both before delivery, as in *placenta previa,* or after delivery when the normal *decidua basalis* separates. Naturally the complete *placenta accreta* will bleed furiously when its margin is manually separated by the clinician. In summary, the clinical aspects of these anomalies of implantation challenge the clinical judgment of the obstetrician and are dangerous to the patient, but these are diagnostically quite simple for the pathologist.

As a final diagnostic tip to pathologists about ectopic pregnancies, it is the author's experience that (a) The endometrium is not diagnostic of anything.[117] The endometrium at the time the patient is first seen may have sloughed off its decidua and the patient subsequently may have begun a new menstrual cycle.

In general, the more healthy the conceptus, the healthier is the corpus luteum and hence the decidua. Since most ectopic pregnancies have begun to involute when first seen clinically, the chorionic gonadotropin tests may be negative, the embryo dead, resorbed, or initially absent, and the chorion undergoing atrophy. It is a pathologic truism that any hemorrhage within a fallopian tube is the result of an ectopic pregnancy, unless proven otherwise. The conceptus is usually dying or dead. It may be difficult or impossible to demonstrate trophoblast or chorionic villi even with serial gross step sections through the hemorrhage.

(b) If the clinician expects the laboratory to help him make or confirm the clinical diagnosis of ectopic pregnancy, he is unwise if not outrightly foolish. While he is waiting for an equivocal report, the patient may die. The author was once partly responsible for a patient's death by assuring a senior obstetrician that a large sheet of decidua passed by the patient could not possibly have come from an ectopic pregnancy, even though no chorionic villi could be found. The author was wrong. The patient died on the operating table of a ruptured tubo-ovarian mass containing a living five-month conceptus. The patient, a dancer at a night club, had the most acutely inflamed tubo-ovarian mass that the author had ever witnessed. That patient taught the author that his laboratory, in general, was of little help in the preoperative diagnosis of ectopic pregnancy.

(c) If the clinical history suggests an ectopic pregnancy and the uterine cavity yields gross chorionic villi which are easily identified under the binocular dissecting microscope, then it is statistically unlikely that the patient has both an intra-uterine and extra-uterine pregnancy. Such a likelihood is a rarity, even though the author, while an obstetrical clinician, has seen two examples. (Both intra-uterine pregnancies went to term, curiously enough. One ectopic was ovarian and one was tubal.) Ordinarily when the symptoms suggest an ectopic pregnancy with uterine bleeding from a demonstrated intra-uterine pregnancy, the associated pelvic pathology is most likely to be a corpus luteum cyst or some other ovarian enlargement. Its tenderness on palpation, however, suggests the diagnosis of ectopic pregnancy.

The author's final thought on ectopic pregnancies is that there

is no such thing as a typical one, either clinically or pathologically. Perhaps this is true of all disease. Some philosopher, I believe
Trousseau, once said that "there are no diseases, only sick
patients."

PREMATURE SEPARATION

The problem of premature separation of the normally implanted
placenta is also a simple one from a diagnostic standpoint. The
so-called toxic separation (Fig. 172) is of the concealed type and
is associated with fulminating clinical toxemia of the hypertensive albuminuric type. The essential pathologic lesion involves
the spiral arterioles resulting in spasm and/or thrombosis with
ensuing decidual necrosis and hemorrhage. The full-blown stage,
with massive retroplacental hemorrhage, has obliterated the early
histopathologic details. The patient is acutely ill with *abruptio
placentae*. This is usually clinically evident but may be masked as
in eclampsia. Such was the case illustrated in Figure 172. The
condition was recognized only at autopsy. It is the firm conviction
of the author that toxic separation of the placenta is merely a
manifestation of the toxemic pathologic process elsewhere: arteriolar spasm (as seen in eye grounds and nail beds *in vivo*)
with more or less thrombosis, necrosis, and hemorrhage of the
tissue supplied by the affected vessel. A review of the whole
process, as a potential part of the generalized Schwartzman phenomenon, was published by McKay and associates in 1953.[100]

The nontoxic separation of the placenta is associated with the
normal necrosis and/or degeneration of the *decidua basalis* and
its immediately adjacent *decidua vera*. In the latter location lies
the large venous drainage of the margin of the placenta. These
veins appear as a discontinuous series of venous lakes, whose
wall toward the placental margin resembles the cribriform plate
of the skull. The marginal blood of the placenta oozes through
these fine holes or pores into the endometrial veins and thence
into the general venous circulation.

The margin of each cotyledon has a similar, though smaller,
corona of venous structures. These drain the cotyledon as do
those larger veins at the margin of the placenta. Indeed, the so-
called marginal venous sinus is probably merely the hypertrophied

and dilated vein of the margin of a cotyledon which happens to be at the margin of the placenta.

In any event, nontoxic separation results from the rupture of these venous vessels, wherever they may be located. Since the veins draining the placenta have little strength other than the surrounding decidua (the normal placenta would not separate otherwise), a breakdown of the decidua may involve the thin wall of a vein. As term approaches, the decidua becomes very edematous and focally moth-eaten; it is this sort of condition, together with focal necrosis which involves *all* normal placental sites, that causes the separation of the normally implanted placenta of the nontoxic patient. The reader is referred to the article by Sexton *et al.* for a resumé of this problem.[121]

CHAPTER IX

EXAMINATION OF THE PLACENTA

A S with any organ, the gross and microscopic examination
may be either cursory or detailed. The thoroughness with
which any organ is examined in a pathology laboratory is a
function of the interest and material in the particular hospital:
the interest of the pathologist and his trainees, the time available
for a particular examination, and finally the training and experience of the examiner.

Over the years there have been myriads of organ examination
forms prepared to help train residents, to speed up tissue interpretation, and to record data uniformly for coding or for research
purposes. Such a placental examination form evolved at the
Boston Lying-in Hospital. It began about 1946 or 1947 when
Dr. Robert Scully, now at the Massachusetts General Hospital,
was a resident pathologist in the author's laboratory. It has
gradually become the detailed four-page form whose gross and
microscopic notations number sixty and sixty-nine items respectively. These have been prepared by the Perinatal Research
Branch of the National Institute of Neurological Diseases and
Blindness. They are now in use by thirteen medical centers
engaged in a collaborative effort studying fifty thousand patients
to gather all the parameters surrounding the prenatal history,
birth history, postnatal development, and childhood growth until
school age. This collaborative effort is called M.I.H. or COLR
Project.

Many persons have been responsible for the present forms,
but Dr. Kurt Benirschke, when pathologist at the Boston Lying-in
Hospital, took a leading role in its preparation. The placental
examinations have been the responsibility of Dr. Shirley Driscoll,
associate pathologist of that hospital. The author is indebted
to her for the succinct statement that these modifications were

made "in order to accomplish three specific goals: 1) to standardize terminology, 2) to permit specific coding of the data directly from these forms, and 3) to minimize narrative descriptions." Thus, these sheets "have interest and validity only within a collaborative study." The author is grateful to Dr. Zekin A. Shakhashiri, acting chief of the N.I.N.D.B., Perinatal Research Branch, for permission to use these forms. They appear in the Appendix to this monograph with appropriate comments.

Whether or not the reader wishes to use any part of these forms for recording data from placental examinations, these forms do give a complete resumé of what should be looked for and/or what may be found when the placenta is meticulously examined. A simple perusal of the items in the gross and microscopic forms will teach the pathologist reader how to examine a placenta grossly, how to select blocks for microscopic sections, and how the latter should be interpreted. The placenta follows all the same general principles of anatomy, physiology, and pathology as does any other organ. It is helpful, however, to keep in mind that the greatest part of the placenta is a part of the ovum but that there are always maternal *decidua basalis* fused to the floor of the placenta and a variable amount of *decidua vera* adherent to the *decidua capsularis* covering the external surface of the *chorion laeve*. The examiner can roughly reconstitute the ruptured, empty ovisac by inserting his hand into the amniotic cavity through the rupture in the "membranes," the fused *chorion laeve* and amnion. This maneuver gives the examiner a thorough view of the maternal surface which has been created by the cleavage through the spongy layer of the decidua. The maternal surface of the membranes and placenta, although more or less smooth and shiny, will reveal microscopically the presence of torn decidua. The latter splits easily because of its edema, lack of collagen, and thin-walled vessels. (This is fortunate; otherwise, every placenta would become adherent to tissues and this would preclude its separation.)

An additional fact should be kept in mind when examining the maternal surface. The remnants of torn vessels, both veins and arteries, may often be seen grossly but always with the binocular dissecting microscope if the pathologist is interested.

Accurate tissue sections give the pathologist an actual biopsy of maternal vessels and hence a clue to placental site maternal vascular physiology and pathology. The toxemic patient and/or one with renal disease may well show a beautiful acute atheroma of spiral arterioles as they course diagonally through the placental floor. The author had already seen this in routine material by the early 1940's. There has been a recent review by Brosens, 1964,[11] with a good Bibliography.

Although the placental tissue is soft and apparently solid, it is in fact a mass of villous tissue surrounded or bathed by maternal blood. With simple blunt finger dissection, the main stem and main branches of a cotyledon, derived from a primary villus, may be easily found. Since the maternal blood is within a space, the intervillous space, and *not* within a vessel, there is no atherosclerosis in contact with maternal blood in the intervillous space. There are, however, typical laminated thrombi which may arise through stasis or by gradual fibrin deposition on degenerated trophoblastic surfaces of the "ceiling," the villi themselves, or the "floor" of the placenta. Most of these thrombi do no harm to the fetus since they do not often enmesh villi with subsequent infarction. Moreover, the placenta has a vast functional reserve estimated at about 50 per cent. Actually, it is the speed with which feto-maternal exchange is altered—whether by placental separation, villous infarction, or intervillous thrombosis—and the extent of the process which determine the prognosis of the fetus.

It should never be forgotten that the viability of the placental tissue is a function of maternal and not fetal blood supply. Thus infarcts of the placenta are due to obstruction of maternal blood to, through, or from the placenta and not to thrombosis of the fetal vessels. One needs to reflect that fetal death or absence does not cause placental necrosis but merely an atrophy or disappearance of villous vessels and sometimes hydatidiform "degeneration" of the villous stroma. The site of the maternal vascular obstruction, as in any other organ, will determine the location, size, shape, color, and consistency of the infarct. In general, arteriolar obstruction causes a dry granular infarct, either red or yellow, whereas a venous obstruction results in

FIGURE 176. *(Upper left)* Attachment of placenta (4½ months) to uterus. B.L.I.H. S-35-706, H + E, × 50.

FIGURE 177. *(Upper right)* Attachment of 7-month placenta to uterus. This is particularly good to show Rohr's stria at top of basal plate and Nitabuch's stria below the basal plate. At right center, these two striae fuse and become indistinguishable as pregnancy progresses. Much of the picture shows the thick, normal decidua basalis. B.L.I.H. S-34-165, H + E, × 50. Previously published by Irving and Hertig.[78] (Courtesy of Surgical Publishing Company of Chicago.)

FIGURE 178. *(Lower)* A term placenta attached to uterus. Note progressive decrease in size of villi, the thinning of the basal plate with just a suggestion of the fused striae of Rohr and Nitabuch, the edema of the decidua, and the prominent mass of chorionic villi within the vein. The myometrium is barely in the picture at the bottom. B.L.I.H. S-34-519, H + E, × 50. Previously published by Irving and Hertig.[78] (Courtesy of Surgical Publishing Company of Chicago.)

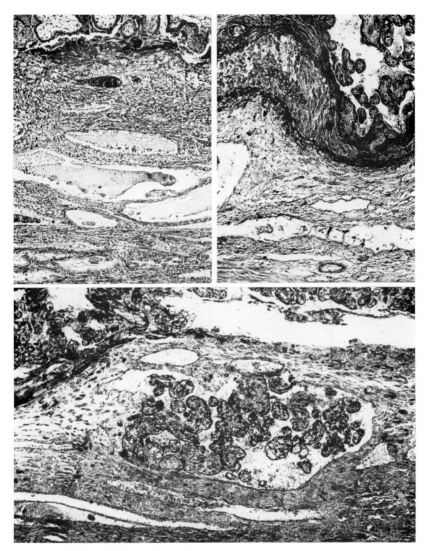

FIGURES 176 to 178 are from the implantation sites of three normal pregnancies of 4½, 7, and 9 months respectively. In each instance the placental tissue is above, the *decidua basalis* in the center, and the myometrium below. All pictures are at 50 diameters of magnification. Note that, with increasing duration of pregnancy, the decidual zone, the future cleavage plane of the placenta, becomes thinner. The large spaces are either glands or veins; the older they are, the more difficult they are to identify as such. Inspissated mucus and blood cells help although not absolutely. The presence of "prolapsed" chorionic villi is normal and occurs in any placental site if enough sections are taken to find it. These are secondary villous branches whose tips are free.

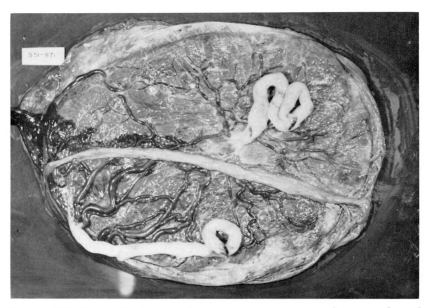

FIGURE 179. Shows the fetal surface, amniotic septum, and two cords and their vascular anastomoses of a typical monovular twin placenta (mono-chorionic-diamniotic). B.L.I.H. S-51-871. About one half natural size. Previously published by Hertig and Gore.[49] (Courtesy of the W. F. Prior Company, and Dr. C. H. Davis and Dr. B. Carter.)

a moist congested infarct. Thus the venous obstruction causes infarction in the true Latin sense of the word, "to stuff."

As a practical point, the membranes are often lacerated and portions thereof are missing, presumably retained within the patient. (See comments later *re* succenturiate lobes.) The amnion is often detached from the chorionic surface except where the cord is attached to the placenta. (It is reminiscent of a pile of clothes discarded on the floor by a sleepy child prior to going to bed.) The careful examiner may find the remnants of a yolk sac (a flattened, yellow and opaque mass of 3 to 5 mm) lying between the amnion and chorion. The anatomic and obstetric books always illustrate it as lying near the base of the cord, but it is seldom found there in the author's experience. In fact, careful search often fails to reveal it at all. It is a matter of no importance, obviously, but medical students and young residents like to see it—a sign of academic sophistication.

Since this is not a monograph about the placenta but about trophoblast, there are but few illustrations of mature placental pathology (Figs. 179 and 182-185). It is hoped that what has been said in previous chapters, this chapter, the remaining chapters, and the Appendix will give the pathologist some feeling for trophoblastic anatomy and pathology.

The careful examination of the placenta from a definite single ovum twin pregnancy and of the fused or separate placentas from a double ovum twin pregnancy or a single ovum twin pregnancy that divided prior to the inception of chorial development is most important for the twins themselves, the parents, and the hospital records. This is not a difficult procedure if approached with a little tender loving care and a modicum of embryological knowledge.

DEFINITE SINGLE OVUM TWIN PLACENTA

A typical example is seen in Figure 179. The single placenta has developed from a single chorion. The embryonic blastomeres have separated during segmentation or sometime *prior* to amnion formation. The latter begins just after implantation. Hence there are *two* amniotic sacs that are normally adherent to each other and to the surface of the chorion. There are also two umbilical cords. The fused amnions thus form the septum between the two amniotic sacs without the interposition of any chorion between. This simple anatomic fact can be easily demonstrated grossly if the examiner will peel the two amnions apart, taking care not to tear the delicate membranes. If preferred, a T-shaped block of tissue may be taken for microscopic examination: the stem of the "T" representing the amniotic septum, and the top of the "T" the reflection of the two amnions upon the surface of the adjacent chorion. The amniotic septum may be anywhere upon the surface of the placenta, but usually it divides it into two somewhat similar sized portions.

As a consequence of the single chorionic structure, there is *always* a demonstrable vascular anastomosis on the fetal surface of the placenta. It is usually arterial to arterial and venous to venous, although arterial to venous may occur. Such anastomoses are usually quite visible but may require the injection of radio-opaque material to demonstrate vascular connections between the two fetal circulations. It is helpful for the pathologist and the clinician to know which twin was attached to which cord since the babies may be of different size and viability. (I believe it is legally important, also, as to which twin is born first.) Therefore it is important to correlate the placental mass and circulation with its respective twin. The two cords may be attached anywhere on the surface of the placenta and/or membranes.

If the twin pregnancy is monochorionic, there may rarely be only one amnion, the so-called monoamniotic twin pregnancy. Care must be taken by the pathologist to be sure that the septum between a once diamniotic monochorionic twin placenta has not been broken, either during pregnancy, delivery, or the handling of the specimen afterwards. If so, the remnants of the septum will always be found if carefully searched for. This embryologic anomaly, monoamniotic twin pregnancy, stems from the splitting of the germ disk *after* the single amnion is formed. It should be emphasized that there is a whole series of such monoamniotic twinning ranging from the complete variety just mentioned to the incomplete or conjoined twins, including the famous Siamese variety of legendary fame. All conjoined twins, produced by failure of separation of two germ disks, have only one amnion and often only one umbilical cord. The early nineteen-day stage of such a conjoined twin with but a single amnion is to be seen in Figure 180. For comparison with the

$\rightarrow$

FIGURE 180. (*Upper*) These conjoined embryos are near the implantation pole but not precisely in its axis. Had they survived, they would have been joined in their longitudinal axes lying within a single amnion and undoubtedly attached by a single cord to the margin of the placenta. Carnegie No. 8727, section 84-1-3, F.H.W. S-49-3680, × 35. Previously published by Hertig.[46] (Courtesy of Dr. Kurt Benirschke and Springer-Verlag, and the Carnegie Institution of Washington.)

FIGURE 181. (*Lower*) This single normal embryo of 19 days shows the expectedly large yolk sac with hematopoietic foci, the small amniotic cavity, the early body stalk, and the allantoic diverticulum. Carnegie No. 8671, section 10-4-3, × 35. From the Free Hospital for Women. This specimen also shown previously in Figs. 45 to 47, 90 and 93. (Courtesy of Carnegie Institution of Washington.)

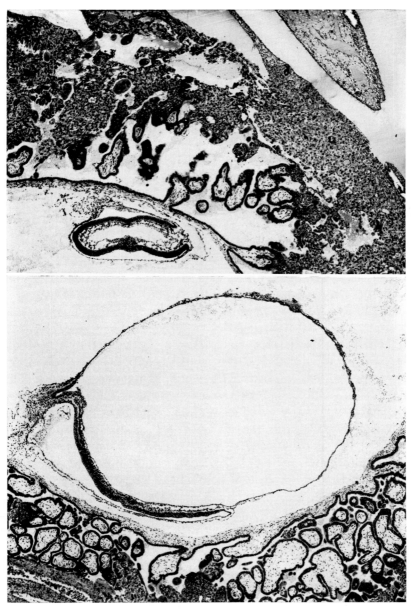

Figures 180 and 181 contrast two 19-day human ova, the upper contains a conjoined germ disk within a single amnion; the lower contains a single embryonic germ disk. Unfortunately (or fortunately) the conjoined twins, actually not yet separated, are cut transversely, whereas the singleton is cut longitudinally.

normal single nineteen-day embryo, the reader is referred to Figure 181. The latter specimen has been used in previous chapters (as Figs. 45-47, 90 and 93) to illustrate various aspects of placentation, embryonic development, or umbilical cord formation.

Whether the monoamniotic twins are conjoined or separate, the prognosis is bad for the offspring. The separate twins get snarled up in each other's cords and often die. The conjoined twins make the newspapers but usually die just the same.

DICHORIONIC TWIN PLACENTA

This may show variable degrees of fusion. Indeed, the two chorions may have implanted so closely together that the placenta appears, on superficial inspection, to be a single organ. Nevertheless there is always gross and microscopic evidence of two chorions. The septum between the amniotic sacs, if fused, will show the layering of amnion, *chorion laeve, chorion laeve,* and amnion in a microscopic section. Grossly, when the elements of the septum are peeled apart, it will also be evident that the chorionic component will be continuous with the chorionic membrane of its respective placenta. Moreover the vessels in man are never anastomotic, at least in the author's experience. This, of course, is at variance with the anastomosis of dizygotic heterosexual twins in cattle resulting in the production of so-called freemartins.

The interested reader is referred to the classic article by Corner on the embryological mechanism of twinning.[17] Also the writings of Benirschke, the modern authority on twinning, may interest the pathologist.[5, 6] The latter reference is a masterful summary of the placenta with an excellent discussion of its pathophysiologic implications. A recent article on monochorionic twins is by Bleisch,[7] a former resident pathologist at the Boston Lying-in Hospital.

PLACENTA SUCCENTURIATA

Another grossly evident anomaly of chorionic formation of great clinical importance to the patient is the formation of one or more succenturiate lobes of the placenta. These are rounded symmetrical masses of placental tissue usually lying anywhere within the "membranes," or more accurately within the *chorion laeve*. These isolated cotyledons are due to persistence of a single, isolated primary villus. The specimen illustrated in Figure 182 shows such structures, one tiny and two large, associated with a somewhat irregularly shaped placenta. The vascular connection with the main chorionic circulation is clearly seen, especially in the case of the tiny accessory lobe.

The cause of this anomaly is not completely known. In the presently illustrated specimen, it looks as though the irregular lobulation of the main placental mass was due to aplasia or atrophy of some areas and hyperplasia or hypertrophy in others. (This may also result in the "bald" chorion, previously described.) This might be considered teleologically as a compensatory phenomenon. When the anomalous lobe occurs out in the "membranes," well away from the main placental mass, it can only mean that the primordial villus secured a good maternal blood supply from the adjacent *decidua vera*. This could well happen in the light of the poor viability of the decidua capsularis. As a matter of comparative anatomical interest, the macaque monkey forms an entire secondary placenta by this mechanism. The reason for such a phenomenon lies in the fact that the monkey blastocyst is only superficially implanted or attached at its primary site. Hence the exposed chorion is never protected by *decidua capsularis,* imperfect though it be, as is the case in man.

The clinical importance of the lesion lies in the fact that retention of a succenturiate lobe *may* result in subinvolution of the uterus and postpartum hemorrhage. Therefore, since the succenturiate lobe may be associated with a normal-appearing placenta, it is necessary for the pathologist to determine whether defects in the "membranes" show torn vessels at their margins. If so, a succenturiate lobe has been retained because such structures are *always* connected with the main chorionic circulation even though "membranes" intervene. It is obvious from a consideration of the developing chorion that at one time the entire chorionic surface was covered with villi and that each villus was an integral part of the entire interconnected chorionic circulation. Simply stated, the succenturiate lobe is the persistence of a primary chorionic villus of the *chorion laeve* that grows, develops, and maintains its connection with the chorionic circulation but secures a new secondary maternal blood supply from beyond the main placental mass.

A multilobed placenta (Fig. 183) superficially resembles two large succenturiate lobes. The mechanism here, however, is different. Such misshapen placentas are the result of atrophy or aplasia of trophoblast (primary villi) of the placental mass with corresponding or compensatory growth of the placentogenic tissue that remains. The cord may be attached to any part of these bizarre multilobulated placentas, whereas it is rarely, if ever, attached to a succenturiate lobe, at least in the author's experience. By chance it could happen if the embryo lay at some distance from the implantation pole.

When the cord is membranously inserted, as it is in the five-month abortion seen in Figure 140, the persisting blood vessels lie within the *chorion laeve* and connect with the main placental vessels. Such anomalies of cord insertion are a function of the position of the embryonic mass vis-à-vis the implantation pole, as mentioned earlier in Chapter V. The clinical importance of the membranous insertion of the cord is twofold: if the vessels lie over the internal cervical os, they are subject to either pressure and/or rupture. Both of these conditions seriously endanger the baby's life during labor. Incidentally, rupture of such a vessel in *vasa praevia* is the only cause of uterine bleeding of fetal origin occurring during labor. The author once observed a perfect example of *vasa praevia* in which the baby was delivered through a rupture which was completely surrounded by the enormously prominent umbilical vessels. The baby was, in fact, delivered

$\rightarrow$

FIGURE 182. *(Upper)* This picture shows, particularly well, three succenturiate lobes of varying sizes at "5:30, 9, and 11 o'clock." Note the vascular connections of these accessory lobes or cotyledons with the main chorionic circulation. B.L.I.H. S-52-1401.

FIGURE 183. *(Lower)* A typical bilobed placenta whose umbilical cord has a marginal insertion. This type of placenta could have arisen from an ovum whose trophoblast was slightly hypoplastic as shown in Figs. 122 and 123. B.L.I.H. S-52-429.

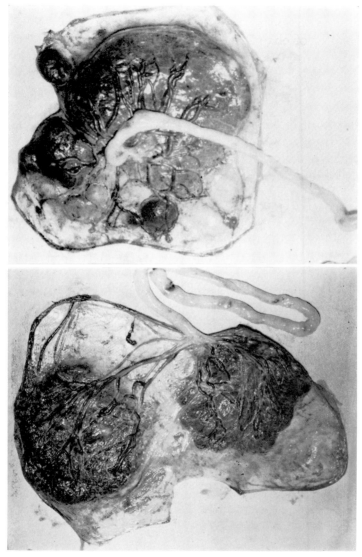

FIGURES 182 and 183 show anomalous shapes of two placentas associated with failure or abnormal persistence of primary chorionic villi. Both approximately one half natural size. Previously published by Hertig and Gore.[49] (Courtesy of the W. F. Prior Company, and Dr. C. H. Davis and Dr. B. Carter.)

through a vascular arch! The baby was normal and did not have any alteration of fetal heart rate during labor. Naturally, it is a matter of chance whether vessels within the membranous chorion lie over the internal cervical os. Usually, they do not; if they do, it is mere chance that they are so accurately placed that they rupture or bleed. Perhaps elasticity of vessels allows them to be pushed aside as the baby is delivered.

Hemorrhage into cord is an uncommon gross finding (Fig. 184). It results from a rupture of a basal chorionic or umbilical vessel. The fetal blood dissects its path through the loose mesenchyme of the chorionic membrane into the Wharton's jelly of the cord. It could conceivably assume serious proportions but never has in the author's experience.

Hemangioma of the placenta is a common benign tumor-like growth which probably should be classed as hamartoma. A typical example is seen in Figure 185. Such "tumors" may be single or multiple, large or small. They have a characteristic firm, uniform, rubbery consistency and are of a deep plum color. They ooze fetal blood from their cut surface owing to their origin from chorionic blood vessels. Microscopically they resemble a mass of small, capillary endothelial vessels which freely anastomose with one another. The chorionic angioma is the one exception to the general rule that chorionic tissue depends for its viability on a maternal rather than on a fetal source of its blood supply. Occasionally the venous drainage of an angioma may become thrombosed and the angioma thus infarcted.

→

FIGURE 184. *(Upper)* This shows an umbilical cord with a massive hematoma which arose from one of the umbilical vessels. The etiology is unknown, although occult pressure from a fetal part is a possibility. B.L.I.H. S-48-989. Previously published by Hertig and Gore.[49] (Courtesy of the W. F. Prior Company, and Dr. C. H. Davis and Dr. B. Carter.)

FIGURE 185. *(Lower)* A mature placenta containing several typical lobulated hemangiomas or chorionic hamartomas of chorionic villous origin. These are of no clinical significance to the mother or baby in the author's experience. B.L.I.H. S-55-1867. Previously published by Hertig and Gore.[49] (Courtesy of the W. F. Prior Company, and Dr. C. H. Davis and Dr. B. Carter.)

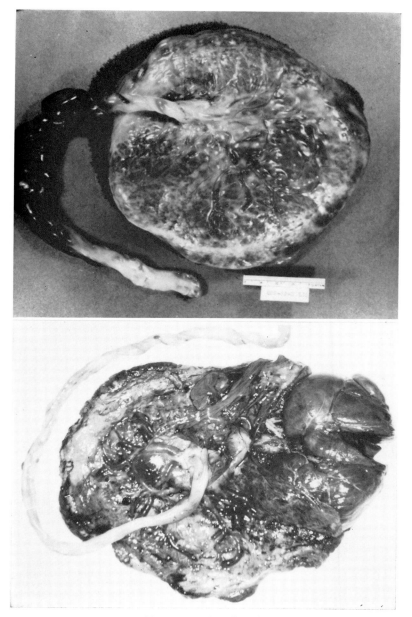

FIGURES 184 and 185

Rarely can choriocarcinoma arise from, or at least be found in, a mature placenta. Dr. Shirley Driscoll of the Boston Lying-in Hospital has reported such a lesion.[25] More recently, Brewer and Gerbie[10] have reported two. Also, these typical malignant trophoblastic tumors may follow a term pregnancy, the tumor having been missed at delivery. Such cases usually give a history of someone's failure to examine the placenta. This will be spoken of in the final chapter.

CHAPTER X

HYDATIDIFORM MOLE

A. GENESIS

THE accumulation of fluid within the stroma of chorionic villi has been noted for hundreds of years, supposedly as early as the third century B.C. There is a legendary story concerning Margaret, Countess of Henneberg, who expelled grapelike vesicles characteristic of this chorionic disease in the year 1276. It was thought that each of these vesicles was a separate conceptus, and so each one was baptized alternately as a boy and as a girl.[128]

The earliest hydatidiform mole recorded in this country appears to be that of Anne Hutchinson, a resident of the early Massachusetts Bay Colony. The following account is from Governor Winthrop's Journal as recorded by Anya Seton on page 323 of her historical novel, *The Winthrop Woman*.[120] A colleague of the present author, Miss Margaret Richardson, noted this bit of historical obstetrical pathology and published it in the *New England Journal of Medicine* in 1959.[114] The gross description of the mole is worth quoting because of its vivid accuracy:

"Mrs. Hutchinson, six weeks before her delivery, perceived her body to be greatly distempered, and her spirits failing, and in that regard doubtful of life, she sent to me, etc. and not long after (in immoderato fluore uterino) it was brought to light, and I was called to see it, where I beheld, first unwashed, (and afterwards in warm water,) several lumps, every one of them greatly confused, and if you consider each of them according to the representation of the whole, they were altogether without form; but if they were considered in respect of the parts of each lump of flesh, then there was a representation of innumerable distinct bodies in the form of a globe, not much unlike the swims of some fish, so confusedly knit together by so many several strings, (which I conceived were the beginnings of veins and nerves,) so that it was impossible either to number the small round pieces in every

225

FIGURE 186. *(Upper left)* A normal chorionic villus of 7½ weeks' menstrual age. The chorionic membrane is represented at the bottom by the square bit of tissue. Note the uniformity of the main stem, the main branches, and the secondary branches thereof. The basal plate or the placenta is artifactitiously absent. F.H.W. S-39-216 × 10.

FIGURE 187. *(Upper right)* The normal pregnancy of 7½ weeks' menstrual age containing a normal embryo measuring 19 mm from crown to rump and from which the villus seen in Fig. 186 was removed. The entire specimen consists of the posterior half of the uterus, the cervix was toward the lower right. The *decidua capsularis* and *chorion laeve* have been removed, leaving a square defect. The amnion has been incised and retracted. F.H.W. S-36-216, × 0.85.

FIGURE 188. *(Lower left)* An originally intact pathologic ovum of about 9 weeks' menstrual age, containing an empty chorionic sac and showing early hydatidiform swelling of its villi; one in greater detail can be seen in Fig. 189. B.L.I.H. S-39-612, × 1.65.

FIGURE 189. *(Lower right)* The chorionic villus from "11 o'clock" of the chorion shown in Fig. 188. The chorionic membrane is seen on edge at bottom of picture. Note fusiform swelling of villous branches and relative constriction of main stem and proximal portions of branches attached thereto. B.L.I.H. S-39-612, × 12.6.

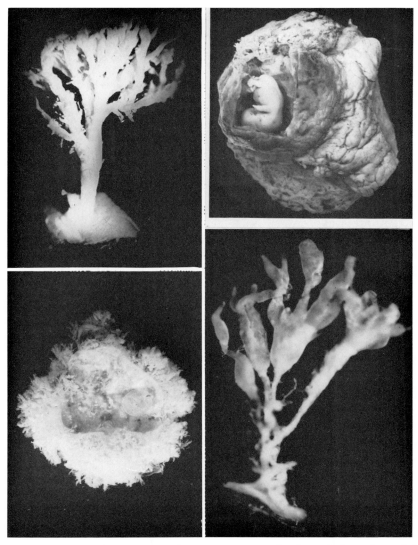

FIGURES 186 to 189 compare and contrast a normal ovisac of about 8 weeks' menstrual age with a pathologic or "blighted" ovum which spontaneously aborted at about 9 weeks. In each instance, a typical villus was dissected from each chorion and photographed under fluid with a Zeiss stereomicroscope. Previously published by Hertig and Edmonds.[48] (Courtesy of the American Medical Association.)

lump, much less to discern from whence every string did fetch
its original, they were so snarled one within another. The small
globes I likewise opened, and perceived the matter of them (setting
aside the membrane in which it was involved,) to be partly wind
and partly water. Of these several lumps there were about twenty-
six, according to the relation of those, who more narrowly searched
into the number of them. I took notice of six or seven of some
bigness; the rest both in matter and form; and the whole was like
the (blank) of the liver; being similar and every where like itself.
When I had opened it, the matter seemed to be blood congealed."
The governour, not satisfied with this relation, spoke after with
the said Mr. Clarke, who thus cleared all the doubts: The lumps
were twenty-six or twenty-seven, distinct and not joined together;
there were no secundine after them; six of them were as great as
his fist, and one as great as two fists; the rest each less than the
other, and the smallest about the bigness of the top of his thumb.
The globes were round things, included in the lumps, about the
bigness of a small Indian bean, and like the pearl in a man's eye.
The two lumps, which differed from the rest, were like liver or
congealed blood, and had no small globes in them, as the rest had.

It is a sad thought that Anne Hutchinson was driven from
the Massachusetts Bay Colony because of her abnormal pregnancy and finally came to reside in Narragansett Bay. Her name
is perpetuated not only in medical writings but by her statue
on the lawn in front of the Massachusetts State House in Boston,
and by the naming of the Hutchinson River with its parkways in
the state of New York.

Hertig and Edmonds published an account of the histogenesis
of this hydropic change, based upon the examination of 1,027
spontaneously aborted ova and seventy-four hydatidiform moles
examined in the Boston Lying-in Hospital's Laboratory of

$\rightarrow$

FIGURE 190. (*Upper*) Note uniformly loose, normal, mesenchymal type of
stroma, the thin-walled capillaries, and the thick, even layer of trophoblast.
Histologic details are not necessary for the purposes of this illustration.
B.L.I.H. S-39-690, $\times$ 75.

FIGURE 191. (*Lower*) Note, in contrast to above, that these villi show
locules or localized areas of fluid collected within their stroma. The
trophoblastic epithelium is normal. This is early hydatidiform swelling
in the villus, but the pregnancy is *not a hydatidiform mole!* B.L.I.H.
S-35-445, $\times$ 75.

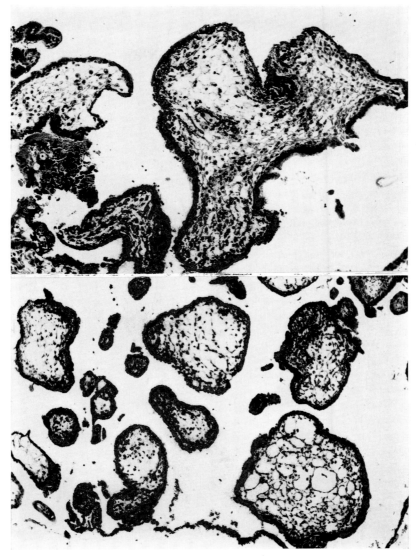

Figures 190 and 191 compare and contrast early chorionic villi of about 9 to 10 weeks' menstrual age: the normal is above, and the abnormal with early hydropic swelling of its stroma is below. The comparable, though not identical gross chorions, are to be seen in Figs. 187 and 188 respectively. Previously published by Hertig and Edmonds.[48] (Courtesy of the American Medical Association.)

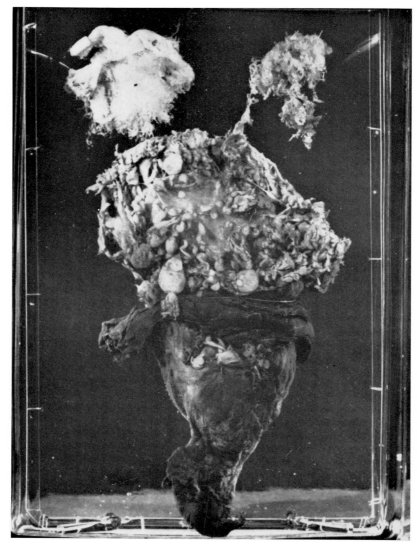

FIGURE 192. Three specimens of "blighted" or pathologic ova showing progressive hydatidiform swelling of their villous stroma. The upper left specimen is a typical pathologic ovum, comparable to that in Figs. 188 and 189. The upper right specimen is only a portion of a transitional hydatidiform mole whose hydropic villi are only slightly evident at this magnification. The main specimen of pyramidal or cone shape is a perfect

Pathology from 1934 through 1939.[48] The material from the abortions has been mentioned in Chapter VII, and the molar material, a part of an ultimately much larger series, will be discussed later in this chapter.

The essential gross and microscopic features of the formative stages in this biologically interesting and clinically important abnormality are to be seen in Figures 186 to 199. (Early stages have been illustrated in Chapter VII, Figs. 143-148.) There are only a few salient points that need to be emphasized about hydatidiform moles to a group of pathologists.

The early stage of this swelling, not a degeneration but rather an accumulation of normal intercellular fluid within the stroma of the villus, is very common. It occurs in 66.9 per cent of a large series, 487, of "blighted" or pathologic ova. Since these defective ova constitute slightly less than 50 per cent of all abortuses and the latter in turn constitute at least 10 per cent of all clinical pregnancies, early hydropic swelling as a morphologic entity occurs in slightly over 3 per cent of all pregnancies! It should be emphasized here that these early swellings of the villous branches do not constitute a true hydatidiform mole.

A casual glance at Figure 189 and comparison with Figure 199 will show the great difference in the gross appearance of the two conditions. The microscopic appearance of the trophoblast of a blighted ovum with early stromal swelling is normal (Fig. 191), whereas the trophoblast of a true mole, as will be discussed later, shows all gradations of hyperplasia and neoplasia. Moreover, a true hydatidiform mole is quite uncommon, about one in two thousand pregnancies in the United States.

A true hydatidiform mole is a temporary missed abortion of a blighted ovum with marked hydatidiform swelling of its villi and variable trophoblastic proliferation. The average menstrual age of a large series of blighted ova with hydropic swelling is

---

←

cast of the uterus, the blood clot having prolapsed through the cervix. This represents a classic example of a transitional hydatidiform mole with easily visible hydropic villi. The intact chorionic sac was empty on transillumination. From the Boston Lying-in Hospital Museum. Main (lower) specimen B.L.I.H. S-35-75. Approximately natural size.

about ten weeks; the somewhat larger series of nonpathologic ova with much less frequent hydropic swelling (about 10%), fifteen weeks; the occasional transitional mole, sixteen weeks; and the true mole, twenty weeks. Thus the longer the true "blighted" or pathologic ovum is retained *in utero* prior to expulsion, the greater is the degree of hydropic swelling.

If the pathologist receives the entire molar specimen and it has not been broken up during delivery, he will always find evidence of the original chorionic sac as shown in Figures 195, 196, and 198. (Various of the author's colleagues in obstetrics and pathology thought this a foolish concept and did not believe it. Dr. Harold Sheehan of Liverpool once discussed this matter with the author at a Red Sox baseball game, he being uninterested in the game but keenly interested in obstetric pathology. Nevertheless, he listened to the concept about the genesis of moles and said he would try and prove or disprove it. Some years later he found perfect evidence in the specimen shown in Fig. 196. The latter is a postmortem specimen of an intact molar pregnancy whose empty chorionic cavity is well shown within the mass of hydropic villi.)

The probable sequence of events in the development of swelling in the hydropic villus is (a) the early death or absence of

$\rightarrow$

FIGURE 193. *(Upper)* An opened chorionic sac containing, in turn, an empty amniotic sac. The grossly evident hydatidiform swelling of many of the chorionic villi is pathognomonic of a transitional hydatidiform mole. The blood clot lies within the intervillous space. The menstrual age is about 20 weeks. B.L.I.H. S-39-286, A.F.I.P. Acc. No. 218754-541. About natural size. Previously published by Hertig and Edmonds.[48] (Courtesy of the American Medical Association.)

FIGURE 194. *(Lower)* A chorionic villus from a transitional hydatidiform mole comparable to that seen above. Note coalescence of isolated locules of intercellular fluid to form central cavity such as is present in all typical hydatidiform molar villi. Note further the absence of blood vessels and the absence of any significant trophoblastic overgrowth. Indeed, the solid mass of trophoblast at right lower corner has undergone "physiologic" fibrinoid and hyaline degeneration. B.L.I.H. S-39-327, A.F.I.P. Acc. No. 218754-485, × 50. Previously published by Hertig and Mansell.[53] (Courtesy of the Armed Forces Institute of Pathology.)

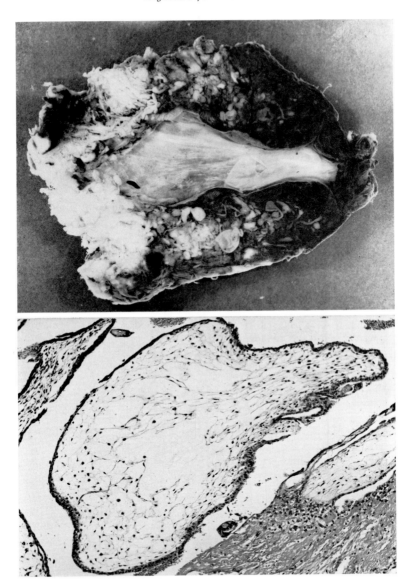

FIGURES 193 and 194 show the gross and microscopic features, respectively, of a transitional hydatidiform mole. Both specimens come from the Boston Lying-in Hospital Laboratory of Pathology.

FIGURES 195 to 198 show various anatomic aspects of the relationship of the hydatidiform molar villi to the chorionic membrane, from which they arose and to which they still may be attached by tenuous thread-like remnants of the villous stems. Many molar villi, however, are isolated from the chorion and/or their fellows, perhaps artifactitiously, owing to the trauma of delivery.

FIGURE 195. *(Upper)* The opened chorionic sac, lined by amnion, of a classic hydatidiform mole of 16 weeks' menstrual age removed by hysterectomy. The mole is still *in situ,* the posterior wall of the bivalved uterus being faintly seen at the top of the picture. Specimen photographed under fluid at approximately four fifths natural size. B.L.I.H. S-39-1144. Previously published by Hertig and Edmonds.[48] (Courtesy of the American Medical Association.)

FIGURE 196. *(Lower left)* The best example of an intact, hemisected uterus containing a hydatidiform mole known to the author. The globular shape of the uterus with the hemorrhage into the uterine cavity, owing to disruption of the intervillous space, is apparent. (All molar pregnancies bleed from this mechanism.) The oval-shaped empty chorionic sac is plainly evident at left center. A.F.I.P. Acc. No. 218754-486. Previously published by Hertig and Mansell.[53] (Courtesy of Dr. Harold L. Sheehan, Liverpool, England, and the Armed Forces Institute of Pathology.)

FIGURE 197. *(Center right)* A typical hydatidiform unit of a molar pregnancy to emphasize the variable swelling in a segment of a villus and the tenuous, thread-like attachment of the swelling to its fellows and/or the villus. B.L.I.H. S-39-1099. Approximately nine tenths natural size.

FIGURE 198. *(Lower right)* From the same specimen as in Fig. 197 but showing the empty, opened chorionic sac. B.L.I.H. S-39-1099, × 0.9.

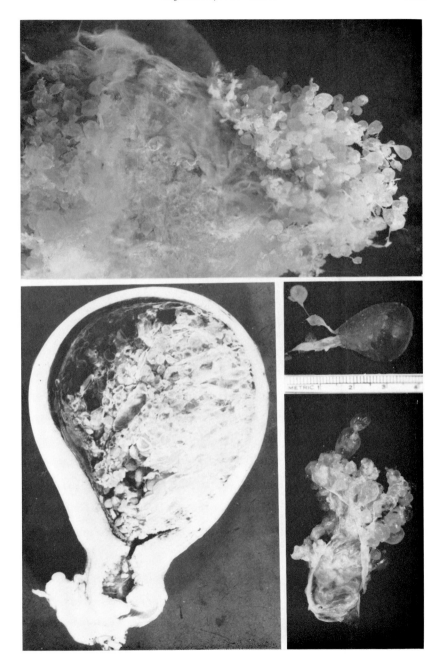

FIGURE 199. A classic hydatidiform mole photographed under fluid to show all the gross anatomic features of the lesion. The specimen was removed at hysterectomy by Dr. Christopher J. Duncan at the Free Hospital for Women. The chorionic sac containing the macerated somewhat stunted embryo with early limb bud formation was originally intact. (A slightly younger normal embryo of this development may be seen in Fig. 166.) This embryo developed for about 32 days and died, although the molar pregnancy went on for many weeks thereafter. The extension of the head is an artifact of fixation, although associated with maceration of the embryo. The chorionic sac, opened by the author for photographic purposes, is seen at upper right. Plainly evident are the tiny opaque foci of trophoblastic growth on the surface of the distended villi. Carnegie No. 8723, sequence 1, × 2. F.H.W. S-49-788, A.F.I.P. Acc. No. 218754-487. Previously published by Hertig.[38] (Courtesy of Grune and Stratton, Dr. S. H. Sturgis, and Carnegie Institution of Washington.)

the embryo, (b) a disappearance of villous blood vessels, (c) the accumulation of stromal fluid through the activity of a still functioning trophoblast, and (d) the ultimate globular swelling of the branch(es) of the involved villus. The actual mechanisms have been discussed for over a hundred years. The interested reader is referred to author's resumé of the various theories published in 1940.[48]

Suffice it to say, hydropic swelling is not a degeneration and it is not truly a pathological process, rather it is due to the persistent normal activity of immature trophoblast in the absence of a functioning chorionic circulation. It occurs normally at junction of the *chorion laeve* and *chorion frondosum* of the normal developing placenta if one takes care to look for it. It occurs in otherwise normal placentas if the blood vessel primordia fail to coalesce with their fellows. It does not happen with any frequency following fetal death per se after the first ten weeks as cited above. The ten weeks' blighted ova show the lesion in two thirds of the specimens, whereas the non-pathological ova with normal albeit dead fetuses of fifteen weeks show only about 10 per cent hydropic swelling. Thus the degree of looseness of stroma and immaturity of the trophoblast appear to be important factors in the pathogenesis of hydropic swelling.

The author is convinced that these two factors evoke some primitive urge or latent growth factor in trophoblast. It is as though the rounded vesicle reverts to the type of growth and invasive activity seen in the early ovum discussed in Chapter IV. Whether this is either good logical or good biological reasoning, the fact remains that the more dangerous the hydatidiform vesicle becomes clinically the more it resembles an immature ovum trophoblastically.

McKay,[97] while collaborating with the author, wrote a short and lucid summary of the pathophysiology of hydatidiform "degeneration" as follows:

> . . . it is one of the curious facts to be observed in the routine obstetric pathology laboratory that early in gestation when the embryo dies, or the fetal-villous blood vessels fail to connect, the connective tissue of the villi becomes distended with fluid, so-called hydatidiform "degeneration." On the contrary, when a fetus dies

after the fifth month of gestation, the villi do not accumulate fluid but become hyalinized, fibrotic, and decrease in size. This difference in response on the part of the placenta to the death of the embryo may be explained by at least two possible mechanisms: (1) there may be a change in the water binding capacity of the ground substance of the stroma, or (2) there may be a change in the permeability of the trophoblast to fluid transfer.

As a final point, the reader is referred to the several papers by McKay and associates[101, 102] which give the chemical composition of fluid from hydatidiform molar villi, normal early chorions, and their associated amniotic sacs. Suffice it to say here, the trophoblast of moles and young chorions is physiologically similar. It is able to concentrate substances in strengths different than in the maternal plasma. It is able to maintain a fluid milieu that is osmotically lower than that of the mother's blood. In short, there is a true placental barrier and it is largely, if not wholly, of trophoblastic nature.

B. GROUPING

It is generally accepted by pathologists and obstetricians that there is a wide spectrum of trophoblastic growth and differentiation in a hydatidiform mole. This becomes readily apparent if one has the opportunity to see a large number of specimens. It is less apparent to the individual physician who may personally see one or two of these specimens during his professional life.

That the hydatidiform mole is followed by or associated with sequelae of serious clinical import is universally acknowledged. Not as well understood or remembered is the clinical fact that over 80 per cent of moles have a benign course, and that half of the affected patients subsequently become pregnant. Only a small proportion, 2.5 per cent, eventuate in choriocarcinoma, *a true neoplasm*. A somewhat greater number, 16 per cent, are followed by local invasion by one or more hydropic villi, which may very rarely be carried to distant foci. Nevertheless these *invasive moles are not true neoplasms*, in the author's opinion, any more than the rare *placenta increta* and the universal deportation of trophoblast to the lungs in normal pregnancy constitute neoplasia. True enough, normal trophoblast has cancer-like qualities, at least temporarily, as has been mentioned before.

The histologic interpretation of an individual hydatidiform mole seems to typify the situation of the treatment and evaluation of any uncommon or rare lesion; the clinician tends to treat the current patient as he did the last one, and similarly the pathologist tends to interpret the current specimen as he did the previous one of the same category. Nevertheless, each hydatidiform mole or each choriocarcinoma is a distinct entity even though their respective incidences are uncommon and rare, respectively. Thus the morphologic variations of these lesions tend to follow a normal population or bell-shaped curve if one sees enough specimens.

It is the purpose of this chapter, with its many illustrations gleaned from the author's files, to give the practicing pathologist an idea of the great morphologic variation among hydatidiform moles and the potential prognostic significance of these variations. Much of the information has been published before by the author and his colleagues, Hertig and Sheldon in 1947, and Hertig and Mansell in 1956. Thus, many of the illustrations have been published before in one or the other or both of these papers. The first one, in a obstetrical journal,[64] the pathologists will probably not have seen. The other, in *Atlas of Tumor Pathology*,[53] is usually available in most laboratories of general pathology. Therefore, the text of this chapter will be somewhat brief; the pictures with legends speak for themselves.

As an initial statement, it is all too common for medical personnel, be they obstetricians, pathologists, or medical students, to link together the entities of hydatidiform mole and choriocarcinoma. This is unfortunate. Although these lesions may on occasion be related sequentially, they are entirely different clinicopathologic entities. One need only recall that hydatidiform mole can give rise to an invasive mole, whereas any type of pregnancy can eventuate in a choriocarcinoma. To be sure, the more pathologic a pregnancy, the more apt it is to be followed by a choriocarcinoma, as demonstrated in the final illustration (Fig. 274).

Another concept that seems hard to instill is the fact that a hydatidiform mole *always* is a new, albeit pathologic, pregnancy as described in the first section of this chapter. It *never* follows a normal pregnancy owing to "retained secundines."

The only practical reason for the histological grouping of hydatidiform moles, as with the grading of true tumors, is for prognostic purposes. To be sure, it is fun to classify any variety of living organism, the taxonomist's delight. The usually busy pathologist is, however, not generally taxonomically inclined. He has far too many things to do, all of them bearing upon the diagnosis and prognosis of disease, whether he be an anatomic and/or clinical pathologist.

The author's original grouping of hydatidiform moles began in 1932, as part of his diagnostic interest in trophoblast. At that time the prognosis of choriocarcinoma, the relatively rare sequel to a molar pregnancy, was all but hopeless. Therefore it seemed reasonable to see if one, using accepted histopathologic criteria, could separate in advance those moles which were destined to have a fatal prognosis from those with a favorable outcome. It became evident after about fifteen years of careful histopathologic and clinical correlation of two hundred moles that, although there was a general correlation between the way a mole looked and the way it acted, there were significant exceptions. Thus, although no obviously benign mole (Group 1) ever got the patient or her uterus in trouble, other moles with even minimal trophoblastic atypia might be followed by serious sequelae. In the author's initial experience, choriocarcinoma never followed an apparently innocuous mole of the first four groups; this series sequel was confined to Groups V and VI. Nevertheless, Little and his colleagues,[86] in data as yet unpublished, showed that the present author's series of 205 moles examined (in consultation) from 1943 to 1952 yielded a significant number of choriocarcinomas following the Group IV moles (Fig. 224). In material seen since that time, choriocarcinoma has followed moles histologically more benign.

At this point it is appropriate to give both the author's original grouping, which he still follows, and the subsequent simplified version which, however, he does not use. The apparently illogical reason for this is that there seems to be a great morphologic spectrum in moles, as can readily be appreciated by glancing at Figures 200 to 223 and at Table III.

"Malignancy" in Table III includes the sequelae to hydatidi-

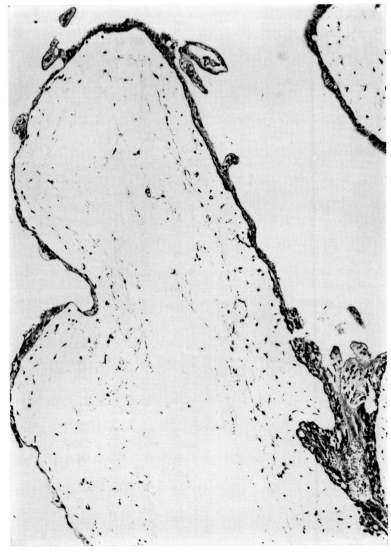

FIGURE 200. A benign hydatidiform mole of Hertig and Sheldon Group I. Although the trophoblast is quite viable, it has undergone neither growth nor undifferentiation. B.L.I.H. S-37-375, A.F.I.P. Acc. No. 218754-549, × 100. Previously published by Hertig and Mansell.[53] (Courtesy of the Armed Forces Institute of Pathology.)

FIGURE 201. *(Upper)* The stroma of two molar villi can be seen at upper left and in the lower portion of the picture. The upper left trophoblast is normal, but that below has vacuolated syncytiotrophoblast and dysplastic (the author prefers and uses the term anaplastic) cytotrophoblast. This was considered to be Group II mole, probably underdiagnosed. B.L.I.H. S-43-203, A.F.I.P. Acc. No. 218754-550, × 120. Previously published by Hertig and Sheldon.[64] (Courtesy of the C. V. Mosby Company.)

FIGURE 202. *(Lower)* The curetted placental site from a Group III mole. The maternal portion of the placental site is not shown. Although much of this trophoblast from the floor of the original immature placenta has undergone fibrinoid degeneration, usually a good prognostic sign, there is still disturbing viable trophoblast on the surface. The trophoblast in curettings of any mole usually looks worse than that of the original mole, which is why all curettings should be carefully and separately examined! B.L.I.H. CS-53-26, A.F.I.P. Acc. No. 218754-497, × 115. Previously published by Hertig and Mansell.[53] (Courtesy of the Armed Forces Institute of Pathology, Dr. B. Weisl and Dr. W. Studdiford.)

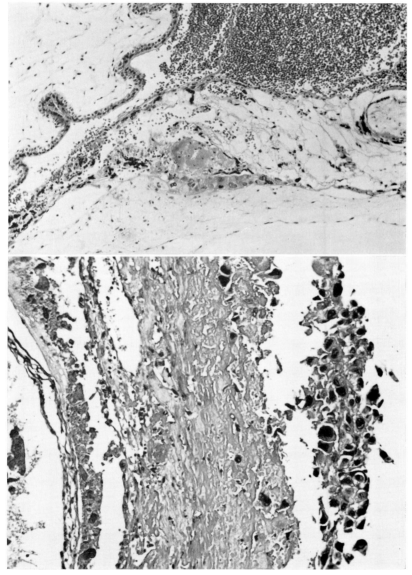

FIGURES 201 and 202 are from two different hydatidiform moles of morphologically low malignant potential. Both, however, were followed by an invasive mole (chorioadenoma destruens) although the patients survived following hysterectomy.

FIGURE 203. *(Upper)* Predominantly syncytiotrophoblastic proliferation. In the light of Tao's newer data, it is clear that the cytotrophoblast at the right has given, and is still giving, rise to the syncytiotrophoblast. B.L.I.H. S-39-1408, A.F.I.P. Acc. No. 218754-552, × 150.

FIGURE 204. *(Lower)* An apparently free-lying mass of predominantly cytotrophoblast from the same mole as above. In spite of the normal trophoblast below, moles often have these masses of trophoblast which seem to lie free but are actually and usually attached to a villus elsewhere. Compare with Figs. 205, 207, 209, 210, 212, 215, 218, 220 and 222 to show the origin of such trophoblastic masses. B.L.I.H. S-39-1048, A.F.I.P. Acc. No. 218754-551, × 150.

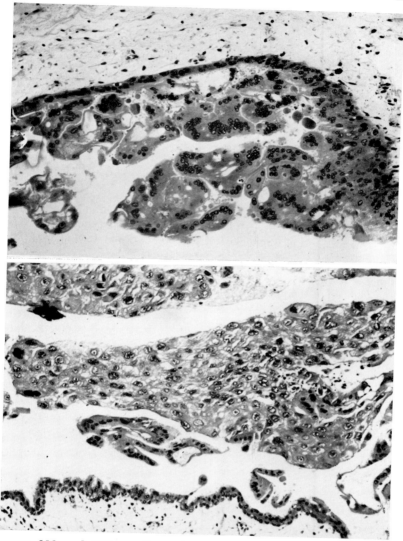

Figures 203 and 204 are from the same Group IV mole sent for the author's original study by the late Dr. Ralph Miller of Dartmouth Medical School (033-430). Although this trophoblast disturbed both Dr. Miller and the author (and still does), the patient did not develop any serious sequelae. This illustrates superbly that trophoblast varies within the same mole and that disturbing trophoblast does not necessarily imply bad prognosis. Previously published by Hertig and Sheldon.[64] (Courtesy of the C. V. Mosby Company.)

FIGURE 205. *(Upper)* Note classic evidence of trophoblastic immaturity or hyperplasia: vacuolated syncytiotrophoblast surrounding foci of cytotrophoblast. This mimics the trophoblast of the 11- to 12-day ovum (Figs. 26-29 and 30-36. A.F.I.P. Acc. No. 218754-492, × 195.

FIGURE 206. *(Lower)* The placental site curettings obtained at the time of the evacuation of the mole seen above. Note immature trophoblast attached to walls of vein and lying within its lumen. This may well represent tangential section of an invasive hydropic villus such as was actually found in the uterus removed surgically. A.F.I.P. Acc. No. 218754-507, × 52.

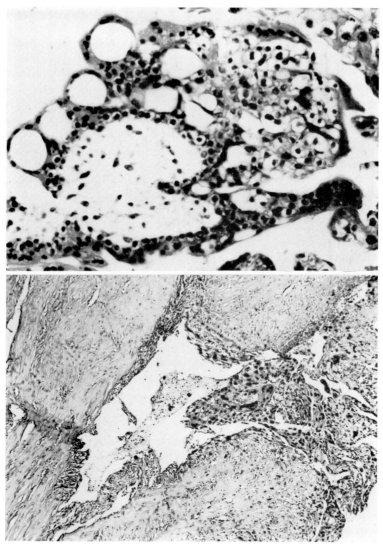

FIGURES 205 and 206 are from a molar pregnancy, Group IV; the upper is from the mole itself, and the lower is from uterine curettings. The latter enabled the author to suspect an invasive mole which was confirmed at hysterectomy. Rarely is the pathologist fortunate enough to be presented with this pathognomonic picture. B.L.I.H. CS-53-18. Previously published by Hertig and Mansell.[53] (Courtesy of the Armed Forces Institute of Pathology.)

FIGURE 207. *(Upper)* Note variations in trophoblastic growth still attached to villus and the independent or "tissue culture" growth along surface of blood clot at left. A.F.I.P. Acc. No. 512921-19021, × 40.

FIGURE 208. *(Lower)* Note immature but benign-appearing trophoblast comparable to that in Fig. 205. B.L.I.H. S-52-209, A.F.I.P. Acc. No. 514647, 52-1461, × 75. Previously published by Hertig.[40] (Courtesy of the American Society of Clinical Pathologists.)

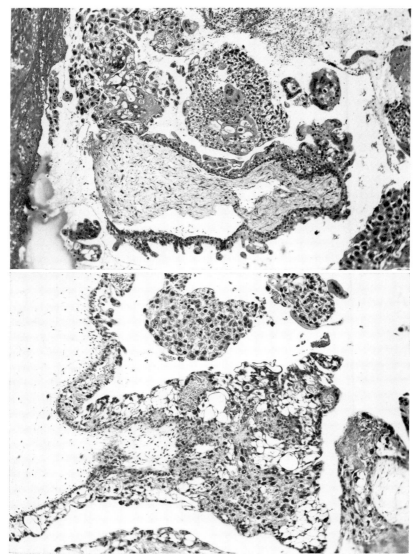

FIGURES 207 and 208 represent two different hydatidiform moles of Group IV; the majority of moles fall in this group, possibly malignant, as shown by the bell-shaped curve (Fig. 224).

FIGURE 209. *(Upper left)* Note mixture of immature but benign-appearing trophoblast comparable to that in Fig. 205. A.F.I.P. Acc. No. 218754-233D, × 145.

FIGURE 210. *(Upper right)* Note predominant vacuolated syncytiotrophoblast with fibrinoid degeneration or necrosis of cytotrophoblast. A.F.I.P. Acc. No. 218754-233C, × 150.

FIGURE 211. *(Lower)* The most disturbing portion of this mole owing to hyperplastic and somewhat dysplastic (anaplastic) trophoblast but without active growth. The extensive fibrinoid necrosis, a normal aging process in the maturing placenta, is reassuring to the pathologist. A.F.I.P. Acc. No. 218754-233A, × 200.

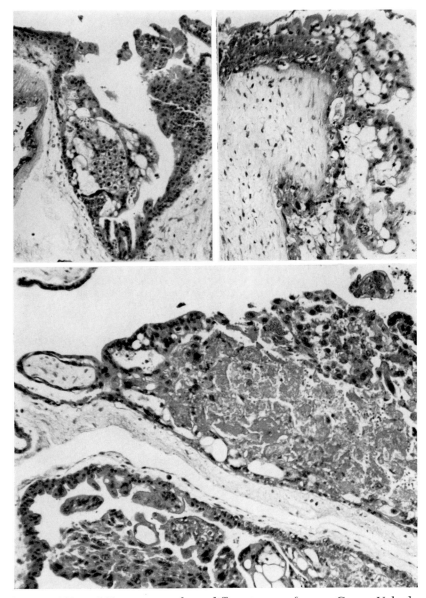

FIGURES 209 to 211 represent three different areas from a Group V hydatidiform mole to show variations in trophoblastic morphology and its dysplastic pattern. This indicates that it is necessary to take many sections to sample a mole adequately. B.L.I.H. CS-50-47.

FIGURE 212. *(Upper)* Note dysplasia of trophoblast, the apparent loss of basement membrane, and the invasion of the villous stroma by trophoblast. The latter is uncommon. Note further that the placental site trophoblast (Fig. 213), although disturbing, does not resemble that of the original mole. A.F.I.P. Acc. No. 218754-555, × 150. Previously published by Hertig and Sheldon.[64] (Courtesy of the C. V. Mosby Company.)

FIGURE 213. *(Lower)* The curetted placental site associated with mole illustrated above. Note trophoblast above separated from decidua below by a fibrinoid layer analogous to Nitabuch's layer (Fig. 177). This may well be a "protective" layer that inhibits invasion. Whether this very immature trophoblast is truly neoplastic, a choriocarcinoma *in situ,* is a matter of opinion. The author believes so. In any event the uterus was *not* removed and the patient remained well for five years. × 110.

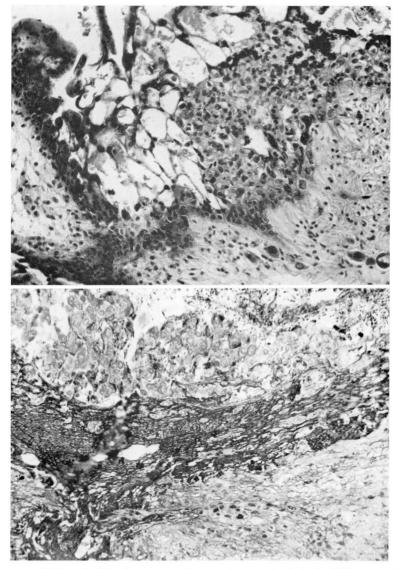

FIGURES 212 and 213 show a malignant (appearing) hydatidiform mole, Group VI, and its associated placental site. B.L.I.H. S-34-662.

FIGURE 214. *(Upper)* A low-power view to show the massive amount of trophoblast arising from this single villus. A.F.I.P. Acc. No. 482478-4, × 48.

FIGURE 215. *(Lower)* A higher-power detail of the above showing a perfect replica of an early intervillous space, two primordial villi, and the basal plate or "floor" of an immature placenta. A.F.I.P. Acc. No. 482478-2, × 114.

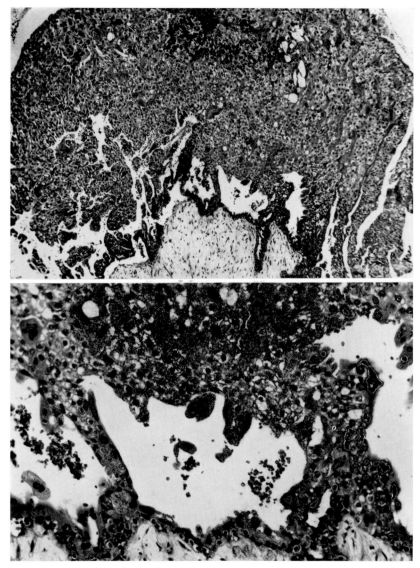

FIGURES 214 and 215 are from a Group VI or malignant mole in which the trophoblast shows maximal proliferation. It was followed by an invasive mole. Note its immature character and its mimicry of the 13-day trophoblast (Figs. 38 and 39).

FIGURE 216. *(Upper left)* Original curettings showing placental site above and markedly pleomorphic trophoblast below. B.L.I.H. S-35-1035, A.F.I.P. Acc. No. 218754-557, × 50. Previously published by Hertig and Sheldon.[64] (Courtesy of the C. V. Mosby Company.)

FIGURE 217. *(Upper right)* Higher-power detail of Fig. 216. Note extreme hyperchromatism and pleomorphism of trophoblast. B.L.I.H. S-35-1035, × 150.

FIGURE 218. *(Lower left)* A retained hydropic villus removed at the second curettage performed for bleeding, fever, and elevated chorionic gonado-tropin. Note extreme pleomorphism of trophoblast. B.L.I.H. S-36-19. A.F.I.P. Acc. No. 218754-556, × 130. Previously published by Hertig and Sheldon.[64] (Courtesy of the C. V. Mosby Company.)

FIGURE 219. *(Lower right)* The placental site in the uterus removed sur-gically several days after the second curettage. Note trophoblast within the large vein of the myometrium. This is consistent with the appearance of a tangential section from an invasive mole, although it may be an exaggeration of the normal growth of trophoblast within placental site veins. B.L.I.H. S-36-37, × 50. Previously published by Hertig and Shel-don.[64] (Courtesy of the C. V. Mosby Company.)

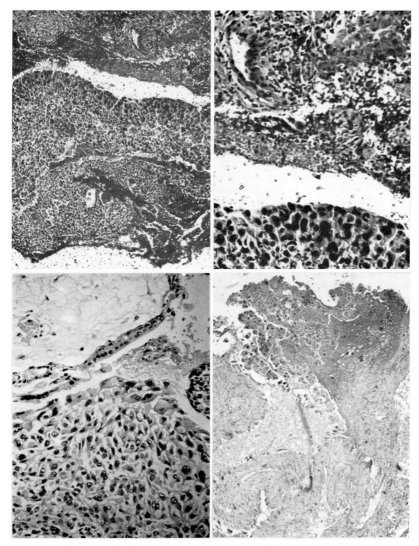

FIGURES 216 to 219, from a Group VI or malignant mole, illustrate the marked growth and anaplasia (dysplasia) which may be encountered, although the sequel may be only minimal trophoblastic invasion of the excised uterus. The patient was alive and well at least ten years following hysterectomy.

TABLE III

HYDATIDIFORM MOLE CLASSIFICATION

Group	Name	Histologic Criteria	Number of Cases	Number of Malignancies
I	Benign	None to slight hyperplasia of trophoblast	22	0
II	Probably benign	Slight to moderate hyperplasia	30	2
III	Possibly benign	Hyperplasia with slight anaplasia	33	4
IV	Possibly malignant	Moderate anaplasia with hyperplasia	59	10
V	Probably malignant	Marked anaplasia with hyperplasia	39	20
VI	Malignant	Exuberant trophoblastic growth (variable mitotic activity) with marked anaplasia and often evidence of endometrial invasion	17	17
		Total	200	53

The original grouping of 200 hydatidiform moles as proposed by Hertig and Sheldon. Previously published by Hertig and Sheldon.[64]

form mole such as chorionepithelioma *in situ*, syncytial endometritis, invasive mole, and true choriocarcinoma. Strictly speaking, these complications might better be called choriomas or in modern terminology "trophoblastic disease." There are insufficient data to be sure of the roles of chorionepithelioma *in situ* and syncytial endometritis so that only invasive mole and choriocarcinoma are included in "trophoblastic disease." It is the latter group which Roy Hertz and his colleagues[33, 118] have treated so successfully and to which reference will be made later. The morphologic aspects of the four choriomas which may follow a hydatidiform mole are

Chorionepithelioma *in situ* (Figs. 253-255).

Syncytial endometritis (Fig. 175).

Invasive mole (Figs. 225, 227, 230, and 231, see also Chapter X-C and X-D).

Choriocarcinoma (See Chapter XI-A, XI-B, and XI-C).

TABLE IV

FOLLOW-UP DATA ON CHORIONIC MALIGNANCIES

Grade	Cases	Subsequently Pregnant	Living and Well with uterus	without uterus	No Data	Died	Cured (%)	Remarks
Chorionepithelioma *in situ*	7	2	2	3	0	0	100	no deaths
Syncytial endometritis	9	0	2	6	0	1	89	1 death sepsis
Chorioadenoma destruens	32	0	0	27	4	1	97	1 death sepsis
Choriocarcinoma	5	0	0	0	0	5	0	5 deaths choriocarcinoma
Total	53	2	4	36	4	7	86.6	

The variety of chorionic malignancies which followed the 200 hydatidiform moles tabulated in Table III. Previously published by Hertig and Sheldon.[64]

TABLE V

SIMPLIFIED CLASSIFICATION OF HYDATIDIFORM MOLES

New Grade	New Name	Old Group	Old Name
1	Apparently benign	Group I	Benign
2	Potentially malignant	Group II	Probably benign
		Group III	Possibly benign
		Group IV	Possibly malignant
3	Apparently malignant	Group V	Probably malignant
		Group VI	Malignant

This table was previously published by Hertig and Mansell.[53]

Although the three grades are simpler, the author does not use this classification, even though it has some practicality.

If there is admittedly no perfect correlation between the morphologic appearance of a well-studied mole and its clinical outcome,[77] why bother to examine the specimen? In all probability, refined histochemical techniques will ultimately show important biologic differences not brought out by the classic hematoxylin and eosin stain. Even now, the somewhat crude histochemical techniques used by Bur and his associates[13] indicate a difference between the trophoblast of the noninvasive mole and the invasive mole. Also he showed that of three typical choriocarcinomas, the one from the patient who survived, in spite of metastasis but without treatment other than hysterectomy, was different from those two that killed the patients. The nonfatal one had a ribonucleoprotein (RNP) which was digestible by ribonuclease and comparable to benign trophoblast, whereas the two fatal choriocarcinomas showed a ribonucleoprotein which was undigestible by commercial ribonuclease.

In any event, the careful histopathological examination of multiple molar sections (5 to 10 good paraffin blocks) AND of the separated curettings gives a fairly good estimate of prognosis. If for no other reason, the pathological examination of a mole gives the clinician a good idea of just how worried he should be about his patient. If the mole is a Group I, there is very little need for worry. If the mole is a Group II, III or IV, there is an increasing chance of an invasive mole. If the mole possesses those nasty disturbing morphologic characteristics of the Groups V and VI, the patient has about a fifty-fifty chance of getting into serious trouble from *either* an invasive mole or a choriocarcinoma.

As a general principle, the author and his colleagues have been unable to pinpoint which of the sequelae will follow, even though intelligently worried by the appearance of the mole.[30] The reason for this is quite simple. It is manifestly impossible to diagnose the critical intramyometrial lesion from even curetted fragments, let alone from the mole lying within the uterine

$\rightarrow$

FIGURE 220. *(Upper)* The extreme pleomorphism of the trophoblast is obvious. Although this trophoblast appears neoplastic and alarmed both Dr. B. Earle Clark, the donor pathologist, and the author, it *does not* look like the choriocarcinoma that killed the patient sixteen months later.

FIGURE 221. *(Lower)* A typical choriocarcinoma, metastatic to the kidney, present at autopsy sixteen months after evacuation of hydatidiform mole seen above. Note that it does *not* resemble the alarmingly pleomorphic trophoblast of the original mole, an invariable generalization in the author's experience.

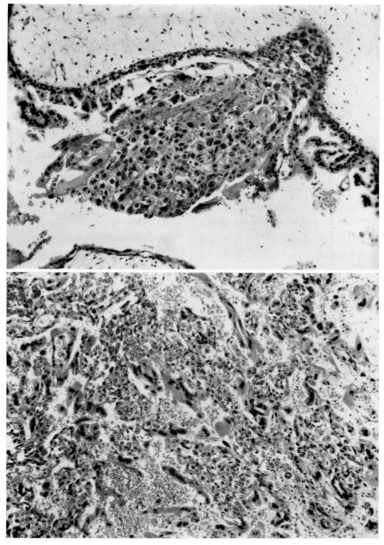

FIGURES 220 and 221 are from a Group VI or malignant mole and the subsequent choriocarcinomatous metastasis to the kidney. Rhode Island Hospital, S-39-1852 and A-41-38 respectively: B.L.I.H. S-39-910 and A.F.I.P. Acc. Nos. 218754-562 and -563. Both × 110. Previously published by Hertig and Mansell.[53] (Courtesy of the Armed Forces Institute of Pathology.)

cavity. This important and obvious fact is often overlooked; the ordinary tumor which the pathologist sees is a part of the host, the hydatidiform mole is within the host(ess) but not really a part of her.

As a practical fact, the author has seldom diagnosed a chorio-carcinoma or an invasive mole from even the wildest molar trophoblast. As mentioned above, these lesions are intramyo-metrial. If the pathologist chances to secure a bit of myometrium with trophoblast attached, he can suspect the diagnosis of an invasive mole (Fig. 206). If the curettings should by rare chance contain obvious choriocarcinoma at the time of molar evacuation and curettage, well and good. The trouble is that the ultimate choriocarcinoma is almost never far enough ad-vanced to yield, at this time, the typical morphologic pattern of this tumor. A typical choriocarcinoma, once on a microscopic slide, is usually very easy to diagnose. Moreover, the mole which gives rise to choriocarcinoma does not precisely resemble the ultimate tumor, as can readily be appreciated in comparing Figures 220 with 221, and 222 with 223.

Actually the worst-looking, apparently neoplastic molar tropho-blast in the author's experience is to be seen in Figures 216 to 218. This patient with an obvious VI mole survived the original evacuation, two curettages with one perforation of the uterus, an acute and chronic endomyometritis, and an ultimate hyster-ectomy! (This was before the antibiotics and during the early days of sulfonamides.) She had only a tiny amount of residual trophoblast as seen in Figure 219. She survived at least ten

→

FIGURE 222. (*Upper*) A mass of malignant-appearing trophoblast arising from the hydropic villus in the upper part of the picture. Note extreme variation in the appearance of cytotrophoblast. The trophoblast at the right is so undifferentiated that it is difficult to categorize as either syncytio-trophoblast or cytotrophoblast.

FIGURE 223. (*Lower*) The cerebral metastasis which caused the death of the patient ten months after evacuation of the mole illustrated above. Note that this choriocarcinoma does not resemble its parental molar trophoblast, nor is it precisely like the choriocarcinoma shown in Fig. 221. This generalization is probably the single most important thing for a pathologist to remember about these treacherous, albeit rare, lesions.

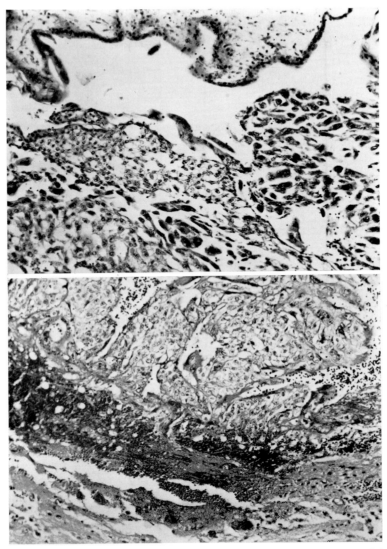

FIGURES 222 and 223 from another Group VI or malignant hydatidiform mole which illustrates the general principle that the malignant-appearing trophoblast which precedes, and presumably gives rise to, a choriocarcinoma does not resemble that malignant tumor. Leary Laboratory of Boston, P-36-1370 and P-37-855, respectively; and A.F.I.P. Acc. Nos. 218754-560 and -561 respectively, × 110. Previously published by Hertig and Sheldon.[64] (Courtesy of the C. V. Mosby Company.)

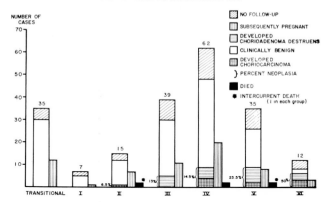

FOLLOW-UP AND NEOPLASIA IN 205 HYDATIDIFORM MOLES
BOSTON LYING-IN HOSPITAL CONSULTATION 1943-1952

Figure 224. A bar graph to illustrate the number of hydatidiform moles seen (in consultation) by the author from 1943 to 1952, their original grouping and the follow-up histories on the 205 patients from whom the specimens were obtained. The data were assembled and analyzed by Dr. A. Brian Little but never published. To be noted are the following: (a) The ratio of transitional moles to ordinary moles—35 to 170. (b) The bell-shaped population curve of distribution of groups—the majority are of Group IV. (c) The absence of clinical sequelae in Group I. (d) The increasing incidence of invasive mole (chorioadenoma destruens) and choriocarcinoma as the molar trophoblast becomes more undifferentiated.

years. (The author used to see her and her doctor-husband at the Boston Symphony concerts, a good way to follow patients.) Whether this is choriocarcinoma (which is doubtful), a placental site with bad trophoblast (which would have involuted), or an invasive mole (tangentially cut), it is impossible to say. The point to emphasize is that bad molar trophoblast is very apt to get the patient and/or her uterus in trouble; whereas, innocuous looking trophoblast tends to cause little serious trouble.

An anecdote that typifies this whole problem concerns the late Doctors Leary, Olga and Timothy, of Boston. This husband-and-wife team of pathologists organized and ran the excellent private laboratory of pathology which was later run by their daughter, Olga Junior. Olga Senior saw the original mole shown in Figure 222 and was properly alarmed. Timothy, famous for his atherosclerotic researches and as well as for being the medical examiner of the South District of Suffolk County, did the postmortem examination on the patient whose cerebral metastasis is seen in Figure 223. During the evening of the day of the autopsy, the following dialogue took place:

> Timothy said, "I did an autopsy on a patient from South Boston today who died of a cerebral choriocarcinoma."
> Olga replied, "What was her name?"
> Timothy answered, "E. McA———."
> Olga very succinctly said, "I was always worried about that mole and have often wondered what had happened to the patient."

C. INVASIVE MOLE
(CHORIOADENOMA DESTRUENS)

This important sequel occurred in 16 per cent of the author's initial series of two hundred hydatidiform moles collected from the eastern half of the United States.[64] This figure remains relatively constant as shown by Little's unpublished data (Fig. 224) using the subsequent series of 205 hydatidiform moles examined and grouped by the author.

Since an invasive mole is one of the two clinically important choriomas or types of trophoblastic disease, it is well to summarize its salient clinical and pathological features.[119] The latter are well shown in Figures 225 to 234.

1. The uterus containing an ordinary mole is usually larger than normal for its gestational age. Therefore it is soft, relatively thin-walled, and subject to operative perforation. It must be remembered, however, that the uterus may be the expected size for the period of gestation or smaller.[24] Nevertheless, when the uterus has been reported as being smaller, the question whether the pregnancy may have been a transitional mole arises.

2. All patients with hydatidiform mole bleed to a greater or lesser degree. Such bleeding is caused by the mechanical disruption of the placenta by the hydropic swelling of the chorionic villi; the chorionic membrane (ceiling) and the basal plate (floor) of the placenta are forcibly separated. Thus the normally controlled blood flow within the intervillous space becomes uncontrolled within the uterine cavity. There is nothing except the degree of patency of the cervix to control bleeding into the vagina.

3. All molar uteri should be carefully curetted, whether the

FIGURES 225 and 226 represent a human uterus containing a hydatidiform mole. A.F.I.P. Acc. No. 482668. Previously published by Hertig and Mansell.[53] (Courtesy of the Armed Forces Institute of Pathology.)

FIGURE 225. *(Upper)* The uterus has been opened anteriorly by a "Y" incision. The mass of molar villi may be seen within the uterine cavity. At the fundus (top) there is a T-shaped dark area representing a tiny focus of molar invasion.

FIGURE 226. *(Lower)* The posterior aspect of the same specimen as above to show the multiple theca lutein ovarian cysts which are the result of stimulation by the HCG of the hydatidiform mole. The ovaries were sectioned after fixation.

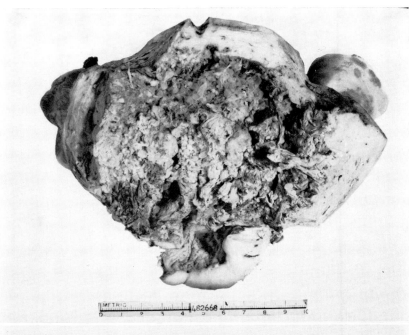

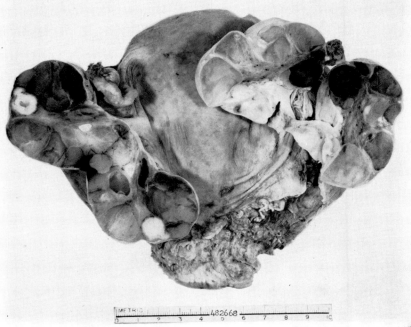

FIGURE 227. *(Upper)* A postmolar uterus opened by the author along the left side and across the fundus to show the irregularly raised thickening associated with a single hydropic villus and accompanying hemorrhage at the left cornu. Note the massive hemorrhage into and from the left ovary. See Fig. 228 for freshly cut surface of ovary. B.L.I.H. S-50-200.

FIGURE 228. *(Center right)* This left ovary has been turned over and upside down to show the freshly cut surface of a recent corpus luteum which has bled superficially and interstitially from an unhealed stigma. The invasive (hydatidiform) mole had not caused cessation of ovulation. B.L.I.H. S-50-200.

FIGURE 229. *(Lower)* An ectopic pregnancy (tubal) to show a small, hydropic, partially vascularized chorionic villus stuck within a vein. Although *not a hydatidiform mole*, this is the most likely mechanism by which the invasive hydatidiform villus gains entrance to the myometrium. A.F.I.P. Acc. No. 129130, × 62. Previously published by Hertig and Mansell.[53] (Courtesy of the Armed Forces Institute of Pathology.)

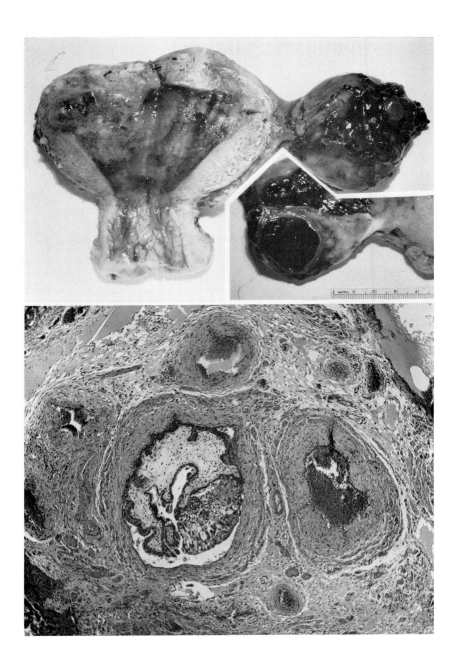

FIGURES 230 and 231 represent, at very low and medium power, the histopathologic features of an invasive hydatidiform mole which has caused destruction of nearly 90 per cent of the uterine wall at the point of invasion. Previously published by Hertig and Mansell.[53] (Courtesy of the Armed Forces Institute of Pathology.)

FIGURE 230. *(Upper)* The typical crater formed by one or more hydatidiform molar villi growing within the uterine veins. The crater is caused by vascular obstruction and trophoblastic growth. The crater, lined largely by necrotic tissue and blood clot, is not completely accessible to the curette. Even if it were, the active trophoblastic cause of the lesion is below the surface of the crater and is, therefore, truly inaccessible in the intact living patient. Several villi within veins are visible at this power, but the best is at the lower left corner and is magnified in Fig. 231. A.F.I.P. Acc. No. 298593-1, × 9.

FIGURE 231. *(Lower)* A hydatidiform molar villus growing within a myometrial vein and invading its wall. Note that the trophoblast is hyperplastic. A tangential section, without the stroma of the villus, might give the pathologist the erroneous idea that this trophoblast is malignant. Without the diagnostic comfort of a villus, hyperplastic, although benign, trophoblast may suggest neoplasia. A.F.I.P. Acc. No. 298593-2, × 48.

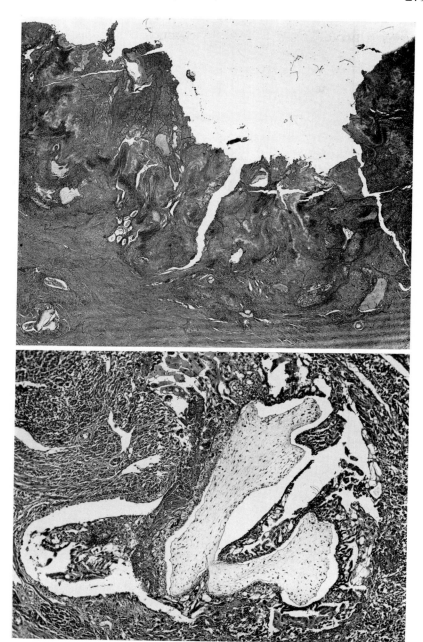

mole is evacuated per vaginum or by hysterotomy. The reason for this is twofold: (a) to remove as much trophoblast as possible and (b) to give the pathologist the most diagnostically significant material. Curettings must be kept separate from the main mass of molar tissue for complete histopathologic examination.

4. The presence of an invasive mole complicating an ordinary molar pregnancy cannot be foretold by (a) the size of the uterus, (b) the amount of bleeding, (c) the curettings (except very rarely), (d) the human chorionic gonadotropin (HCG) titer or the immediate postmolar clinical course. The reason for the silence of this important lesion lies in its gross and microscopic anatomy.

5. The lesion at first is small, as seen in the fundus in Figure 225. It always, in the author's experience, lies in the upper corpus and often in the cornu as in Figures 227 and 234.

6. The mechanism by which this lesion begins is unknown, although it appears to be caused by chorionic villi growing in or prolapsing into myometrial veins as seen in Figures 229 to 231. The stroma of the villus continues to swell and the trophoblast undergoes continuing growth.

7. A crater, usually solitary but occasionally multiple, forms

→

FIGURE 232. *(Upper left)* The posterior serosal surface of the cornual portion of a uterus showing an invasive mole which has perforated and now lies exposed to the peritoneal cavity. See Fig. 233 for frontally sectioned uterus to show this same invasive mole within the myometrium. B.L.I.H. S-40-256.

FIGURE 233. *(Upper right)* Same specimen as shown in Fig. 232 but viewed from the opposite side. The uterus has been opened frontally. Note hemorrhagic area at cornu within the myometrium. Note further the hydropic villus at the top where it has penetrated the serosa. B.L.I.H. S-40-256.

FIGURE 234. *(Lower)* A classic example of an invasive mole. Note circumscribed dark area at left cornu. The uterus has been bisected in the frontal plane. Note the mass of trophoblast at left side in parametrial vessels. This patient was cured by hysterectomy and bilateral salpingo-oophorectomy. B.L.I.H. S-46-1417. Previously published by Hertig and Mansell.[53] (Courtesy of Dr. Harry Finkel, Boston, Mass., and the Armed Forces Institute of Pathology.)

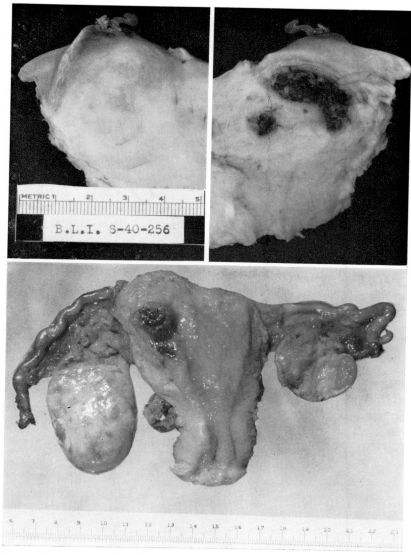

FIGURES 232, 233, and 234 show two sequelae to an invasive hydatidiform mole—perforation and vascular permeation.

by a process of infarction caused by plugged vessels and growth of trophoblast as seen in Figure 230. The crater, inaccessible to the curette contains a mixture of trophoblast, necrotic myometrium, and blood clot. Unless multiple sections of the entire crater are taken by the pathologist, the villus or villi may be missed. The invasive trophoblast may, however, resemble choriocarcinoma enough to result in the false diagnosis of the latter neoplasm. An invasive mole is *not* a neoplasm per se any more than *placenta accreta, increta,* or *percreta* are neoplasms. True, this trophoblast invades, destroys, may perforate and even metastasize, but so does normal trophoblast within limits.

8. The complications of an invasive mole are (a) vaginal bleeding, (b) perforation (Figs. 232 and 233), (c) permeation by trophoblast of uterine blood vessels to distant sites in the pelvis (Fig. 234) and (d) very rarely the development of true neoplasia, choriocarcinoma. The author knows of only one bona fide case of choriocarcinoma superimposed upon an invasive mole: that reported by Hunter in his master's degree thesis material at the Mayo Clinic.

9. On rare occasions, molar villi are deported to the vagina and to the lung. In the latter location they continue to grow and may either perforate the pleura resulting in hemothorax or metastasize as trophoblast and/or villi to the brain. The author has seen material from four patients whose lung lesions contained histologically demonstrated molar villi. Two died with cerebral hemorrhage. One of these was from the Queen Mary Hospital in Hong Kong, and the material was shown me by Dr. Hou Pao-Chang.[73] The other was from Rhode Island (Medical Examiner: Dr. Arthur O'Dea, F.H.W. CS-58-20).[107] The other two with lung lesions were from Hartford, Connecticut (courtesy of Dr. William A. Schear, B.L.I.H. CS-57-130) and from Minneapolis (courtesy of Dr. John I. Coe, B.L.I.H. CS-57-52). These have been reported by Bardawil and Toy.[3] The mysterious thing about the fatal cerebral hemorrhage that may be a part of this syndrome is that the offending trophoblast and/or villus cannot be found. This syndrome is not to be confused with the ordinary cerebral metastasis of choriocarcinoma.

10. The villi and/or trophoblast deported to the vagina,

whether from an ordinary mole or an invasive mole, do not seem to have much viability. Very often this "metastatic" material disappears after an incisional biopsy even though it is realized that the entire lesion has not been removed.

11. Probably the most common complication of any hydatidiform mole, whether invasive or not, is the presence of multiple bilateral theca lutein cysts of the ovary. These probably are the results of the HCG stimulation from the trophoblast, an autonomous Aschheim-Zondek test as it were. This is merely an exaggeration of the response seen in all normal ovaries to the presence of a pregnancy. All normal ovaries in normal pregnancy show some degree of theca lutein hyperplasia of involuting graafian follicles. Such cystic ovaries, in response to a hydatidiform mole, are to be seen in Figure 226. It is important to remember that such ovaries, no matter how big and ugly they are, will involute once the trophoblastic stimulus is completely removed.

12. Another important thing to remember about invasive moles, as about trophoblast in general, is their inherent tendency to undergo spontaneous involution. There is no way of predicting which invasive mole will disappear and which will continue to grow. Indeed the author has seen examples of "burned out" invasive moles. They resemble the old ectopic pregnancy in which the tube is massively distorted by hemorrhage, although serial blocks reveal no viable trophoblast. It is the author's impression that recently excised molar uteri frequently have tiny foci of molar invasion such as seen in Figure 225. Molar uteri removed some weeks later, for whatever reason, tend to have no such lesions. It suggests that some of these tiny foci die out as do some of the more mature invasive foci.

Discussion

With the modern methods of chemotherapy now available for the treatment of trophoblastic disease, it is important to stress that the invasive mole is one of the two intra-uterine types of chorioma or trophoblastic disease amenable to such treatment. Choriocarcinoma, to be discussed later, is the other type. If metastases occur, they are almost certain to be the result of choriocarcinoma, although rarely they may actually be deported hydropic villi as mentioned above.

When there is evidence of trophoblastic disease confined to the uterus, it is often difficult or even impossible to determine by pathologic or clinical or endocrinologic means whether the lesion is an invasive mole or a choriocarcinoma. Both may be well buried in the myometrium and hence inaccessible to the curette. If one finds innocuous trophoblast and/or villi attached to myometrium, the diagnosis is easy. Likewise the abundant curettings of the typical plexiform choriocarcinoma are diagnostically very simple. The difficulty lies in the frequent lack of diagnostically significant tissue from such trophoblastic lesions. This, in substance, is why Roy Hertz and his disciples have coined and used so successfully the term, trophoblastic disease, in treating their patients. If there are metastases, the lesion is most probably a choriocarcinoma. If there are no metastases, the intra-uterine lesion may be either an invasive mole or a choriocarcinoma resulting from any type of pregnancy. At this point, chemotherapy is indicated in an attempt to preserve the childbearing function. If clinical complication such as uncontrolled uterine bleeding, rising HCG titer in spite of adequate chemotherapy, or intractable toxicity to the drug(s) arises, then hysterectomy is employed. Ironically, only then may the pathologist and clinician know which variety of trophoblastic disease had been being treated!

Rarely one may excise locally an invasive mole and preserve childbearing function. The author knows of one such case. The difficulty, however, is to be sure of the nature of the lesion prior to local surgery. The presence of continued bleeding, an apparently normally involuting uterus, a low or absent HCG titer, determined by routine pregnancy test, and the surgeon's ability to feel a uterine crater without securing significant trophoblast for the pathologist all suggest an invasive mole.

As with all biologic phenomena there is a spectrum of size, growth, and activity. Occasionally one encounters an early invasive mole (Figs. 227 and 228) of such size, location, and endocrine activity that it fails to suppress ovulation. The patient in question passed a hydatidiform mole but thereafter never quite returned to normal with respect to uterine involution, resumption of normal menstruation, or a sense of well being. There was evidence by uterine biopsy of ovulation. Finally the patient had shoulder pain which suggested intraperitoneal hemorrhage. The surgeon, Dr. Crawford W. Hinman of the Boston Lying-in Hospital, asked the author to see the uterus and adnexa while they were within the patient. The uterus was slightly enlarged and soft, but one ovary was massively enlarged and hemorrhagic. The lesion proved to be a recent corpus luteum bleeding from the unhealed stigma, although the possibility that it was a bleeding theca lutein cyst was raised. It was thought initially that the uterus contained an invasive mole or a choriocarcinoma with extension, deportation, or metastasis to the ovary. One ovary was saved because of the statistical rarity of ovarian involvement by metastatic trophoblast.

This case is cited in some detail to indicate that each invasive mole is a law unto itself. It is difficult to diagnose except in the excised uterus. The dilemma lies in the fact that it cannot be differentiated easily from a choriocarcinoma in the absence of metastases. Be that as it may, it is a common type of trophoblastic disease confined to the uterus and should be treated conservatively by either chemotherapy or local surgery, unless clinical circumstances force one to do additional surgery.

In view of the fact that about 2.5 per cent of hydatidiform moles become choriocarcinomas, 16 per cent become invasive moles, and a few deport their villi and/or trophoblast, there is growing evidence that all molar patients and those with any other variety of trophoblastic disease should have all surgical manipulation under the protection of chemotherapy. Dr. John Lewis, a disciple of Roy Hertz, has recently reported a series of patients with trophoblastic disease in which he has enunciated this general principle.[85] These sixteen patients were treated at the Boston Lying-in and other Boston hospitals. Dr. Hazel Gore and the author examined all of the pathologic material from these patients.

The general interest in, and success with, chemotherapy has led to the formation in New England of a Trophoblastic Disease Center.[44] Dr. Donald Goldstein is in charge of this center, one of two in the country. Again, Dr. Hazel Gore and the author examine the material sent in, some of it from beyond the limits of New England. During the first year (July 1, 1965 to June 30, 1966) thirty-four patients were treated who had suspected or definite trophoblastic disease.

D. HISTOCHEMISTRY OF NORMAL, MOLAR, AND MALIGNANT TROPHOBLAST

Some aspects of the histochemistry of the thirteen-day ovum have already been shown in Figures 76 to 87. In this section will be recorded some additional observations made in the author's laboratory on normal developing trophoblast by McKay and associates[97] and on molar and malignant trophoblast by Bur and associates.[13] Some of these observations are to be seen in Figures 235 to 249. McKay's study was undertaken to elucidate the changing metabolism in the placenta during its total developmental span. Bur's study was undertaken to determine whether significant histochemical differences between the trophoblast of benign hydatidiform moles, invasive moles, and choriocarcinoma could be demonstrated. There were fifteen benign moles, two invasive moles, and three choriocarcinomas in this series. All patients, with the exception of two with benign moles, were followed for a period of ten or more years.

This study revealed no significant diagnostic differences in any type of trophoblast with respect to the phosphatases, 5-nucleotidase nonspecific esterase, glycogen, glycoprotein, and inorganic iron of both valances. An example of the essential similarity of distribution of alkaline phosphatase in normal, molar, and malignant trophoblast is to be seen in Figures 235 to 237. It will be seen that the enzyme is confined to the syncytiotrophoblast. Although the enzyme is beautifully concentrated in the brush border of normal trophoblast, as seen in Figures 80 to 82 and 235, its distribution in choriocarcinoma is patchy, as seen in Figure 237. There appears to be a spectrum of increasing patchiness as trophoblast becomes more malignant. Thus, the enzyme is uniformly distributed in the trophoblast of developing placentas and benign moles; it is only slightly patchy in invasive moles, but it is distinctly so in choriocarcinomas. Even though there is a slight difference in alkaline phosphatase distribution of various types of trophoblast, it is obviously of no diagnostic significance. The usual gross and microscopic morphology is of more importance.

The distribution of glycogen and glycoprotein in all types of trophoblast is to be seen in Figures 83 to 87 and 238 to 249. Glycogen is normally prominent in cytotrophoblast and absent in syncytiotrophoblast after the eighth week. Moles and choriocarcinoma resemble first trimester trophoblast more than mature normal trophoblast, as might be expected. The glycogen in these abnormal placental tissues is somewhat increased as compared to the normal. This could be due to (a) the persistence of primitive trophoblast, (b) the lack of a fetus with subsequent nonutilization of glycogen, or (c) the deposition of glycogen in hypoxic tissues as McKay and associates showed in normal placentas.[97]

Glycoprotein is increased somewhat in the syncytiotrophoblast of moles and choriocarcinomas (Figs. 241, 243, and 245) as compared to normal placentas. It is also increased in the cytotrophoblast of moles and choriocarcinomas as compared to immature normal placental trophoblast. This might reflect the known increase in HCG hormone production of such tissues. Although chorionic gonadotropin is known to be a glycoprotein and the hormone has been localized to the syncytiotrophoblast by Midgely and Pierce,[103, 110] it has been shown by Tao[142] that cytotrophoblast gives rise to syncytiotrophoblast. The precursors of the hormone may well be formed in the cytotrophoblast and the hormone finally produced in the syncytiotrophoblast. In any event the stains for glycogen and glycoprotein are not diagnostically helpful in separating benign, potentially malignant, and malignant trophoblast, one from another. The nonfatal case of choriocarcinoma did, however, show intranuclear staining (PAS digested), whereas the two fatal cases did not. A large series will show whether this observation is significant or not.

An interesting and potentially useful fact, however, did emerge from Bur's study. McKay originally showed that placental site giant cells in normal pregnancy were derived from primitive cytotrophoblast. Bur showed, for the invasive mole at least, that *both* types of trophoblast are involved in the production of giant

FIGURE 235. *(Upper)* A normal chorion (Harvard Fetus No. 5) at 6 weeks' menstrual age. Note localization of enzyme in syncytiotrophoblast and its absence from the Langhans' epithelium. A higher-power view of a younger specimen at 13 days may be seen in Figs. 81 and 82. Previously published by McKay *et al.*[97] (Courtesy of American College of Obstetricians and Gynecologists, and Hoeber Medical Division of Harper and Brothers.)

FIGURE 236. *(Lower left)* An invasive hydatidiform molar villus. Note similarity to an early ovum with branching primordial villi. Note further a distribution of the enzyme in syncytiotrophoblast comparable to that in Fig. 235 (normal) and in Fig. 237 (malignant). Harvard Case No. 3. Previously published by Bur *et al.*[13] (Courtesy of American College of Obstetricians and Gynecologists, and Hoeber Medical Division of Harper and Brothers.)

FIGURE 237. *(Lower right)* A typical plexiform choriocarcinoma which terminated fatally. Note enzyme in syncytiotrophoblast, albeit patchy in density. Note further the absence of the enzyme in the cytotrophoblast, a feature which characterized this latter tissue whether normal, benign, or malignant. Harvard Case No. 1. Previously published by Bur *et al.*[13] (Courtesy of American College of Obstetricians and Gynecologists, and Hoeber Medical Division of Harper and Brothers.)

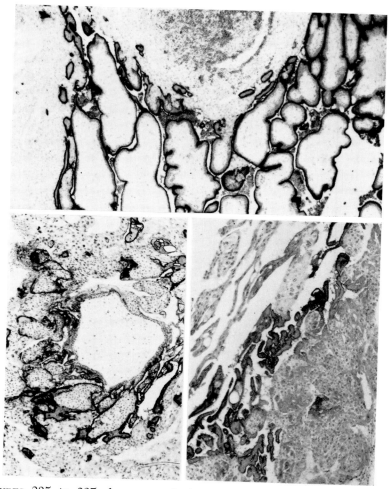

Figures 235 to 237 show normal chorionic villi at 6 weeks' menstrual age, an invasive hydatidiform molar villus, and typical plexiform choriocarcinoma, all reacted for alkaline phosphatase.

FIGURE 238. *(Upper left)* Two immature chorionic villi of the first trimester to show the cell column cytotrophoblast heavily laden with glycogen. Note that the larger cells (top) toward the basal plate ("floor") of the placenta are larger and contain more glycogen. Note that the syncytium on the outer surface of the villus is relatively devoid of glycogen although the Langhans' epithelium contains some. Harvard Fetus No. 5.

FIGURE 239. *(Upper right)* This is the control section for that seen in Fig. 238. Note presence of glycoprotein in stroma of villus, in syncytiotrophoblast, and some in the cytoplasm of the Langhans' epithelium.

FIGURE 240. *(Lower left)* A noninvasive hydatidiform mole (Harvard Case No. 8). Note prominent staining for glycogen in cytotrophoblast and relative absence in the vacuolated syncytiotrophoblast.

FIGURE 241. *(Lower right)* Amylase-digested control for Fig. 240. Glycoprotein is more pronounced than in normal villi, as seen in Fig. 239.

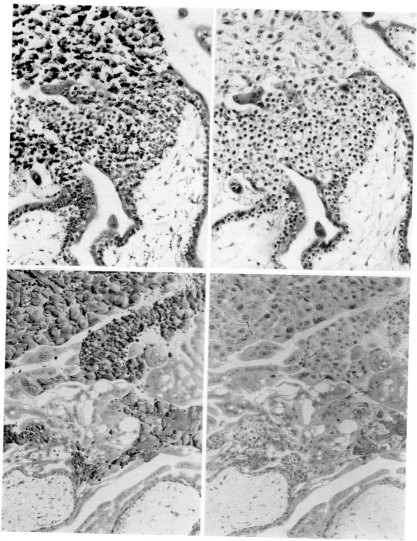

Figures 238 to 241 are stained for glycogen on the left and glycoprotein on the right; the technique was PAS stain with salivary (amylase) digestion on contiguous serial sections. Above is a 6 weeks' menstrual age normal placenta; below is a benign hydatidiform molar villus. All sections × 140. Figs. 238 and 239 previously published by McKay *et al.*[97] Figs. 240 and 241 previously published by Bur *et al.*[13] (All courtesy of American College of Obstetricians and Gynecologists, and Hoeber Medical Division of Harper and Brothers.)

FIGURE 242. *(Upper left)* Note presence of glycogen in the cytotrophoblast and virtual absence in syncytiotrophoblast. Maternal tissue below is being invaded by placental site giant cells which also, because of predominant cytotrophoblastic origin, contain glycogen.

FIGURE 243. *(Upper right)* Note slight amounts of glycoprotein in the trophoblast. The large dark area in lower center represents fibrinoid material which is common to all trophoblast of whatever type and is always positive for glycoprotein.

FIGURE 244. *(Lower left)* Typical plexiform choriocarcinoma (same case as Fig. 237) showing glycogen distributed irregularly throughout the cytotrophoblast.

FIGURE 245. *(Lower right)* Amylase-digested control for Fig. 244 to show moderate amounts of glycoprotein in trophoblast—more in the syncytiotrophoblast than in the cytotrophoblast.

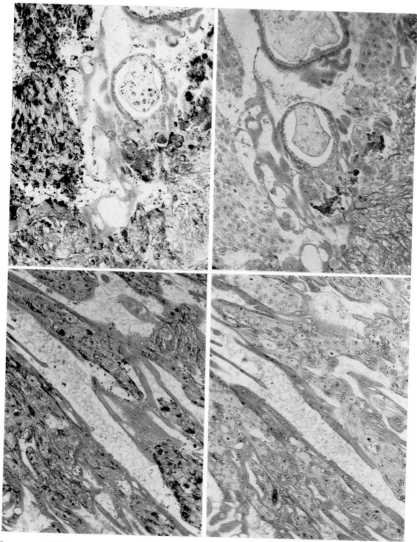

FIGURES 242 to 245 compare an invasive hydatidiform mole (Harvard Case No. 4) with a typical choriocarcinoma (Harvard Case No. 1). Each specimen was stained by the PAS technique on the left and with suitable contiguous serial sections digested by amylase on the right. All sections × 140. Previously published by Bur *et al.*[13] (Courtesy of American College of Obstetricians and Gynecologists, and Hoeber Medical Division of Harper and Brothers.)

FIGURE 246. (*Upper left*) Normal placental site at 6 weeks' menstrual age to show prominent, glycogen-laden giant cells of cytotrophoblastic origin infiltrating the decidua. Endometrial glands are in center and below. Harvard Fetus No. 5.

FIGURE 247. (*Upper right*) An immature, fatal choriocarcinoma invading the uterus and one of its blood vessels, probably a vein. Note resemblance to malignant-appearing placental site giant cells. Contrast this somewhat atypical choriocarcinoma with that shown in Figs. 237, 244, and 245.

FIGURE 248. (*Lower left*) Trophoblast from an invasive hydatidiform mole, above, invading myometrium below. The two types of trophoblast (cytotrophoblast on left and syncytiotrophoblast at right) are clearly seen above and below a fibrinoid layer of Nitabuch's or Rohr's type. Compare with amylase-digested control in Fig. 249.

FIGURE 249. (*Lower right*) An amylase-digested control to invasive hydatidiform mole in Fig. 248. Note prominent fibrinoid stria containing large amounts of glycoprotein. Note further that, above the stria, the two types of trophoblast are easily distinguished: the cytotrophoblast (left and center) is largely devoid of glycoprotein; the large syncytiotrophoblastic mass (upper right) contains significant amounts of glycoprotein. Below the stria, this distinction is lost, as though the invaded myometrium had "used up" or in some way altered the glycoprotein or the syncytiotrophoblastic element. This picture lends weight to the concept that placental site giant cells are of double origin from the invading trophoblast.

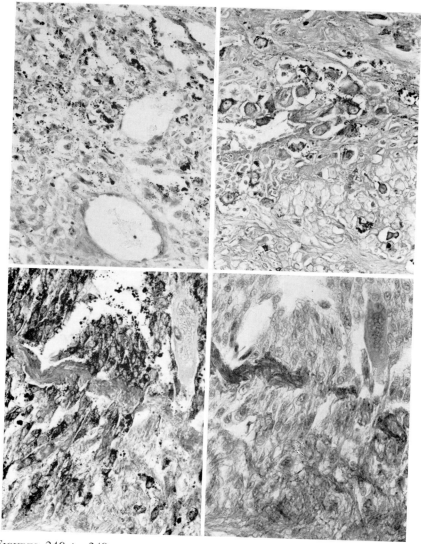

Figures 246 to 249 compare a normal first trimester placental site with an immature fatal choriocarcinoma and with the placental site of an invasive hydatidiform mole. All are stained by the PAS technique for glycogen and glycoprotein, but only one (Fig. 249) shows an amylase-digested control. Previously published by Bur *et al.*[13] (Courtesy of American College of Obstetricians and Gynecologists, and Hoeber Medical Division of Harper and Brothers.)

cells within the myometrium. The author has seen early syncytio-trophoblast of the thirteen- to fourteen-day ovum actually invading the *decidua basalis* and has assumed from the multinucleated nature of giant cells that syncytiotrophoblast was the only source. Thus the separate observations of McKay and of Bur indicate that both types of trophoblast participate in the formation of these tumor-like invasive cells that are pathognomonic of a placental site. The normal early placental site giant cells from the thirteen-day ovum may be seen in Figure 39, those of the six-week pregnancy (menstrual age) in Figure 246, and those of the invasive mole in Figures 248 and 249.

Bur showed two other facts of potential biologic significance. Placental site giant cells, irrespective of whether they are associated with normal benign, potentially malignant, or malignant trophoblast possess some of the histochemical characteristics of malignant trophoblast associated with fatal choriocarcinoma. Both the giant cells and the tumor are strongly basophilic owing to the presence of ribonucleoprotein (RNP). Both resist prolonged digestion by RNase.

A similar difference was found between normal trophoblast and fatal choriocarcinoma. The more malignant trophoblast becomes, the more it resists RNase digestion. Bur reported an apparently typical choriocarcinoma with pulmonary metastases (case 21) which regressed following hysterectomy. The patient was alive and well more than ten years later. Her uterine tumor was much less resistant to RNase digestion than the other two cases of choriocarcinoma, both of which terminated fatally. Further work will determine whether this is a valid observation when applied to a large series of cases. Certainly the metastases of some choriocarcinomas in the past have spontaneously disappeared when the primary tumor in the uterus was removed. Furthermore, some choriocarcinomas now respond well to chemotherapy and others do not. There are no data, other than Bur's preliminary observations, as to why some typical choriocarcinomas have a good prognosis and why others do not. The ones that get well, whether spontaneously or with chemotherapy, may be "sheep dressed in wolves' clothing."

CHAPTER XI

CHORIOCARCINOMA

A. ANATOMIC PATHOLOGY

B Y definition, choriocarcinoma is a malignant epithelial tumor composed of pure trophoblast. There are no chorionic villi present. The tumor metastasizes exclusively by the blood stream. In its initial metastases, it tends to go to the lung, although the vagina may be involved. The secondary metastases from the lung may be in any organ but tend to be in the brain, upper gastrointestinal tract, liver, and kidney.

Choriocarcinoma may arise from any type of pregnancy in any location (Fig. 274). There are no precise figures as to how often a particular type of pregnancy is associated with or followed by choriocarcinoma. The author's figure (Hertig and Sheldon, 1947) of 2.5 per cent of two hundred randomly selected hydatidiform moles giving rise to this malignant trophoblastic tumor is probably representative of the malignant potential of this type of pregnancy in this country. It is well known that hydatidiform moles and choriocarcinomas are common in the Orient. It is generally accepted that choriocarcinoma is preceded by moles in about 50 per cent, abortion in 25 per cent, and normal pregnancy in 25 per cent of cases. Based on this assumption and the relative prevalence of the four main types of pregnancy, the tendency of any type to undergo malignant change is estimated to be as shown in Figure 274. Dr. John I. Brewer,* in a personal communication,[9] indicates that he has found that approximately one third of choriocarcinomas are preceded by normal pregnancy, one third by mole, and one third by abortion. It is generally agreed that ectopic pregnancy may precede choriocarcinoma,

---

* Dr. Brewer is in charge of the Mathieu Chorionepithelioma Registry in Chicago, Illinois, and directs the only other treatment center for this disease. The second treatment center is in Boston, Massachusetts.

but only rarely. During his professional career, the author has seen but six or seven examples involving either tube or ovary.

Prior to discussing choriocarcinoma, the various morphologic entities which may be the precursors of and/or may be confused with this truly malignant neoplasm should be discussed briefly.

Chorionepithelioma *In Situ*

The early or *in situ* stage of the tumor has neither been studied extensively nor has it been particularly well-documented. Indeed it has not been generally accepted as a clinicopathologic entity. So far as the author is aware, he is the only one who believes that such a lesion exists. Logically and biologically there should be such a lesion. All other cancers, when well-studied histogenetically, show such an early stage. Here illustrated in Figures 250 and 252 to 255 are two cases from the author's files. One (Figs. 250 and 252) followed a full-term delivery by caesarean section. Some months postpartum, owing to rheumatic heart disease, uterine bleeding, and a positive Friedman's test for HCG, a hysterectomy was completed but without prior dilatation and curettage. It was assumed that the patient had again become pregnant and hence the pregnancy should be therapeutically interrupted and the patient sterilized. There was no new pregnancy but a placental polyp within the base of which was a mass of pure very undifferentiated trophoblast surrounded by an area of decidual tissue. The patient made an uneventful recovery and was alive and well at least five years later. There is obviously no proof that this malignant-appearing trophoblast, left undistrubed, would have gone on to become an undoubted choriocarcinoma. Suffice it to say that when choriocarcinoma is associated with normal pregnancy and the placenta is available for examination, it has been shown to arise either within the placenta[25] or in the basal plate, "floor," of the organ.[92]

Most choriocarcinomas following normal pregnancy must arise from bits of adherent trophoblast, possibly focal *placenta accreta,* or from the placental site giant cells. It is possible that the normal intravascularly growing trophoblast of the placental site may give rise to the tumor. Certainly the vast majority of these patients destined to develop such tumors show clinical evidence of retention of secundines, subinvolution of the uterus (and presumably the placental site), and uterovaginal bleeding. Whether the tumor arose *pari passu* with the pregnancy or from retained trophoblast that underwent subsequent malignant change is not usually subject to proof.

This triad of symptoms or signs, retention of trophoblast, subinvolution and bleeding, is comparatively so common and choriocarcinomas so rare that the possibility of cancer following a normal pregnancy is seldom entertained except as a last resort. The clinical and pathological pitfalls in this as well as other choriomas will be discussed later. It is well recognized, however, that the obtaining of sufficient diagnostically suitable material from a subinvoluted placental site, either with or without retained trophoblast, is difficult. It is a clinicopathologic truism that no other lesion in postpartum obstetrics causes so much bleeding and shows so little cause for that bleeding when placed under the pathologist's microscope as does the subinvoluted placental site.

Part of this is due to technical difficulty: a curettage is always a blind operation. Placental sites of placental polyps are notoriously hard to remove. A glance at a normally involuting placental site (Fig. 251) explains some of the difficulty. The area is raised, hyalinized, and undermined by the regenerating endometrium. A placental site bleeds because this hyalinized, necrotic, and inflamed decidua crumbles away, exposing nonthrombosed, physiologically thickened vessels in the basal endometrium and underlying myometrium. These opened vessels comprise the origin of the bleeding. The late great obstetrician, John Whitridge Williams, wrote in a posthumously published article,[147] the only definitive classic work on the subject of the involution in the normal placental site.

The second case of choriocarcinoma *in situ* here illustrated (Figs. 253-255) followed a hydatidiform mole in a very young primigravid patient. Her uterus failed to involute and she continued to bleed vaginally. At curettage, about twenty fragments of endomyometrial tissue were removed, counted, and individually embedded for section. In only one of these, shown in Figure 253, was there any trophoblast. This lesion, entirely within the myometrium, is obviously growing in and destroying maternal

FIGURE 250. *(Upper left)* A portion of a placental polyp attached to the uterine wall. The base of the placental polyp contains a mass of pure, malignant-appearing trophoblast, the higher-power detail of which is seen in Fig. 252. Much of the polyp is composed of blood clot and hemorrhagic necrotic decidua. B.L.I.H. S-32-373, A.F.I.P. Acc. No. 218754-564, × 5.

FIGURE 251. *(Upper right)* A normally involuting placental site following a term pregnancy. Note hyalinized raised tissue, the placental site, which is being undermined by the regenerating endometrium. A.F.I.P. Acc. No. 319653, 52-1397, × 40.

FIGURE 252. *(Lower)* A higher-power detail of a portion of the trophoblast in the base of the placental polyp seen in Fig. 250. Note two types of trophoblast. The syncytiotrophoblastic masses contain lacunae, primitive anlagen of the intervillous space. The isolated cells are cytotrophoblast. The general pleomorphism and hyperchromatism are evident. The lack of mitoses is not of diagnostic significance. There is a fibrinoid stria between the trophoblast and the decidua. B.L.I.H. S-32-373, A.F.I.P. Acc. No. 218754-565, × 150.

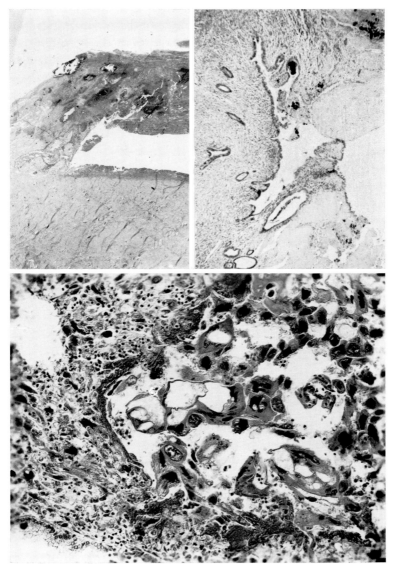

Figures 250 and 252 show what the author interprets as a "chorionepithelioma *in situ*" following a normal pregnancy as compared to a normally involuting placental site following a term pregnancy (Fig. 251). Figs. 250 and 252 previously published by Hertig and Mansell.[53] (Courtesy of the Armed Forces Institute of Pathology.)

tissue. True serial sections revealed no chorionic villi. It has all the morphologic hallmarks of malignant trophoblast, as seen in Figures 254 and 255. Nevertheless, after a hysterectomy completed some days later, there was not only no tumor but no endometrium either! At least the patient was spared the complications of a complete *placenta accreta* in subsequent pregnancies. The patient was alive and well some years later. This case was one of seven examples of chorioepithelioma *in situ* which followed the two hundred moles reported by Hertig and Sheldon[64] in 1947. These cases are summarized in Table IV in Chapter X-B. Most of these early debatable lesions followed moles of the higher grouping of malignant potential (i.e. Groups V and VI).

Whether these tiny foci of malignant-appearing trophoblast are, indeed, the early stage of choriocarcinoma is unknown. The author believes that they are. It is doubtful that choriocarcinoma, rare as it is, follows any different histogenetic path in its development than that path trod by the more mundane carcinomas such as those of the uterus, cervix, or corpus. They do not spring, as was said of Minerva, "full grown and clad in armor."[32] There is little if any reason to suspect that a choriocarcinoma develops *de novo* as a full-fledged tumor irrespective of what type of pregnancy is its progenitor.

The whole argument over whether carcinoma *in situ* is a valid biological phenomenon now seems fruitless. That lesion of the cervix presently is designated officially as carcinoma, stage O. Nevertheless, the author well remembers that in 1939 the members of the New England Society of Pathologists, when asked by

→

FIGURE 253. *(Upper left)* The entire lesion showing destruction of myometrial tissue by an expanding trophoblastic growth which probably began in a blood vessel. See Figs. 254 and 255 for histologic detail. × 18.

FIGURE 254. *(Upper right)* A very undifferentiated mass of pure trophoblast lying within a vascular and/or hemorrhagic space. × 200.

FIGURE 255. *(Lower)* Another field of pure trophoblast lying within the vein seen in the lower portion of Fig. 253. Note the spectrum of differentiation or undifferentiation. The portion on the left is approaching the type seen in Fig. 254; that on the right more nearly resembles that of a typical choriocarcinoma seen in Fig. 260. × 125.

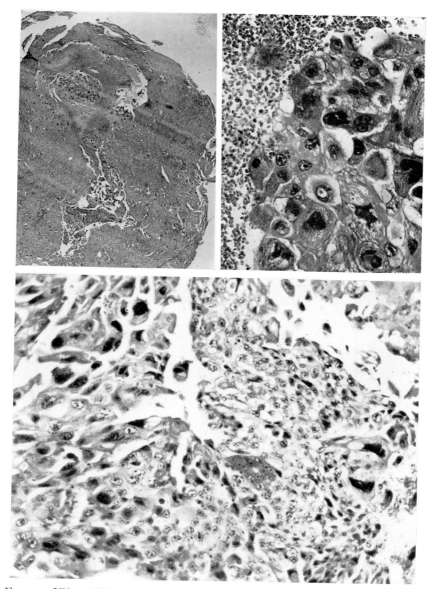

FIGURES 253 to 255 show the trophoblastic lesion, chorionepithelioma *in situ,* which followed a very undifferentiated hydatidiform mole. Serial sections proved that there were no chorionic villi present. B.L.I.H. S-38-917, A.F.I.P. Acc. No. 218754-567, -568, and 9748, respectively. Figs. 253 and 254 previously published by Hertig and Mansell.[53] (Courtesy of the Armed Forces Institute of Pathology.)

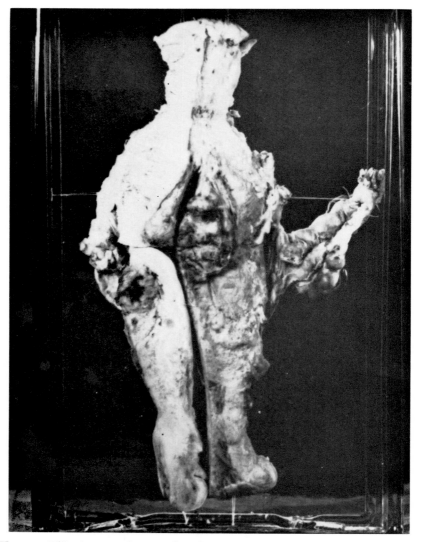

FIGURE 256. A typical example of an invasive mole or *chorioadenoma destruens* (CAD). The uterus has been opened laterally and bivalved to show the entire endometrial surface. One wall has been sagittally sectioned and the portion on the left rotated outwardly at 90° to reveal the characteristic crater or excavation. The latter communicated with the uterine cavity by a very narrow opening. The placental site is seen in the upper corpus and fundus as a raised plaque. The uterus was removed because

Dr. Paul A. Younge of the Free Hospital for Women to interpret and diagnose such lesions, responded much as did the farmer when he saw a giraffe and commented, "There ain't any such animal." With the establishment of treatment centers for trophoblastic disease such as are now present in Chicago and Boston, more data probably will be forthcoming on the significant histogenetic stages of choriocarcinoma.

Syncytial Endometritis

For purposes of completeness, this controversial and sometimes overdiagnosed lesion should be mentioned. Although it is probably not a true chorioma, the author is sure that it contributes to the spectrum of trophoblastic disease. This lesion is well illustrated in Figure 175. It probably represents an accentuation of the placental site giant cell morphology, so well seen in Figures 173 and 174. The diagnostic difficulty with syncytial endometritis is that, as with all lesions, it possesses a morphologic spectrum. The author believes that its more florid manifestation in Figure 175 merges into the chorionepithelioma *in situ* discussed above. Whether or not syncytial endometritis is a valid chorioma, its more disturbing manifestations are most apt to follow very malignant-appearing moles. Both of these controversial lesions, chorionepithelioma and syncytial endometritis, are curable if removed by curettage. At least in the author's experience, such patients remain alive and well whether the uterus is removed or not.

Invasive Mole (Chorioadenoma Destruens or C.A.D.)

The name chorioadenoma destruens was coined by the late oncologic pathologist James Ewing. He thus separated the relatively common sequel to hydatidiform mole from the less

---

←

of persistent bleeding following a very disturbing looking hydatidiform mole. The patient died of generalized peritonitis but without evidence of other trophoblastic disease. B.L.I.H. S-34-585. A.F.I.P. Acc. No. 218754-571. About natural size. (Harvard Medical School students refer to this as the "gingerbread man"). Previously published by Hertig and Sheldon.[64] (Courtesy of the C. V. Mosby Company.)

FIGURES 257 and 258 represent an invasive mole and choriocarcinoma, respectively to compare and contrast the salient microscopic features of these two lesions. Previously published by Hertig and Mansell.[53] (Courtesy of the Armed Forces Institute of Pathology.)

FIGURE 257. *(Upper)* This is a high-power detail of the invasive hydropic villus that lay just beneath the crater shown in Fig. 230 and at medium power in Fig. 231. Note hydropic avascular stroma above and fairly well-organized trophoblast below which mimics that of the 11- to 12-day ovum. Note inflammatory cells and placental site giant cells within the surrounding myometrium. A.F.I.P. Acc. No. 298593-3, × 90.

FIGURE 258. *(Lower)* A typical choriocarcinoma, left, invading the myometrium. Note plexiform pattern of tumor, lack of fibrinoid stria or capsule at margin, and vascular permeation of vessel at right. A.F.I.P. Acc. No. 284811-20063, × 70.

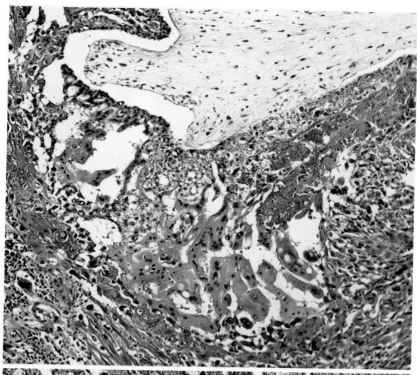

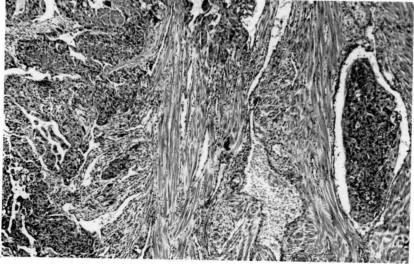

common one, choriocarcinoma. Ewing implied in his designation that C.A.D. was a glandular tumor. This is bad terminology since the lesion is not a tumor in the strict sense of the word any more than normal first trimester trophoblast or a *placenta increta* is a tumor. Moreover, the lesion is not glandular, although the trophoblast elaborates a protein hormone, HCG, and steroid hormones as well. Nevertheless the lesion is real, potentially or actually dangerous, and can be accurately separated from non-metastatic choriocarcinoma only by examination of the complete uterus. From curettings, the diagnosis of C.A.D. is nearly impossible unless the pathologist is fortunate enough to see molar chorionic villi and/or trophoblast attached directly to myometrium. (This same difficulty obtains in diagnosing *placenta accreta, increta,* or *percreta.*) Choriocarcinoma can be diagnosed from curettings *only* by finding the typical plexiform pattern (Figs. 260 and 261) or the atypical and immature patterns (Figs. 247, 262, and 263).

Although invasive moles have been discussed and illustrated thoroughly in Chapter X-C, typical gross and microscopic examples of this lesion are shown in Figures 256 and 257 respectively. Realizing that there is always a spectrum of gross and microscopic morphology in any disease, the essential differences between these two lesions are as follows:

1. Gross

A. Chorioadenoma destruens, C.A.D., or invasive mole is usually a solitary, punched-out crater located in the corpus and often in one cornu (Fig. 256). The crater may or may not communicate with the endometrial cavity. It *always* contains one or more villi within the cavity, within the hemorrhagic necrotic tissue forming the margin of the crater or in the viable myometrium bordering the crater. If the lesion has involuted, the crater and cavity are filled with old, clotted blood, but no viable villi or trophoblast is seen. Adequate sections in number *and* extent must be taken, or the diagnosis may be confused with choriocarcinoma.

B. Choriocarcinoma may be located anywhere in the uterus, cervix, fallopian tube, or ovary (Fig. 259). It is conceivable that

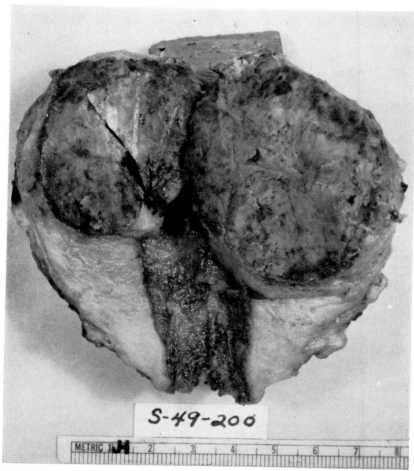

FIGURE 259. A classic, well-advanced choriocarcinoma of the uterus removed eight months after a normal pregnancy. A portion of one wall of the supracervically removed uterus has been dissected away. Note the hemorrhagic margin of the solid mass, the site of viable tumor, whereas the more central portion is opaque and necrotic. The patient died approximately ten months after the hysterectomy with pulmonary metastases. Massachusetts Memorial Hospitals S-49-200. Previously published by Hertig.[38] (Courtesy of Dr. Rudolph Osgood, Attleboro, Mass., and Grune and Stratton.)

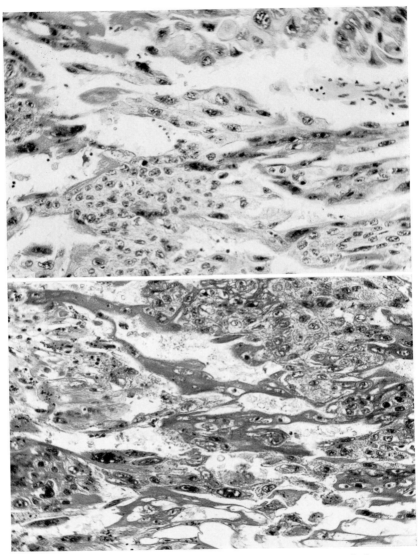

FIGURES 260 and 261 represent a classic choriocarcinoma of the uterus. Both pictures show the plexiform pattern composed of cytotrophoblastic cords covered by syncytiotrophoblast enclosing a labyrinth containing maternal blood. Fig. 260 shows less syncytium; Fig. 261 shows more, including that containing vacuoles. The latter is due to the formation of lacunae which are identical with the precursors of the intervillous space

it could occur as a primary tumor at the placental site of an abdominal pregnancy, but this is only of academic interest owing to the rarity of both conditions. Primary ovarian chorio-carcinoma, a teratoma, is extremely rare, but such tumors are grossly characteristic when they occur, usually in young girls. The typical gross appearance of a choriocarcinoma, whether primary or metastatic, is that of an irregular but circumscribed solid hemorrhagic lesion of any size which infiltrates the surrounding tissue. Central necrosis of the tumor and blood clot comprise the rule, especially in lesions of more than one centimeter. (The very nature of the intrinsic blood supply, blood spaces lined by syncytiotrophoblast, leads to thrombosis and infarction. The author supposes that primary choriocarcinoma may spontaneously involute, as may choriocarcinomatous metastases, but he has never seen one such a lesion histologically. The possible exception may be the vaginal metastasis which often "looks sick" trophoblastically and more often than not tends to disappear spontaneously after an incisional biopsy.)

2. *Microscopic*

A. Chorioadenoma destruens, C.A.D., or invasive mole, when adequately sectioned, shows the characteristic pattern seen in Figures 230, 231, 236, 248, 249, and 257. The stroma of the villus is avascular and edematous or hydropic. The trophoblast may be actively proliferating or quiescent, but it tends to mimic an early ovum of the eleven- to twelve-day stages (Figs. 26-36). There is an abortive attempt at primitive intervillous space formation, nodular proliferation of the inner-lying cytotrophoblast, and invasion of the myometrium by the outer-lying syncytio-trophoblast. There are always placental site giant cells in the myometrium. The villus or villi may lie within a recognizable vascular space, a vein, but the latter may have been destroyed by the growing trophoblast. In summary, the living margin of an invasive mole looks like an immature implantation site but

←

of the early previllous ovum. A.F.I.P. Acc. Nos. 283272-20061 and -20062. Both × 185. Previously published by Hertig and Mansell.[53] (Courtesy of the Armed Forces Institute of Pathology.)

without the presence of decidua. The microscopic appearance of the crater itself is disappointing. One may find surface growth of trophoblast similar to the placental "floor" pattern, but often it reveals only necrotic myometrium, old and recent blood clot.

B. Choriocarcinoma, by contrast, never has an organoid or definitive chorionic villus. The trophoblast may show all degrees of differentiation, but classically it resembles the plexiform pattern of *pure trophoblast* of the thirteen-day, early, villous ovum (Figs. 37-39 and 80-87). The anastomosing cords of cyto-trophoblast are covered by immature syncytiotrophoblast which has formed an intercommunicating labyrinthine space containing maternal blood (Figs. 237, 244, 245, 258, 260, and 261). There are usually no placental site giant cells and no "floor" on the basal placental plate. There is usually no Nitabuch's stria. The tumor blends into the myometrium; its vascular spaces are connected directly to the uterine vessels. The latter often have easily recognizable permeations of viable tumor within their lumens (Fig. 258). (The lack of placental site giant cells may be of prognostic significance since Bur's nonfatal case had such giant cells, whereas the two fatal cases did not.[13])

Choriocarcinomas are usually well differentiated (Figs. 260 and 261) but may be poorly differentiated (Figs. 262 and 263). A small atypical inaccessible lesion within the myometrium is well nigh impossible to diagnose from curetted material. A curettage also may obtain only the peripheral, superficial portion of the lesion. If the main portion of the lesion is curetted, the tissue obtained is usually abundant, granular to friable, red

---

$\rightarrow$

FIGURE 262. (*Upper*) Note position within the myometrium and hence its inaccessibility to the surgeon's curette. The pattern to the right is fairly typical of this tumor, but much of it is solid as seen in Fig. 263, × 58.

FIGURE 263. (*Lower*) Note solid nature of tumor with admixture of cyto-trophoblast and syncytiotrophoblast. There is only one significant inter-villous space or lacuna. This is very immature or poorly differentiated trophoblast. It is reminiscent of the 7- and 8-day ova. Compare this atypical pattern with the typical form of the tumor in Figs. 260 and 261. × 165.

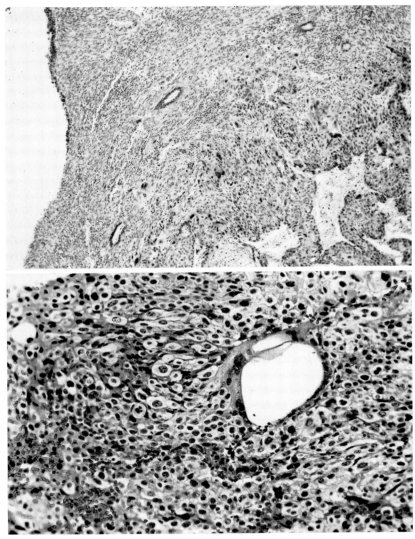

F<small>IGURES</small> 262 and 263 are from an atypical choriocarcinoma which lay
within the myometrium and did not communicate with the uterine cavity.
A.F.I.P. Acc. No. 304903. Previously published by Hertig and Mansell.[53]
(Courtesy of the Armed Forces Institute of Pathology.)

and hemorrhagic. Microscopically the diagnosis is obvious because of exuberant plexiform immature trophoblast.

B. DIAGNOSTIC GENERALIZATIONS

Specific diagnostic pitfalls and suggestions for avoiding them have been made at appropriate places throughout the monograph. Owing to the intrinsic biologically malignant nature of normal immature trophoblast, diagnostic mistakes will be made by pathologists even though they have long familiarity with and respect for trophoblastic neoplasia. Only recently the author made such an error. A slide sent in consultation revealed a large sheet of very immature trophoblast with no chorionic villi. The absence of villi and the plane of section suggested the diagnosis of choriocarcinoma. Such a diagnosis had also been suggested by the contributing pathologist. Later sections of additional material revealed the true nature of the trophoblast—that of an early abortion with chorionic villi. The history of the patient should have made one cautious; a recent marriage with subsequent missed period only 2 or 3 weeks before the uterine bleeding and curettage. Such a history is more in keeping with a spontaneous abortion than a choriocarcinoma. Also the author disregarded another useful rule or generalization. Choriocarcinoma is rarely diagnosed from the initial curettage, whether it be done for a spontaneous abortion, a hydatidiform mole or uterine subinvolution.

Some generalizations or rules follow which the author and his colleagues have found to be helpful over the years.

1. All spontaneous abortions should be carefully examined grossly under the binocular dissecting microscope. In this way the gross morphology of the ovisac and embryo may be appreciated. Curetted material should also be examined in this way so that appropriate tissue may be selected for section. It goes without saying that residual gross material should be saved until a satisfactory final microscopic diagnosis is made. It is possible, though unlikely, that undifferentiated trophoblast suggestive of malignant neoplasia may be found in material from an abortus.

2. A gross hydatidiform mole should have at least 8-10 areas, not just individual hydropic villi, selected for microscopic section. Blood clot should also be included since trophoblast is to be found

within and on its surface. It will be remembered that this blood clot, although now in the uterine cavity, is actually analogous to blood which should be in the intervillous space. The latter has been disrupted by the growth of the hydropic vesicles and subsequent distortion of the normal relationships between the chorionic membrane and "floor" of the placenta.

3. The curettings from a hydatidiform mole should be meticulously prepared for multiple level sections. *All material* including blood clot should be sectioned. Invasion by and/or neoplasia of trophobast may occur anywhere over the uterine surface although such changes appear to be most likely at the original placental site. The microscopic appearance of initially curetted trophoblast from a molar pregnancy is almost always less differentiated than that of the mole itself. Such curettings sample what is analogous to a placental "floor" and usually contain a few retained molar villi as well. (Molar villi are in contact with the *entire* endometrial surface not just the original placental site.) Successive curettages for continued bleeding following a molar pregnancy tend to contain fewer villi but more trophoblast. The later curettage tends to become diagnostic of choriocarcinoma, should such occur, but is generally not diagnostic of invasive mole. Subinvolution of the placental site, with or without retained benign trophoblast, occurs following molar pregnancy as well as other types. On occasion the pathologist is disturbed by what he fails to find in a postabortal, postmolar or postpartum curettage. The history of continued bleeding, subinvolution of the uterus, a persistent or rising HCG titer, no metastases and NO TROPHOBLAST strongly suggests a trophoblastic lesion buried within the myometrium. At this point the clinical decision must be made as to whether to undertake chemotherapy, either alone or in conjunction with surgery.

4. A decidual reaction of the endometrium is usually present at initial curettage for any type of post pregnancy bleeding associated with uterine subinvolution whether trophoblast has been retained or not. Subsequent curettage usually fails to reveal any significant decidual reactions even though there is viable endometrium in the uterus, and trophoblast somewhere in the body. Apparently endometrium must go through its usual evolutionary

estrogen-progesterone cycle in order to form decidua. Incidentally, the curetted endometrium from an ectopic pregnancy is not diagnostic; it may be proliferative, secretory, decidual or resting (involuted).

5. For some unknown reason, the vaginal "metastases" from ordinary moles, invasive moles or even on occasion from true choriocarcinoma do not behave as do ordinary trophoblastic metastases. They frequently involute following an incisional biopsy.

6. If a postmolar patient develops metastatic choriocarcinoma, the uterus when removed surgically or at postmortem examination is apparently free from choriocarcinoma in about 50% of these patients. The cause for this is unknown but may be due to a) overlooking a tiny primary lesion, b) involution of the primary lesion or c) an initially malignant bit of trophoblast gaining entrance to the uterine veins without subsequent trace. An unlikely possibility is the subsequent malignant change of an initially benign bit of trophoblast and/or villus. This seems farfetched but nothing about trophoblast should seem surprising. (Since this is the Weller Lecture Monograph I am sure that Dr. Weller would like this anecdote told. A favorite technician of his had a malignant mole and all who saw it so agreed. An immediate hysterectomy—within 24 hours—was done at Dr. Weller's suggestion. Serial blocking revealed no trophoblastic neoplasm in the uterus. Nevertheless, 10 months later a solitary pulmonary lesion, not a deported villus, was successfully resected. The patient is alive and well many years later. The author believes that this little story epitomizes the many enigmatic facets of trophoblastic disease! Almost nothing that trophoblast does or does not do should surprise anyone who has had any experience with this tissue.)

7. The spontaneous disappearance of metastases (so diagnosed by X-ray) following removal of a primary choriocarcinoma appears to occur in 1 to 2% of patients. About 4% of patients with metastases survive 5 years or more without tumor; the metastases having been removed surgically or having disappeared spontaneously. On the other hand, about 14% of patients with morphologically proven choriocarcinoma with and without metastases, lived 5 years or more without tumor following simple hysterectomy and/or removal of the metastases. The author once exam-

ined material from such a series of "cured" patients (21/147) in discussing a paper by John I. Brewer.[10A] No histologic differences could be found between the tumors from these patients who survived and the tumors from any patient who died. Reference must be made again here, however, to Bur's work[13] which showed that one of three proven cases of choriocarcinoma with pulmonary metastases was histochemically different than the other two. This patient lived and the other two died. (See Chapter X-D for details of this case.) To be sure, the metastases did not disappear *until* the primary uterine tumor was removed. (This phenomenon seems analogous to the disappearance of placental site giant cells following delivery of the placenta.)

8. For some reason, not well understood, the trophoblast of even the most malignant appearing mole does not accurately resemble the choriocarcinoma that arises from or is in association with it. This fact is perhaps related to the dissatisfaction of other authors with the present author's histologic grouping of hydatidiform moles. Whether this classification is valid in other hands is beside the point but as employed by Hertig and Gore, it proves useful to them. The general principle holds true that the more malignant the histologic pattern of the mole, the more likely the development of sequelae. The author feels that all too often insufficient molar or curetted material is examined to give an adequate picture of the malignant potential of any one mole. *Everyone, including Hertig and Gore, agrees that histologic grouping, or grading fails to pinpoint the prognosis in any specific patient.* Nevertheless, it is of great comfort to these authors and their clinical colleagues that a benign appearing mole causes little worry and that a malignant appearing one is apt to cause a great deal.

9. Metastases from choriocarcinoma may take diverse forms. They may remain dormant for many years but usually manifest themselves within a few months. They may destroy tissue and cause signs of dysfunction of the organ or system within which they lie. Pulmonary, pleural, vaginal, cerebral, intraperitoneal, gastrointestinal, and renal hemorrhage are associated with this neoplasm. On rare occasions the metastatic form of the disease in the lung results in death from *cor pulmonale* years after the initial pregnancy which gave rise to the pulmonary intravascular

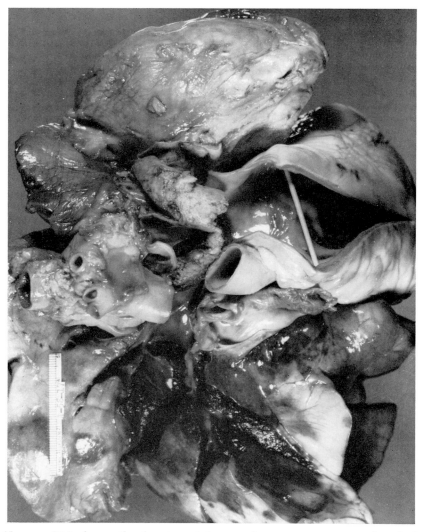

FIGURE 264 shows the heart and lungs of a young woman who died suddenly of *cor pulmonale*. Her obstetrical history revealed the passage of a hydatidiform mole four and one-half years prior to her death. This molar pregnancy was subsequently followed by six spontaneous miscarriages over the intervening years. A year before her death, she had "pneumonia" but no hemoptysis. This chest trouble again occurred six months before her death, but at that time the gonadotropin excretion in 24 hours was 4,800 international units. A thoracotomy two months prior growth (Figures 264 to 266). The oddest, and rarest, evidence of metastatic choriocarcinoma known to the author is the case reported by Mercer and associates[102A] of the Cleveland Clinic. A plum colored lesion in the upper gum of a one month old baby proved to be a typical choriocarcinoma. Investigation of the mother revealed that she too had the same disease. Unfortunately no data were available as to the gross and microscopic examination of the placenta. Incidentally, careful gross examination of the term placenta will reveal choriocarcinoma in about 1 out of 12,000 consecutive ward patients as shown by Driscoll[25] of the Boston Lying-in Hospital in her Maternal and Infant Health Study. It must be emphasized that not all choriocarcinomas of the term placenta cause infant or maternal mortality. Dr. Driscoll's case was non-fatal; the lesion apparently confined to the placenta although Dr. Mercer's case was fatal for both mother and child.

10. And finally, the enlarged cystic ovaries of patients with hydatidiform mole and choriocarcinoma will regress when the trophoblastic lesion is removed or caused to disappear by chemotherapy. Experienced clinicians now know this but the author has observed the accumulation of this wisdom during his professional life time. One of his more pleasurable experiences as a hospital pathologist was to prevent a distinguished obstetrician from removing two large cystic ovaries from a resident's wife who had just had a hydatidiform mole delivered by hysterotomy. (The patient subsequently had several children.)

These items, ten in number, are not given in the sense of Commandments but the information within them has helped the author and his colleagues during the past 35 years.

←

to death revealed pulmonary infarction, but no metastatic disease was demonstrated. Nor was there any trophoblast in the uterus removed shortly thereafter. Only at postmortem examination was discovered the true (trophoblastic) nature of the pulmonary thrombosis which led to her death from *cor pulmonale*. Note the saddle-shaped mass of pure trophoblast and blood clot within the pulmonary artery, just beyond the matchstick which props open the right ventricle. It is obvious from such a history that the source of this trophoblast is unknown. See Figs. 265 and 266 for microscopic details of a similar lesion. H.M.S. CS-64-520. (Courtesy of Dr. Andrew J. McQueeney, Santa Barbara, California.)

FIGURE 265. *(Upper left)* A small pulmonary artery showing a mass of undifferentiated trophoblast. Note the wall of vessel has not been destroyed and the lumen of the vessel has not yet been entirely obliterated. × 112.

FIGURE 266. *(Lower)* A low-power view of an intravascular trophoblastic growth (tumor embolus-thrombus) within the pulmonary artery (from same patient as material in Fig. 265). Note again that the vessel wall has not been destroyed. Note further the central necrosis within tumor mass (intravascular "choriocarcinoma") which characterizes the majority of choriocarcinomas whether they be primary or secondary in nature. There is, however, viable tumor lying free within the lumen, above the occlusive mass and below the loose blood clot. × 70.

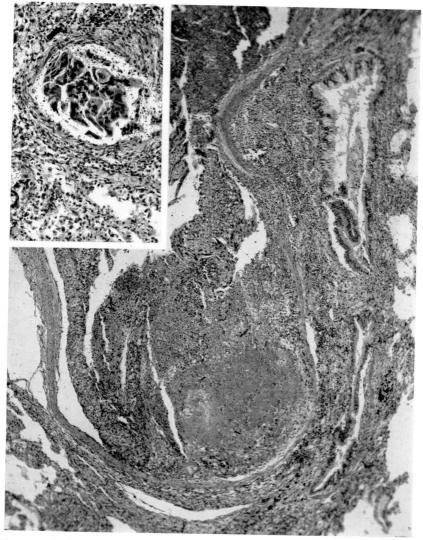

FIGURES 265 and 266 are microscopic details of pulmonary intravascular growth of trophoblast following pregnancy. The patient died of *cor pulmonale*, as did the patient whose heart and lungs are seen in Fig. 264. A.F.I.P. Acc. Nos. 283959-20063 and -20061 respectively. Previously published by Hertig and Mansell.[53] (Courtesy of the Armed Forces Institute of Pathology.)

C. TREATMENT OF TROPHOBLASTIC DISEASE

The pathologist is necessarily drawn into the problems associated with the treatment of these uncommon conditions. The spectrum of morphologic lesions which encompass trophoblastic disease has already been fully discussed and illustrated in other parts of this monograph. The ease and the difficulty of diagnoses have been stressed.

For purposes of treatment, the term "trophoblastic disease" includes any tumor or tumor-like lesion that is associated with or follows any type of pregnancy. Such morphologic variants are choriocarcinoma, choriocarcinoma *in situ*, syncytial endometritis and invasive hydatidiform mole. Because an apparently uncomplicated hydatidiform mole may be followed by invasive mole and choriocarcinoma, the modern thought is to include all moles in the category of trophoblastic disease. This seems reasonable to the author.

Roy Hertz and his colleagues[64A, 64B] coined this term about ten years ago to include all neoplastic complications of pregnancy. Although they realized that any type of pregnancy may have neoplastic sequelae, it was often difficult and sometimes impossible to define the precise anatomic pathology of the uterine complication which gave rise to metastases. Indeed, these authors showed very clearly that once a metastasis had occurred that metastasis was almost certain to be a choriocarcinoma.[64A] Hertz and his colleagues also stressed the frequent difficulty, as the author already has, of making a proper diagnosis when the trophoblastic disease is confined to the uterus. Thus there are two general categories of trophoblastic disease; with and without metastases.

It is universally agreed that the proper therapy for metastatic trophoblastic disease is chemotherapy. The most modern summary of this problem is to be found in Ross, Goldstein, Hertz, Lipsett and Odell in 1965.[118] In essence, these authors found that among 50 patients with metastatic disease:

1) The sequential use of methotrexate and actinomycin D led to "complete remission" in 37 of their 50 patients. Such remission rates were independent of which agent was used first. The necessi-

ty for such sequential use lies in the fact that each agent cures a significant proportion of patients refractory to the other agent.

2) The prognosis in these 37 cured patients was a function of the interval of time before treatment was undertaken and the chorionic gonadotropin titer of the patient when first seen. If the patient was first treated prior to 4 months—dated from either delivery or, if uncertain, the onset of symptoms, the prognosis was good. Moreover, if the HCG titer was less than 1×10^6 units the outlook was favorable. If both these factors were favorable the response to chemotherapy was 95%. On the contrary, if both of these parameters were exceeded, the response was only 36%.

3) Secondary metastases from lung to brain or liver were less favorable than metastases to lung alone. (The author would add jejunum and kidney.)

The problems of how to treat properly the trophoblastic disease still confined to the uterus is less clear-cut. (See Figures 267-273 for two such cases.) It is generally agreed that if the preservation of reproductive function is imperative, chemotherapy is indicated. It must be pointed out, however, that surgery may be necessary to control bleeding or to eradicate persisting foci of trophoblastic disease which are refractory to chemotherapy. Lewis and associates[85] have discussed this problem in a recent paper with a thorough review of the literature and a report of 8 of their patients with trophoblastic disease confined to the uterus. (They also reported 8 patients with metastatic lesions.) These authors raise the very real issue as to whether all surgical procedures whether diagnostic or therapeutic, should not be carried on "under cover" of chemotherapy. Although their series is not large enough for definite conclusions, such a regimen makes very good biological and clinical sense.

Trophoblast, whether benign or malignant, is notorious for its vascular metastasis. It has been shown that trophoblast in general is adversely affected by chemotherapeutic agents. It would seem sensible that all surgical procedures undertaken for conditions likely to give rise to or aggravate trophoblastic dissemination should be "covered" by some chemotherapeutic agent. Such conditions are:

1. Persistent postpartum bleeding

FIGURE 267. *(Upper left)* Curettings, June, 1961. Note that the trophoblast appears malignant. × 200.

FIGURE 268. *(Lower left)* Trophoblast recovered in October, 1961. × 200.

FIGURE 269. *(Lower right)* Corpus luteum of the pregnancy (abortion) which presumably gave rise to the choriocarcinoma. There is still some activity to be noted in the granulosa lutein cells, but the theca lutein cells have been "used up," a physiologic phenomenon in pregnancy irrespective of the type. This was removed at laparotomy in October. × 200.

FIGURE 270. *(Upper right)* Trophoblast in December, 1961. × 200.

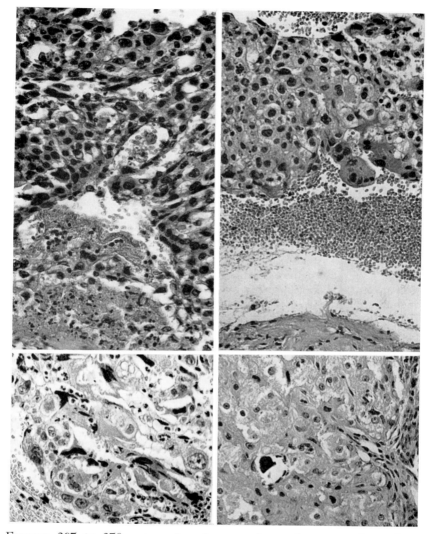

Figures 267 to 270 represent various specimens from a patient whose choriocarcinoma was associated with a spontaneous abortion in June, 1961. She had hemoperitoneum in October and continued to bleed until curettage in December, 1961, when a diagnosis of choriocarcinoma was made. On review, there was choriocarcinoma in both the June curettings and the tissue removed in October. After three courses of methotrexate, there was apparent complete remission. She was delivered by cesarean section of a normal baby in August, 1964. H.M.S. CS-61-722. (Material by courtesy of Dr. Cyril Shier, La Canada, California.)

FIGURE 271. *(Upper left)* The most exuberant trophoblast of the hydatidiform mole—grouped as a IV, Hertig and Sheldon classification. November 12, 1964. × 138.

FIGURE 272. *(Lower)* A uterine curettage following methotrexate therapy. Note pattern of choriocarcinoma but diffuse necrosis. One dead molar villus (not illustrated) was also found in these curettings. February 27, 1965. × 138.

FIGURE 273. *(Upper right)* Viable choriocarcinoma which required hysterectomy on October 21, 1965, approximately one year after the original mole. × 138.

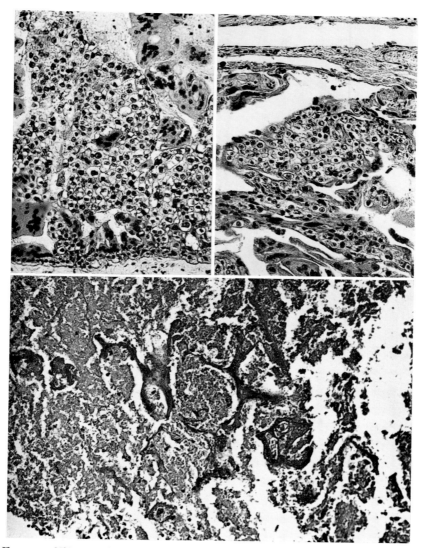

FIGURES 271 to 273 represent a hydatidiform mole from a patient who developed a choriocarcinoma. She was treated by methotrexate therapy with temporary remissions but had a hysterectomy because of persistent elevation of HCG titer. H.M.S. CS-64-726. Figs. 271 and 272 published by Gore and Hertig.[30] (Courtesy of Hoeber Medical Division of Harper and Row.)

2. Persistent postmolar bleeding
3. Persistent postabortal bleeding
4. Persistent or rising titers of HCG without a histologic diagnosis or definite localization of persistent trophoblast.
5. Hydatidiform molar pregnancies *de novo* whether evacuation is to be done by hysterotomy or per vaginam.

It has been repeatedly pointed out by all chemotherapists that the various agents are toxic. Lewis and associates[85] go into some detail about this matter. Suffice it to say here that no chemotherapy for trophoblastic disease should be undertaken by anyone unfamiliar with its use, dangers and toxic manifestations. Lewis points out that for an agent to be effective, it must be given to the point of toxicity. Unfortunately, mere toxicity does not insure therapeutic success.

A word must be said here about the unique role played by the HCG titer in shaping the therapy and determining prognosis for trophoblastic disease. If the titer is high, ordinary tests will suffice. If, however, such tests are negative, the urine must be concentrated by the Kaolin method of Albert[1] and the concentrate bioassayed by the rat hyperemia method.[142A] A truly "negative" test is that which is within the limits delineated by the normal level of pituitary LH (Luteinizing Hormone).

It is imperative that all postmolar patients be followed by weekly HCG tests because Delfs[20A] has shown that:

1. Beyond 8 weeks, 24% of such patients have an elevated or rising titer and

2. Half of such patients have either a choriocarcinoma or an invasive mole. (Hertig and Sheldon[63] showed that the postmolar ratio of such complications was about 1:6.)

The differential diagnosis of normal pregnancy *versus* postmolar complication is a clinicopathologic nightmare. All students of trophoblastic disease have seen subsequent normal pregnancies sacrificed under the guise of some postmolar complication. The author knows of no sure way to tell these two entities apart in the first few months. A diagnostic dilatation and curettage will interrupt a normal pregnancy. A rising HCG titer can be present in such normal pregnancies and reach high levels. (The author well remembers a normal twin pregnancy that was mistaken for

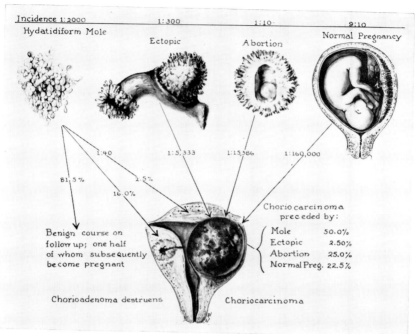

FIGURE 274. A diagram prepared by the author to indicate the relationship of various types of pregnancies to the choriomas of major importance (trophoblastic disease). Note that, although all types of pregnancy may be associated with or followed by choriocarcinoma, *only* a hydatidiform mole may give rise to an invasive mole (chorioadenoma destruens). The tendency of each type of pregnancy to be followed by its sequel(ae) is an estimate based upon the ratios of the kinds of pregnancies and the generally agreed percentages of such pregnancies which precede choriocarcinoma. The figures for hydatidiform mole and its important sequelae are accurate and based upon 200 moles gathered by the author from all over the eastern half of the United States. The drawings are from actual specimens, with the exception of the term uterus. The reader will recognize most of them as having already been published in this monograph. Originally published by Hertig.[38] Modified for Hertig and Mansell.[53] Further modified here because of the improvement in prognosis of choriocarinoma since 1950 when the chart was first made.

a postmolar complication because of such a high titer.) In general, the menstrual or uterine bleeding history is so confused that it is of no help in such patients. The feeling of a normal pregnant uterus at 3 to 4 months is fairly characteristic and does not tend to mimic the *usual* postmolar complication. Nevertheless, it may not be possible to wait long enough to establish pregnancy by such definite tests as x-ray evidence of fetal skeleton or auscultation of the fetal heart. Possibly fetal electrocardiography might be of help but the author knows of no such application of that technique to this problem. The only safe way to prevent the need for such a difficult differential diagnosis is to advise the patient to avoid pregnancy for a year following a hydatidiform mole. Most of the complications of a mole develop within 6 months but some take longer.

Reference has already been made in this monograph to Treatment Centers for Trophoblastic Disease. Roy Hertz established one, the first, some years ago at the National Institutes of Health. His original Center is now largely non-operative owing to the completion of the project for which it was established; the proof that chemotherapeutic agents successfully cured a significant number of choriocarcinomas. Hertz, however, trained a number of younger colleagues in the use of these effective but dangerous agents.

Dr. John Lewis is such a trainee. During his Residency Training program here in Boston, supported in part by the Macy Foundation, he and Goss gathered and treated over a 4 year period the 25 patients referred to above.[85] The author and his colleague, Dr. Hazel Gore, saw all of the histologic material. This constituted an unofficial Treatment Center without government or other formal support. The patients paid for their own treatment; an astounding feat considering the necessary length of hospital stay.

Dr. Donald Goldstein, another Hertz trainee, in conjunction with Dr. Duncan E. Reid, Professor of Obstetrics and Chairman of Obstetrics and Gynecology at Harvard, Dr. Hazel Gore and the author have formed another Treatment Center as of July 1, 1965. This center has formal NIH support for patient care. Within the first year about 30 patients with all manner of trophoblastic disease have been sent to Boston from all over New England and even beyond. The number of patients is increasing.

Dr. John I. Brewer, Professor of Obstetrics and Gynecology at Northwestern, has long headed the Mathieu Chorioepithelioma Registry and now directs in Chicago another Treatment Center for Trophoblastic Disease. It is from such Centers that a much more complete knowledge of all aspects of the biology of trophoblastic disease will be forthcoming.

It has been fun for the author and his colleagues to have observed and participated over the years in the histologic and biologic sequence of events that truly makes trophoblast God's first cancer and man's first cure!

REFERENCES

1. ALBERT, A.: Human urinary gonadotropin. *Recent Progr Hormone Research, 12:*227-301, 1956.
1A. AMOROSO, E. C.: Placentation. In PARKES, A. S.: (Ed.): *Marshall's Physiology of Reproduction,* 3rd ed. London, Longmans, Green and Co., 1952, Vol. II, pp. 127-311.
2. BAER, K. E. VON: Epistola de Ovi Mammalium et Hominis Genesi. Lipsiae, 1827.
3. BARDAWIL, W. A., and TOY, B. L.: The natural history of choriocarcinoma: problems of immunity and spontaneous regression. *Ann NY Acad Sci, 80:*197-261, 1959.
4. BENIRSCHKE, K.: Examination of the placenta. *Obstet Gynec, 18:*309-333, 1961.
5. BENIRSCHKE, K.: Accurate recording of twin placentation. A plea to the obstetrician. *Obstet Gynec, 18:*334-347, 1961.
6. BENIRSCHKE, K., and DRISCOLL, S. G.: The pathology of the human placenta. Reprinted from *Handbuch der Speziellen Pathologischen Anatomie und Histologie.* VII/5. Springer-Verlag New York Inc., 1967.
7. BLEISCH, V. R.: Diagnosis of monochorionic twin placentation. *Amer J Clin Path, 42:*277-284, 1964.
8. BÖVING, B. G.: Anatomical analysis of rabbit trophoblast invasion. *Contrib Embryol, 37:*33-35, 1962.
9. BREWER, J. I., personal communication, 1961.
10. BREWER, J. I., and GERBIE, A. B.: Early development of choriocarcinoma. *Amer J Obstet Gynec, 94:*692-705, 1966.
10A. BREWER, J. J., RINEHART, J. J., and DUNBAR, R. W.: Choriocarcinoma. *Amer J Obstet Gynec, 81:*574-583, 1961.

11. BROSENS, I.: A study of the spiral arteries of the decidua basalis in normotensive and hypertensive pregnancies. *J Obstet Gynaec Brit Comm, 71*:222-230, 1964.

12. BRUMPT, E.: Utilisation des insectes auxiliaires entomophages dans la lutte contre les insectes pathogènes. *Presse Med, 21*:359-361, 1913.

13. BUR, G. E.; HERTIG, A. T.; McKAY, D. G., and ADAMS, E. C.: Histochemical aspects of hydatidiform mole and choriocarcinoma. *Obstet Gynec, 19*:156-182, 1962.

14. COLE, D. F.: The effects of oestradiol on the rat uterus. *J Endocr, 7*:12-23, 1950.

15. CONN, D. L., personal communication, 1967.

16. CORNER, G. W.: The problem of embryonic pathology in mammals, with observations upon intrauterine mortality in the pig. *Amer J Anat, 31*:523-545, 1923.

17. CORNER, G. W.: Observed embryology of human single-ovum twins and other multiple births. *Amer J Obstet Gynec, 70*:933-951, 1955.

18. CORNER, G. W.: Exploring the placental maze. *Amer J Obstet Gynec, 86*:408-418, 1963.

19. CULLEN, T. S.: *Embryology, Anatomy and Diseases of the Umbilicus Together with Diseases of the Urachus.* Philadelphia and London, Saunders, 1916.

20. DALLENBACH-HELLWEG, G., and NETTE, G.: Morphological and histochemical observations on trophoblast and decidua of the basal plate of the human placenta at term. *Amer J Anat, 115*:309-326, 1964.

20A. DELFS, E.: Quantitative chorionic gonadotrophin; prognostic value in hydatidiform mole and chorionepithelioma. *Obstet Gynec, 9*:1-24, 1957.

20B. DELFS, E., and JONES, G. E. S.: Endocrine patterns in abortion. *Obst Gynec Survey, 3*:680-692, 1948.

21. DIAMANDOPOULOS, G., personal communication, 1966.

22. DICKMANN, Z.; CLEWE, T. H.; BONNEY, W. A., JR., and NOYES, R. W.: The human egg in the pronuclear stage. *Anat Rec, 152*:293-302, 1965.

23. *Dorland's Illustrated Medical Dictionary,* 24th ed. Philadelphia and London, Saunders, 1965, p. 1621.

24. DOUGLAS, G. W.: The diagnosis and management of hydatidiform mole. *S Clin N Amer, 37*:379-392, 1957.

25. DRISCOLL, S. G.: Choriocarcinoma: An "incidental finding" within a term placenta. *Obstet Gynec, 21*:96-101, 1963.

26. ELDER, J. H.; HARTMAN, C. G., and HEUSER, C. H.: A ten and one-half day chimpanzee embryo, "Yerkes A." *JAMA, 111*:1156-1159, 1938.

27. Ferin, J., and Gaudefroy, M. (Eds.): *Les Fonctions de Nidation Utérine et Leurs Troubles*. Colloque organisé en collaboration avec la section belge de l'International Fertility Association. Paris, Masson et Cie, 1960.

27A. Flexner, L. B.: The functional role of the placenta. In: Flexner, L. B. (Ed.) Gestation. Transactions of the First Conference, March 9, 10 and 11, 1954. Josiah Macy, Jr. Foundation, New York, 1955.

28. Gemzell, C. A.: The induction of ovulation in the human by human pituitary gonadotropin. In Villee, C. A. (Ed.): *Control of Ovulation*. New York, Pergamon, 1961.

29. Gibson, G. B.: Primary ovarian pregnancy. *J Obstet Gynec Brit Emp, 64*:905-906, 1957.

30. Gore, H., and Hertig, A. T.: Problems in the histologic interpretation of the trophoblast. *Clin Obstet Gynec, 10*:269-289, 1967.

31. Grosser, O.: *Frühentwicklung Eihautbildung und Placentation des Menschen und der Säugetiere. Deutsche Frauenheilkunde*. Fünfter Band. München, Verlag von J. F. Bergman, 1927.

32. Hamilton, E.: *Mythology*. Boston, Little, 1940.

33. Hammond, C. B.; Hertz, R.; Ross, G. T.; Lipsett, M. B., and Odell, W. D.: Primary chemotherapy for nonmetastatic gestational trophoblastic neoplasms. *Amer J Obstet Gynec, 98*:71-78, 1967.

34. Hartman, C. G. (Ed.): *Mechanisms Concerned with Conception*. New York, Pergamon, 1963.

35. Heard, O. O.: Methods used by C. H. Heuser in preparing and sectioning early embryos. *Contrib Embryol, 36*:1-18, 1957.

35A. Hellman, L. M., and Hertig, A. T.: Pathological changes in the placenta associated with erythroblastosis of the fetus. *Amer J Path, 14*:111-120, 1938.

36. Hertig, A. T.: Angiogenesis in the early human chorion and in the primary placenta of the macaque monkey. *Contrib Embryol, 25*:37-82, 1935.

37. Hertig, A. T.: On the development of the amnion and exocoelomic membrane in the pre-villous human ovum. *Yale J Biol Med, 18*:107-115, 1945.

38. Hertig, A. T.: Hydatidiform mole and chorionepithelioma. In Meigs, J. V., and Sturgis, S. H. (Eds.): *Progress in Gynecology*. New York, Grune, 1950, Vol. II.

39. Hertig, A. T.: The pathology of late pregnancy hemorrhage. In Holt, L. E., Jr. (Ed.): *Prematurity, Congenital Malformation and Birth Injury*. New York, Watkins, 1953.

40. Hertig, A. T.: *Seminar on Tumors of the Gynecologic System*. Chicago, American Society of Clinical Pathologists, 1953.

41. Hertig, A. T.: La nidation des oeufs humains fécondés normaux et

anormaux. In *Les Fonctions de Nidation Utérine et Leurs Troubles*. Paris, Masson et Cie, 1960, pp. 169-213.

42. HERTIG, A. T.: Gestational hyperplasia of endometrium. A morphologic correlation of ova, endometrium and corpora lutea of pregnancy. *Lab Invest, 13*:1153-1191, 1964.

43. HERTIG, A. T.: Diseases of placenta and fetal membranes. In *Encyclopaedia Britannica*. Chicago, William Benton, 1964, vol. 17, pp. 988-989.

44. HERTIG, A. T.: Trophoblastic neoplasms, an editorial. *New Eng J Med, 273*:1278-1279, 1965.

45. HERTIG, A. T.: Morphologic criteria of the time of ovulation in the human being. In KEEFER, C. S. (Ed.): *Human Ovulation*. Boston, Little, 1965, pp. 75-83.

46. HERTIG, A. T.: Overall problems in man. In BENIRSCHKE, K. (Ed.): *Conference on Comparative Aspects of Reproductive Failure*. Berlin, Springer-Verlag, 1967, pp. 11-41.

47. HERTIG, A. T.; ADAMS, E. C.; McKAY, D. G.; ROCK, J.; MULLIGAN, W. J., and MENKIN, M. F.: A thirteen-day human ovum studied histochemically. *Amer J Obstet Gynec, 76*:1025-1043, 1958.

48. HERTIG, A. T., and EDMONDS, H. W.: Genesis of hydatidiform mole. *Arch Path (Chicago), 30*:260-291, 1940.

49. HERTIG, A. T., and GORE, H.: Diseases and anomalies of the ovum. In DAVIS, C. H., and CARTER, B. (Eds.): *Gynecology and Obstetrics*. Hagerstown, The W. F. Prior Co., 1959.

50. HERTIG, A. T., and GORE, H.: The female genitalia. In ANDERSON, W. A. D. (Ed.): *Pathology*, 5th ed. St. Louis, Mosby, 1966.

51. HERTIG, A. T., and HERTIG, M.: A technique for the artificial feeding of sandflies *(Phlebotomus)* and mosquitoes. *Science, 65*:328-329, 1927.

52. HERTIG, A. T., and LIVINGSTON, R. G.: Spontaneous, threatened and habitual abortion: its pathogenesis and treatment. *New Eng J Med, 230*:797-806, 1944.

53. HERTIG, A. T., and MANSELL, H.: *Atlas of Tumor Pathology*. Tumors of the female sex organs. Part 1. Hydatidiform mole and choriocarcinoma. Washington, D. C., Armed Forces Institute of Pathology, 1956, sec. ix, fascicle 33.

54. HERTIG, A. T., and ROCK, J.: Two human ova of the pre-villous stage, having an ovulation age of about eleven and twelve days respectively. *Contrib Embryol, 29*:127-156, 1941.

55. HERTIG, A. T., and ROCK, J.: On the development of the early human ovum with special reference to the trophoblast of the previllous stage: a description of 7 normal and 5 pathologic ova. *Amer J Obstet Gynec, 47*:149-184, 1944.

56. HERTIG, A. T., and ROCK, J.: Two human ova of the pre-villous stage,

having a developmental age of about seven and nine days respectively. *Contrib Embryol, 31*:65-84, 1945.

57. HERTIG, A. T., and ROCK, J.: Two human ova of the pre-villous stage, having a developmental age of about eight and nine days respectively. *Contrib Embryol, 33*:169-186, 1949.

58. HERTIG, A. T., and ROCK, J.: A series of potentially abortive ova recovered from fertile women prior to the first missed menstrual period. *Amer J Obstet Gynec, 58*:968-993, 1949.

59. HERTIG, A. T., and ROCK, J.: Abortive human ova and associated endometria. In ENGLE, E. T. (Ed.): *Menstruation and Its Disorders*. Springfield, Thomas, 1950, pp. 96-137.

60. HERTIG, A. T.; ROCK, J., and ADAMS, E. C.: A description of 34 human ova within the first 17 days of development. *Amer J Anat, 98*:435-494, 1956.

61. HERTIG, A. T.; ROCK, J.; ADAMS, E. C., and MENKIN, M. C.: Thirty-four fertilized human ova, good, bad and indifferent, recovered from 210 women of known fertility. A study of biologic wastage in early human pregnancy. *Pediatrics, 23*:202-211, 1959.

62. HERTIG, A. T.; ROCK, J.; ADAMS, E. C., and MULLIGAN, W. J.: On the preimplantation stages of the human ovum: a description of four normal and four abnormal specimens ranging from the second to the fifth day of development. *Contrib Embryol, 35*:199-220, 1954.

63. HERTIG, A. T., and SHELDON, W. H.: Minimal criteria required to prove prima facie case of traumatic abortion or miscarriage. An analysis of 1000 spontaneous abortions. *Ann Surg, 117*:596-606, 1943.

64. HERTIG, A. T., and SHELDON, W. H.: Hydatidiform mole—a pathologico-clinical correlation of 200 cases. *Amer J Obstet Gynec, 53*:1-36, 1947.

64A. HERTZ, R., LEWIS, J., JR., and LIPSETT, M. B.: Five years' experience with the chemotherapy of metastatic choriocarcinoma and related trophoblastic tumors in women. *Amer J Obstet Gynec, 82*:631-640, 1961.

64B. HERTZ, R., ROSS, G. T., and LIPSETT, M. B.: Primary chemotherapy of nonmetastatic trophoblastic disease in women. *Amer J Obstet Gynec, 86*:808-814, 1963.

65. HEUSER, C. H.: A human embryo with 14 pairs of somites. *Contrib Embryol, 22*:135-152, 1930.

66. HEUSER, C. H.: An intrachorial mesothelial membrane in young stages of the monkey (macacus rhesus). *Anat Rec, 52*, suppl. pp. 15-16, 1932.

67. HEUSER, C. H.: A presomite human embryo with definite chorda canal. *Contrib Embryol, 23*:251-267, 1932.

68. HEUSER, C. H., and CORNER, G. W.: Developmental horizons in human embryos. Description of age group X, 4 to 12 somites. *Contrib Embryol*, 36:29-39, 1957.

69. HEUSER, C. H.: ROCK, J., and HERTIG, A. T.: Two human embryos showing early stages of the definitive yolk sac. *Contrib Embryol*, 31:85-99, 1945.

70. HEUSER, C. H., and STREETER, G. L.: Early stages in the development of pig embryos, from the period of initial cleavage to the time of appearance of limb-buds. *Contrib Embryol*, 20:1-29, 1929.

71. HEUSER, C. H., and STREETER, G. L.: Development of the macaque embryo. *Contrib Embryol*, 29:15-55, 1941.

72. HOLDEN, R. B.: Vascular reactions of the uterus of the immature rat. *Endocrinology*, 25:593-596, 1939.

73. HOU, P. C., and PANG, S. C.: Chorionepithelioma: an analytic study of 28 necropsied cases, with special reference to the possibility of spontaneous regression. *J Path Bact*, 72:95-104, 1956.

74. HUBRECHT, A. A. W.: Keimblätterbilderung und Placentation der Igels. *Anat Anz*, 3:510-515, 1888.

75. HUBRECHT, A. A. W.: Studies in mammalian embryology. I. The placentation of *Erinaceous europaeus*, with remarks on the phylogeny of the placenta. *Quart J Micr Sci*, 30:283-404, 1889.

76. HUBRECHT, A. A. W.: *Die Phylogenese des Amnions und die Bedeutung des Trophoblasts*. Verhandelingen der Koninklijke Academie van Wetenschappen te Amsterdam, Dl. IV, 1-67, 1895. Amsterdam, Johannes Muller.

77. HUNT, W.; DOCKERTY, M. B., and RANDALL, L. M.: Hydatidiform mole. A clinicopathologic study involving "grading" as a measure of possible malignant change. *Obstet Gynec*, 1:593-609, 1953.

78. IRVING, F. C., and HERTIG, A. T.: A study of placenta accreta. *Surg Gynec Obstet*, 64:178-200, 1937.

79. KALMAN, S. M.: Some studies on estrogens and uterine permeability. *J Pharmacol Exp Ther*, 115:442-448, 1955.

80. KEEFER, C. S. (Ed.): *Human Ovulation*. Boston, Little, 1965.

81. KISTNER, R. W.; HERTIG, A. T., and REID, D. E.: Simultaneously occurring placenta previa and placenta accreta. *Surg Gynec Obstet*, 94:141-151, 1952.

82. KISTNER, R. W.; HERTIG, A. T., and ROCK, J.: Tubal pregnancy complicating tuberculous salpingitis. *Amer J Obstet Gynec*, 62:1157-1159, 1951.

83. LAMS, H.: Etude de l'oeuf de cobaye aux premiers stades de l'embryogenèse. *Arch Biol (Liege)*, 28:229-323, 1913.

84. LARROUSSE, F.; KING, A. G., and WOLBACH, S. B.: The overwintering in Massachusetts of *Ixodiphagus caucurtei*. *Science*, 67:351-353, 1928.

85. Lewis, J., Jr.; Gore, H.; Hertig, A. T., and Goss, D. A.: Treatment of trophoblastic disease. With rationale for the use of adjunctive chemotherapy at the time of indicated operation. *Amer J Obstet Gynec*, 96:710-722, 1966.

86. Little, A. B.; Thompson, D. W., and Hertig, A. T., personal communication, 1959.

87. Luce, H. R. (Ed.): *Time* THE WEEKLY NEWSMAGAZINE, 45:64-65, 1945.

88. Lund, C. J., and Thiede, H. A. (Eds.): *Transcript of the First Rochester Trophoblast Conference.* November 13 and 14, 1961. Rochester, New York.

89. Lund, C. J., and Thiede, H. A. (Eds.): *Transcript of the Second Rochester Trophoblast Conference.* November 4 and 5, 1963. Rochester, New York.

90. Lund, C. J., and Thiede, H. A. (Eds.): *Transcript of the Third Rochester Trophoblast Conference.* November 1 and 2, 1965. Rochester, New York.

91. MacMahon, B.; Hertig, A., and Ingalls, T.: Association between maternal age and pathologic diagnosis in abortion. *Obstet Gynec*, 4:477-483, 1954.

92. MacRae, D. J.: Chorionepithelioma occurring during pregnancy. *J Obstet Gynaec Brit Emp*, 58:373-380, 1951.

93. Mall, F. P., and Meyer, A. W.: Studies on abortuses: a survey of pathologic ova in the Carnegie Embryological collection. *Contrib Embryol*, 12:1-364, 1921.

94. Martin, C. B.; McGaughey, H. S., Jr.; Kaiser, H. S.; Donner, M. W., and Ramsey, E. M.: Intermittent functioning of the uteroplacental arteries. *Amer J Obstet Gynec*, 90:819-823, 1964.

95. McKay, D. G.; Adams, E. C.; Hertig, A. T., and Danziger, S.: Histochemical horizons in human embryos. I. Five millimeter embryos. Streeter Horizon XIII. *Anat Rec*, 122:125-144, 1955.

96. McKay, D. G.; Hertig, A. T.; Adams, E. C., and Danziger, S.: Histochemical observation on the germ cells of human embryos. *Anat Rec*, 117:201-220, 1953.

97. McKay, D. G.; Hertig, A. T.; Adams, E. C., and Richardson, M. V.: Histochemical observations on the human placenta. *Obstet Gynec*, 12:1-36, 1958.

98. McKay, D. G.; Hertig, A. T.; Bardawil, W. A., and Velardo, J. T.: Histochemical observations on the endometrium. I. Normal endometrium. *Obstet Gynec*, 8:22-39, 1956.

99. McKay, D. G.; Hertig, A. T.; Bardawil, W., and Velardo, J. T.: Histochemical observations on the endometrium. II. Abnormal endometrium. *Obstet Gynec*, 8:140-156, 1956.

100. McKay, D. G.; Merrill, S. J.; Weiner, A. E.; Hertig, A. T., and

REID, D. E.: The pathologic anatomy of eclampsia, bilateral renal cortical necrosis, pituitary necrosis, and other acute fatal complications of pregnancy, and its possible relationship to the generalized Shwartzman phenomenon. *Amer J Obstet Gynec, 66*:507-539, 1953.

101. McKAY, D. G.; RICHARDSON, M. V., and HERTIG, A. T.: Studies of the function of early human trophoblast. III. A study of the protein structure of mole fluid, chorionic and amniotic fluids by paper electrophoresis. *Amer J Obstet Gynec, 75*:699-707, 1958.

102. McKAY, D. G.; ROBY, C. C.; HERTIG, A. T., and RICHARDSON, M. V.: Studies of the function of early human trophoblast. I. Observations on the chemical composition of the fluid of hydatidiform moles. II. Preliminary observations on certain chemical constituents of chorionic and early amniotic fluid. *Amer J Obstet Gynec, 69*:722-734; 735-741, 1955.

102A. MERCER, R. D., LAMMERT, A. C., ANDERSON, R., and HAZARD, J. B.: Choriocarcinoma in mother and infant. *JAMA, 166*:482-483, 1958.

103. MIDGLEY, A. R., JR., and PIERCE, G. B., JR.: Immunohistochemical localization of human chorionic gonadotropin. *J Exp Med, 115*:289-294, 1962.

104. MIDGLEY, A. R., JR.; PIERCE, G. B., JR.; DENEAU, G. A., and GOSLING, J. R. G.: Morphogenesis of syncytiotrophoblast *in vivo:* an autoradiographic demonstration. *Science, 141*:349-350, 1963.

105. NOYES, R. W.; DICKMANN, Z.; CLEWE, T. H., and BONNEY, W. A.: Pronuclear ovum from a patient using an intrauterine contraceptive device. *Science, 147*:744-745, 1965.

106. OBER, W. B., and FASS, R. O.: The early history of choriocarcinoma. *J Hist Med, 16*:49-73, 1961.

107. O'DEA, A. E., personal communication, 1958.

108. PATTEN, B. M.: *Human Embryology,* 2nd ed. Philadelphia and Toronto, Blakiston, 1953.

109. PETERS, H.: Ueber die Einbettung des menschlichen Eies und das früheste bisher bekannte menschliche. *Placentationsstadium.* Leipzig and Vienna. 1899.

110. PIERCE, G. B., JR., and MIDGLEY, A. R., JR.: The origin and function of human syncytiotrophoblastic giant cells. *Amer J Path, 43*:153-173, 1963.

111. PLENTL, A. A. (Ed.): Symposium on the placenta. *Amer J Obstet Gynec* (suppl.), *84*:1535-1798, 1962.

112. RAMSEY, E. M.: Circulation in the intervillous space of the primate placenta. In PLENTL, A. A. (Ed.): *Symposium on the Placenta. Amer J Obstet Gynec, 84*:1649-1663, 1962.

113. REYNOLDS, S. R. M.: Adaptation of uterine blood vessels and accommodation of the products of conception. *Contrib Embryol, 33*:1-19, 1949.

114. RICHARDSON, M. V., and HERTIG, A. T.: New England's first recorded hydatidiform mole. A historical note. *New Eng J Med, 260:*544-545, 1959.

115. ROCK, J., and HERTIG, A. T.: Some aspects of early human development. *Amer J Obstet Gynec, 44:*973-983, 1942.

116. ROCK, J., and HERTIG, A. T.: Information regarding the time of ovulation derived from a study of three unfertilized and 11 fertilized ova. *Amer J Obstet Gynec, 47:*343-356, 1944.

117. ROMNEY, S. L.; HERTIG, A. T., and REID, D. E.: The endometria associated with ectopic pregnancy. A study of 115 cases. *Surg Gynec Obstet, 91:*605-611, 1950.

118. ROSS, G. T.; GOLDSTEIN, D. P.; HERTZ, R.; LIPSETT, M. B., and ODELL, W. D.: Sequential use of methotrexate and actinomycin D in the treatment of metastatic choriocarcinoma and related trophoblastic diseases in women. *Amer J Obstet Gynec, 93:*223-229, 1965.

119. St. Whitelock, O. v. (Ed.): Trophoblast and its tumors. *Ann N Y Acad Sci, 80:*1-284, 1959.

120. SETON, A.: *The Winthrop Woman,* Boston, Houghton, 1958.

121. SEXTON, L. I.; HERTIG, A. T.; REID, D. E.; KELLOGG, F. S., and PATTERSON, W. S.: Premature separation of the normally implanted placenta. *Amer J Obstet Gynec, 59:*13-24, 1950.

122. SHEA, S. M., personal communication, 1966.

123. SHIRODKAR, V. N.: Surgical treatment of habitual abortion. *Tendances Actuelles en Gynecologie et Obstetrique.* Libraire de l'Université Geneva, GEORGE and CIE, S. A., 1955, p. 350.

124. SHIRODKAR, V. N.: New method of operative treatment for habitual abortions in second trimester of pregnancy. *Antiseptic, 52:*299-300, 1955.

125. SIMMONS, R.: The immunologic problem of pregnancy. *Amer J Obstet Gynec, 85:*589-593, 1963.

126. SIMMONS, R., and RUSSELL, P.: Antigenicity of mouse trophoblast. *Ann N Y Acad Sci, 2:*717-732, 1962.

127. SKINNER, H. A.: *The Origin of Medical Terms,* 2nd ed. Baltimore, Williams & Wilkins, 1961.

128. SMALBRAAK, J.: *Trophoblastic Growths.* Amsterdam, Elsevier Publishing Co., 1957.

129. SPAZIANI, E., and SZEGO, C. M.: Further evidence for mediation by histamine of estrogenic stimulation of the rat uterus. *Endocrinology, 64:*713-723, 1959.

130. STREETER, G. L.: A human embryo (Mateer) of the presomite period. *Contrib Embryol, 9:*389-424, 1920.

131. STREETER, G. L.: Weight, sitting height, head size, foot length and menstrual age of the human embryo. *Contrib Embryol, 11:*143-160, 1920.

132. STREETER, G. L.: Developmental horizons in human embryos. Description of age group XI, 13 to 20 somites, and age group XII, 21 to 29 somites. *Contrib Embryol, 30*:211-245, 1942.

133. STREETER, G. L.: Developmental horizons in human embryos. Description of age group XIII, embryos of about 4 or 5 millimeters long, and age group XIV, period of indentation of the lens vesicle. *Contrib Embryol, 31*:27-63, 1945.

134. STREETER, G. L.: Developmental horizons in human embryos. Description of age groups XV, XVI, XVII, and XVIII, being the third issue of a survey of the Carnegie collection. *Contrib Embryol, 32*:133-203, 1948.

135. STREETER, G. L.: Developmental horizons in human embryos. A review of the histogenesis of cartilage and bone. *Contrib Embryol, 33*:149-167, 1949.

136. STREETER, G. L.: Developmental horizons in human embryos. Description of age groups XIX, XX, XXI, XXII, and XXIII, being the fifth issue of a survey of the Carnegie collection. *Contrib Embryol, 34*:165-196, 1951.

137. STREETER, G. L.: Developmental horizons in human embryos; age groups XI to XXIII. Carnegie Institution of Washington, *Embryology* reprint. Volume II, 1951.

138. STRICHT, O. VAN DER: Étude comparée des ovules des mammifères aux différentes périodes de l'ovogenèse, d'après les travaux du Laboratoire d'Histologie et d'Embryologie de l'Université de Gand. *Arch Biol (Liege), 33*:229-300, 1923.

139. SZULMAN, A. E.: Chromosomal aberrations in spontaneous human abortions. *New Eng J Med, 272*:811-818, 1965.

140. TAO, T.-W.: Tissue Culture Studies of Normal Immature Human Placentas with Special Reference to Morphogenesis, Endocrine Function, and Reaggregation. Ph.D. Thesis, Harvard University, 1962.

141. TAO, T.-W.: Aggregation of dissociated human embryonic cells: Interaction of trophoblast with autologous liver and lung. *Exp Cell Res, 36*:275-284, 1964.

142. TAO, T.-W., and HERTIG, A. T.: Viability and differentiation of human trophoblast in organ culture. *Amer J Anat, 116*:315-328, 1965.

142A. TASHIMA, C. K., TIMBERGER, R., BURDICK, R., LEAVY, M., and RAWSON, R.: Cerebrospinal fluid titer of chorionic gonadotropin in patients with intracranial metastatic choriocarcinoma. *J Clin Endocrinology, 25*:1493-1495, 1965.

143. VILLEE, C. A. (Ed.): *The Placenta and Fetal Membranes.* Baltimore, Williams & Wilkins, 1960.

144. WALL, R. L., JR., and HERTIG, A. T.: Habitual abortion. *Amer J Obstet Gynec, 56*:1127-1133, 1948.

145. WHITE, R.; HERTIG, A. T.; ROCK, J., and ADAMS, E. C.: Histologic and histochemical observations on the corpus luteum of human pregnancy with special reference to corpora lutea associated with early normal and abnormal ova. *Contrib Embryol, 34*:55-74, 1951.

146. WILLIAMS, J. W.: Placenta circumvallata. *Amer J Obstet Gynec, 13*:1-16, 1927.

147. WILLIAMS, J. W.: Regeneration of the uterine mucosa after delivery with especial reference to the placental site. *Amer J Obstet Gynec, 22*:664-696, 1931.

148. WISLOCKI, G. B., and BENNETT, H. S.: The histology and cytology of the human and monkey placenta, with special reference to the trophoblast. *Amer J Anat, 73*:335-423, 1943.

149. WISLOCKI, G. B., and DEMPSEY, E. W.: Electron microscopy of the human placenta. *Anat Rec, 123*:133-167, 1955.

150. WISLOCKI, G. B., and PADYKULA, H. A.: Histochemistry and electron microscopy of the placenta. In YOUNG, W. (Ed.): *Sex and Internal Secretion,* 3rd ed. Baltimore, Williams & Wilkins, 1961, vol. 2, pp. 883-957.

151. WISLOCKI, G. B., and STREETER, G. L.: On the placentation of the macaque *(Macaca mulatta),* from the time of implantation until the formation of the definitive placenta. *Contrib Embryol, 27*:1-66, 1938.

152. WITSCHI, E.: Migration of the germ cells of human embryos from the yolk sac to the primitive gonadal folds. *Contrib Embryol, 32*:67-80, 1948.

PLACENTAL EXAMINATION – GROSS

INSTRUCTIONS: (1) For use when crown-rump length of fetus is 16.5 cm. or more (gestational age 20 weeks). (2) Placenta must be fresh when examined. (3) An entry is required for every item except those for twins only. (4) Describe all abnormalities in the space at bottom of second sheet. (5) Prepare at least 3 sections as specified in manual-cord, membrane roll, and placenta.

1. PATIENT'S IDENTIFICATION

2. GROSS EXAMINATION BY

3. TIME
AM
PM
DATE
Mo. Day Year

4. MULTIPLE BIRTHS (Photograph all placentas of multiple births - 35 mm. color)

5. DESIGNATION OF PLACENTA DESCRIBED ON THIS FORM
☐ Twin A 1 ☐ Twin B 2 ☐ Other Multiple Birth (Describe) 3

6. LABELED AT DELY.
☐ No 0 ☐ Yes 1

7. PLACENTAS FUSED
☐ No 0 ☐ Yes (Fill out one form for each fetus) 1

8. IF FUSED PLACENTAS, IS ANASTOMOSIS PRESENT?
☐ No 0 ☐ Yes 1 ☐ Undetermined 2
(Vessels must be injected as described in manual). Describe anastomoses below, indicating whether artery to artery, vein to vein, or artery to vein. Note size of vessels, etc.

9. DIMENSIONS
_____ X _____ X _____ cms
(Largest Diam.) (Smallest Diam.) (Thickness)

10. SHAPE
☐ Round or Oval 1 ☐ Other (Describe) 2

11. CORD

12. LENGTH OF CORD
(Portion attached to placenta plus any loose pieces) _____ cms

13. SHORTEST DISTANCE FROM CORD INSERTION TO PLACENTAL MARGIN
☐ Insertion not membranous 1 ☐ Insertion membranous 2 _____ cms

14. NUMBER OF VESSELS
(Fetal end)
☐ 2 2 ☐ 3 3

15. TRUE KNOT IN CORD
☐ No 0 ☐ Yes 1 (If "yes" take sections as specified in manual)

16. COLOR OF CORD
☐ Normal 0 ☐ Other 1 (Describe)

17. FROZEN SECTION TAKEN
☐ No 0 ☐ Yes 1

18. MEMBRANES AND FETAL SURFACE

19. MEMBRANES COMPLETE
☐ No 0 ☐ Yes 1 ☐ Unable to determine 2

20. DECIDUAL NECROSIS
☐ Not seen grossly 0 ☐ Present (Not massive) 1 ☐ Massive 2

21. MEMBRANES EDEMATOUS
☐ No 0 ☐ Yes 1

22. INSERTION OF MEMBRANES (check two if partial)
☐ Marginal 1 ☐ Circummarginate 2 ☐ Circumvallate 4 ☐ Other (Specify) 8

23. SHORTEST DISTANCE FROM EDGE OF RUPTURE TO PLACENTAL MARGIN _____ cms ☐ Unknown 99

24. COLOR OF FETAL SURFACE
☐ Blue-gray 1 ☐ Green 2 ☐ Brownish-yellow 3 ☐ Other (Specify) 8

25. OPACITY OF MEMBRANES
☐ Not Opaque 0 ☐ Opaque 1

26. SUBCHORIONIC FIBRIN
☐ Not seen 0 ☐ Present (Not massive) 1 ☐ Massive 2 ☐ Patchy 1 ☐ Diffuse 2

27.

28. THROMBOSED FETAL VESSELS
☐ Not seen 0 ☐ Present (Describe: Vein, artery, etc.) 1

29. AMNION NODOSUM
☐ Not seen 0 ☐ Present (Describe) 1

30. CYSTS
☐ Not seen 0 ☐ Present (Describe) 1

31. WEIGHT _____ Gms
(Trim cord and membranes)

32. MATERNAL SURFACE

33. SURFACE
☐₁ Intact ☐₂ Lacerated

34.
☐₁ Complete ☐₂ Incomplete ☐₃ Undetermined

35. DEPRESSED AREA
☐0X None ☐₁ Present

36. IF PRESENT
Size ____ X ____ cms.

37. APPARENTLY CAUSED BY
☐₁ Hemorrhage ☐₂ Atrophy or infarct ☐₈ Other (Describe) ☐₃ Unknown

38. HEMORRHAGE
☐0X None ☐₁ Recent (Elastic) ☐₂ Old (Firm)

39. SIZE
____ cms: ____ X ____ X ____
(Largest diam.) (Small) (Thickness)

40. SHORTEST DISTANCE FROM PERIPHERAL EDGE OF HEMORRHAGE TO PLACENTAL MARGIN ____ cms
☐₁ Location retroplacental ☐₂ Location retromembranous

41. CUT SURFACE

42. INFARCTS: (If none write 0 in all blanks)

43. Pink-Red Infarcts
No. Marginal ____ No. Not Marginal ____

44. Yellow-White Infarcts
No. Marginal ____ No. Not Marginal ____

45. SIZE OF INFARCTS
☐0 Not Applicable (None found) ☐₁ All less than 3 cms. ☐₂ At least one more than 3 cms (infarcts more than 3cms, in largest diam. must be described below)

46. MATERNAL FLOOR INFARCTS (as specified in manual)
☐0 Not seen ☐₁ Present (Describe)

47. COLOR
☐0 Normal ☐₁ Unusually light (pale)

48. CONSISTENCY
☐₁ Firm ☐₂ Spongy ☐₃ Calcification maternal surface only ☐₄ Calcification throughout

49. INTERVILLOUS THROMBOSIS: (If none, write 0 in all blanks)

50. Total number laminated ____

51. No. laminated in marginal sinus ____

52. Total no. not laminated ____

53. No. not laminated in marginal sinus ____

54. TUMOR
☐0 Not seen ☐₁ Present (Describe)

55. HYDATID CHANGE
☐0 Not seen ☐₁ Present (Describe)

56. TRUE CYSTS (in substance) (if none, write 0)
Number present ____

57. GROSS EXAMINATION WAS DONE WITH KNOWLEDGE THAT;
☐₁ Clinical course or outcome for mother or baby was normal ☐₂ Clinical course or outcome for mother or baby was abnormal ☐₃ With no knowledge of the case

58. SPECIAL STUDIES:
☐₁ Photography ☐₂ Virology ☐₃ Histochemistry (Special strain) ☐₈ Other (describe)

59. PRESENCE OF OTHER ABNORMALITIES
☐0 No abnormalities other than those specified above ☐₁ Abnormalities other than those specified above

60. DESCRIPTION OF ABNORMALITIES CHECKED AND OTHER PERTINENT FINDINGS. IDENTIFY EACH COMMENT BY THE CORRESPONDING NUMBER.

PLACENTAL EXAMINATION-MICROSCOPIC

INSTRUCTIONS: (1) For use when crown-rump length of fetus is 16.5 cm. or more (gestational age 20 weeks). (2) An entry is required for every item except those for twins only. (3) Describe all abnormalities in the space at bottom of sheet. (4) Examine at least 3 sections; cord, membrane roll, and placenta. (5) Use ball point pen.

1. PATIENT'S IDENTIFICATION

2. MICROSCOPIC EXAMINATION BY:

3. DATE
Mo.   Day   Year

4. DESIGNATION OF PLACENTA DESCRIBED ON THIS FORM
- Single Birth ☐ 1
- Twin A ☐ 2
- Twin B ☐ 3
- Other Multiple Birth ☐ 4   (Identify below)

5. WAS AMNION AVAILABLE FOR EXAMINATION
- No ☐ 0
- Yes ☐ 1

6. CORD

7. NEUTROPHILIC INFILTRATION
8. Umbilical Vein
- Not seen ☐ 0
- Slight ☐ 1
- Marked ☐ 2

9. Umbilical Artery
- Not seen ☐ 0
- Slight ☐ 1
- Marked ☐ 2

10. Cord Substance
- Not seen ☐ 0
- Slight ☐ 1
- Marked ☐ 2

11. THROMBOSIS OF VESSELS
- Not seen ☐ 0
- Present (Describe) ☐ 1

12. NUMBER OF UMBILICAL ARTERIES
- One ☐ 1
- Two ☐ 2

13. MEMBRANES

14. EPITHELIUM OF AMNION
15. Necrosis
- Not seen ☐ 0
- Present ☐ 1

16. Squamous metaplasia
- Not seen ☐ 0
- Present ☐ 1

17. Amnion Nodosum
- Not seen ☐ 0
- Present ☐ 1

18. Bacterial Colonies
- Not seen ☐ 0
- Present ☐ 1

19. NEUTROPHILIC INFILTRATION OF:
20. Amnion of Membrane Roll
- Not seen ☐ 0
- Slight ☐ 1
- Marked ☐ 2

21. Chorion of Membrane Roll
- Not seen ☐ 0
- Slight ☐ 1
- Marked ☐ 2

22. Amnion of Placental Surface
- Not seen ☐ 0
- Slight ☐ 1
- Marked ☐ 2

23. Chorion of Placental Surface
- Not seen ☐ 0
- Slight ☐ 1
- Marked ☐ 2

24. Fetal Surface Vessels
- Not seen ☐ 0
- Slight ☐ 1
- Marked ☐ 2

25. OTHER FETAL SURFACE VASCULAR CHANGES
- None ☐ 1
- Thrombosis ☐ 2
- Necrosis ☐ 3
- Other (Describe) ☐ 4

26. MACROPHAGES
27. In Amnion or Chorion
- Not seen ☐ 0
- Present (containing no pigment) ☐ 1
- Present (containing meconium) ☐ 2
- Present (containing hemosiderin) ☐ 4
- Present (containing unknown pigment) ☐ 8

28. In Decidua
- Not seen ☐ 0
- Present (containing no pigment) ☐ 1
- Present (containing meconium) ☐ 2
- Present (containing hemosiderin) ☐ 4
- Present (containing unknown pigment) ☐ 8

29. TWIN PLACENTAS ONLY - CLASSIFY DIVIDING MEMBRANES
- Monoamnionic-Monochorionic ☐ 0 (No dividing membranes present)
- Diamnionic-Monochorionic ☐ 1
- Diamnionic-Dichorionic ☐ 2
- Unknown ☐ 9

35. NECROSIS
36. At Margin
☐0 Not marked ☐1 Marked ☐2 Unable to evaluate

37. In Capsularis
☐0 Not marked ☐1 Marked ☐2 Unable to evaluate

38. In Basalis
☐0 Not marked ☐1 Marked ☐2 Unable to evaluate

39. NEUTROPHILIC INFILTRATION
40. At Margin
☐0 Not seen ☐1 Slight ☐2 Marked

41. In Capsularis
☐0 Not seen ☐1 Slight ☐2 Marked

42. In Basalis
☐0 Not seen ☐1 Slight ☐2 Marked

43. LYMPHOCYTIC INFILTRATION
44. At Margin
☐0 Not seen ☐1 Slight ☐2 Marked

45. In Capsularis
☐0 Not seen ☐1 Slight ☐2 Marked

46. In Basalis
☐0 Not seen ☐1 Slight ☐2 Marked

47. CYTOTROPHOBLAST OF COLUMNS
☐0 Average ☐1 Excessive

48. Fibrin Deposition
49. Cystic Change
☐0 Not seen ☐1 Present

50. SYNCYTIUM-NUCLEAR CLUMPING
☐0 Normal (clumps on 30% of villi) ☐1 Less than normal for term placenta ☐2 Excessive for term placenta

51. TERMINAL VILLI

52. LANGHANS' LAYER
☐0 Absent ☐1 Present

53. HOFBAUER CELLS
☐0 Few ☐1 Many

54. STROMAL FIBROSIS
☐0 Not seen ☐1 Present (Describe)

55. PATHOLOGICAL EDEMA
☐0 Not seen ☐1 Present (Describe)

56. MICRO INFARCTS (as specified in manual)
☐0 Not seen ☐1 Present

57. NUCLEATED RBC IN FETAL CIRCULATION
☐0 Not seen ☐1 Present

58. MELANIN
☐0 Not seen ☐1 Slight ☐2 Marked

59. INTERVILLOUS SPACE

60. INTERVILLOUS THROMBI
☐0 Not seen ☐1 Present, RBC intact ☐2 Present, RBC hemolyzed

61. IF THROMBI PRESENT
☐0 No adjacent villous infarction seen ☐1 Adjacent villous infarction seen

62. MARGINAL SINUS THROMBI
☐0 Not seen ☐1 Present, RBC intact ☐2 Present, RBC hemolyzed

63. SICKLING (maternal blood)
☐0 Not noted ☐1 Present

64. APPARENT MATURITY OF PLACENTA
☐1 Under 20 weeks ☐2 20-27 weeks ☐3 28-36 weeks ☐4 37 weeks or over

65. MICROSCOPIC EXAMINATION WAS DONE WITH KNOWLEDGE THAT:
☐1 Clinical course or outcome for mother or baby was normal ☐2 Clinical course or outcome for mother or baby was abnormal ☐3 With no knowledge of the case

66. PRESENCE OF OTHER ABNORMALITIES
☐0 No abnormalities other than those specified above ☐1 Abnormalities other than those specified above

67. DESCRIPTION OF ABNORMALITIES CHECKED AND OTHER PERTINENT FINDINGS. IDENTIFY EACH COMMENT BY THE CORRESPONDING ITEM NUMBER.

68. FINAL DIAGNOSIS

69. DO NOT USE

The following remarks supplement explanations given in Chapters VII, VIII, and IX regarding the items identified by number in the preceding forms of this Appendix. If the items are obviously self-explanatory, no comment is made.

GROSS

22. It is important to notice the type of insertion of the membranes. The marginal type is normal, as is so well seen in Max Brödel's drawing (Fig. 162). The circumvallate type with the rolled, double contoured insertion situated well in from the margin and with a large extrachorionic mass of placenta is prone to undergo separation or rupture of membranes or to be associated with premature labor. The circummarginate placenta, a related but less severe form of the circumvallate placenta, is much less apt to do any of these things that endanger the baby.

23. The distance of the normal rupture from the placental margin gives a general idea of where the placenta was attached vis-à-vis the internal os at full dilatation. Severe laceration of membranes makes any deduction invalid as to placental location *in utero*.

24 and 25. The color of the fetal surface gives some idea of degree of fetal maceration or anoxia. With a macerated fetus, the fetal surface and "membranes" are gray and opaque, the amniotic fluid being turbid. Brownish or greenish yellow color indicates meconium staining owing to hypoxia *in utero*. Some erythroblastotic placentas of the nonhydropic types, not an obvious abnormality, are stained a golden yellow color. This is thought to be due to blood destruction *in utero*. Not all erythroblastotic placentas, however, show such a staining.

29. Amnion nodosum (small opaque plaques) is a reaction to squame cells within the amnion and is associated with oliguria, a feature related to the accompanying fetal kidney disease.

30. Cysts of the fetal surface may be due to massive subchorionic fibrin deposits with secondary liquefaction in their centers or to accumulations of fluid within the space between the chorion and amnion. Neither is of clinical significance.

33. The inspection of the maternal surface is important. It gives a clue about missing placental tissue, degree of infarction,

premature separation, and calcification. The latter, resembling the pattern of old-fashioned lace, is *not* important except that it dulls the technician's knife. It occurs in the aging trophoblast of the placental floor where main villous branches have been long attached. Such an area, but without calcification, may be seen in Figure 178. Calcification extends into the placenta along main villous branches and is seen on the cut surface, hence its mention in item 48.

40. The location of a retroplacental hematoma will give an accurate idea as to whether the hemorrhage was "concealed" and of the toxic variety or whether it was marginal and of the nontoxic type of degenerative origin. The source of these two types of hemorrhages has been discussed in Chapter VIII.

55. True hydatidiform change of villi in the mature or maturing placenta, with a fetus, whether dead or alive, is due to a congenital failure of the originally normal discontinuous villous vessels to coalesce with one another. The author has seen perhaps a dozen of these in his experience, mostly in consultation. If the condition is severe, it will kill the baby. If it occupies one half of a placenta, seen once by the author, it may be a true hydatidiform mole of one twin of a dizygotic twin pregnancy, or a focal area in a normal singleton placenta.

56. Cysts of the placenta result from degeneration of the decidual septa between cotyledons and may result in tearing of adjacent veins draining the cotyledon. When this occurs, there is a true infarction of the placental tissue drained by that vein. This cystic change is also mentioned in the microscopic item number 49.

For some years the presence of blood-filled cystic spaces within the centers of cotyledons has been discussed by anatomists, pathologists, and clinicians rather fruitlessly it seems to the author. These spaces are normal as so beautifully shown by *in vivo* cinematography by Dr. Elizabeth M. Ramsey of the Carnegie Laboratory. She is a pathologist-embryologist who is the world's expert on the anatomy and physiology of uteroplacental circulation in the macaque monkey. Her summary of circulation in the intervillous space of the primate placenta in the 1962 symposium on the placenta, cited before, is well worth reading.[112]

The article by her and her colleagues in 1964 gives the technique and results of a series of radio-angiograms of the uterus performed on five pregnant macaque monkeys.[94] It is a short paper but full of worthwhile data. The blood-filled spaces are due to jets of arteriolar blood entering the cotyledon through the basal plate of the placenta. The amount of blood in any one cotyledon will thus be a function of what phase the arteriolar circulation was in at the time of placental separation. The late great Canadian clinician Goodall thought these spaces were pathological and called the condition "placentosis." Any fresh placenta will show such cystic spaces in the centers of cotyledons if the pathologist takes the trouble to look for them.

MICROSCOPIC EXAMINATION

As stated, a minimum of three sections is necessary: the umbilical cord, a long wide strip of membranes rolled as in a "jelly roll" which can be accurately trimmed after fixation, and a placental section preferably from the margin. Although this is a minimal number, there are often other areas of the ovisac which require microscopic sections as well.

As a practical point, placental tissue is difficult to section unless the knife, a large one, is very sharp. Ordinary scalpels are fine for small definitive sections made by two parallel cuts to include a small lesion or vessel of the decidual surface. The slice thus made is then best excised from the mass with sharp scissors. The pressure from even a sharp knife of any size distorts the edges of the block when it is being excised. In general, the placental blocks should be thicker than those of other tissues owing to the intrinsic nature of placental tissue. Hence they must be definitively trimmed EARLY after partial fixation if good fixation is to be secured. The experienced pathologist need not be reminded that the spleen, because of its blood content, is a difficult organ from which to obtain good sections. The placenta is comparable, and for the same reason. (As a general complaint, the author dislikes to see sections which appear as though they had been hacked out, whatever the organ may be. Such poor blocks resemble the results of sampling by a pet mouse or rat. The author is grateful to Dr. Wolbach for his early *personal* instructions as to how to select and trim blocks for microscopic sections. After all, all procedures can be done aesthetically and correctly or unaesthetically and sloppily!)

6. The section of umbilical cord will reveal evidence of intra-uterine infection, infection after rupture of membranes and absence of a vessel which portends other congenital anomalies in the fetus. Benirschke has pointed out this significant relationship most recently in his text.[6]

13. Membranes will reveal significant anomalies of the amnion and evidence of infection, either before or after rupture of the membranes. The author has searched for years to find anatomic evidence for the etiology of premature rupture of the membranes. Whether such a rupture is due to some intrinsic defect of the membranes, too large an interval os, or too much intra-uterine pressure, he knows not. The exception is the circumvallate placenta whose ovisac is too small for the baby. An interesting but tragic anecdote about bacteria in the margin of a placenta whose membranes had been ruptured manually to produce labor concerns the author's early days (1932) as a placentologist. Streptococci were visualized by gram stain in this specimen from a patient who started, unwittingly, an epidemic of puerperal sepsis during which two normally delivered multiparae died. They had been in contact with the first patient by way of perineal ice bags (now outlawed at the Boston Lying-in Hospital), which were randomly distributed every four hours by the nurse at the patient's request and made only socially clean after each using. The findings of bacteria in the membranes at the margin of the placenta enabled the author to point out that the first patient, who incidentally did not die, had puerperal sepsis and not acute recurrent pyelonephritis as was clinically diagnosed. Once the first patient was isolated *and* the ice bags discontinued, the epidemic stopped. As a further point of satisfaction, this incident resulted in the author being noticed by the staff as a person and not as just another resident in a white suit. It is this sort of true story which prejudices the author, a trustee of the American Board of Pathology, against hospital training programs which say that placentas are "examined only grossly."

42 and 46. With respect to leukocytic infiltration in the *decid-*

ua basalis, it is well to remember that foci of necrosis occur normally in all placental sites, of whatever age. Polymorphonuclear leukocytes are universally associated with the necrosis of a spontaneous abortion. The important thing to determine is whether there is evidence of true infection, either acute or chronic. The *decidua basalis* is not a simple morphologic picture. It has trophoblastic cells, decidual cells, various kinds of leukocytes, and the granulocytes described by Dallenbach-Hellweg and Nette in 1964.[20] The authors show that the trophoblastic cells are hormonally important and that the granulocytes (often confused with leukocytes) contain relaxin.

51. With respect to terminal villi, the truly functional units of the placenta, the pathologist is often hard put to interpret their changes in proper pathophysiological terms. The syncytiotrophoblastic covering of the toxemic villus is prematurely aged or degenerated.[49]

The normal villus after the thirty-fifth week shows a progressive thickening of the subtrophoblastic and capillary basement membranes.[102]

This may well account for progressive loss of permeability to radioactive sodium after the thirty-sixth week, as shown by Flexner.[27A] McKay's data[97] have also shown a premature thickening of these basement membranes in the villi or the placenta from toxemic patients. This could well account for the long, "skinny," underweight babies from toxemic mothers. Also it could account for premature death of babies *in utero* as a complication of maternal toxemia.

The cytotrophoblast of Langhans' type in the normal placenta has all but disappeared. It is present and active, however, in erythroblastosis fetalis and sometimes in the presence of maternal diabetes. It is difficult to evaluate the significance of Hofbauer cells which are normal components of leukocytic type within the villous stroma. The latter may be dense or edematous, depending on what part of the villus one examines. One should beware of interpreting edema, hydropic change, or immaturity unless the part of the villus in question is identifiable.

The normal villus of a placenta accompanying a dead baby shows disappearance of the now nonfunctioning capillaries.

They undergo a kind of acute disuse atrophy and begin to disappear as soon as the baby dies. Actually this is a better index of the length of time the baby has been dead than is the degree of skin and organ maceration. When the stroma is uniformly edematous and immature, containing many vessels crowded with nucleated red cells and hematopoietic foci, the diagnosis of fetal hydrops or erythroblastosis is obvious. The placenta of the icteric phase of erythroblastosis is not, however, so obvious. Hellman and Hertig[35A] showed that, as a group, these placentas were less mature, although individually they were difficult if not impossible to diagnose. The focal edema of the congenitally abnormal villus whose vessels have not coalesced with their fellows is obvious. They are very edematous; there are few, if any, vessels; and the trophoblast is mature. The edematous, mesenchymal, immature stroma of the hydropic erythroblastotic placenta, however, is accompanied by immature trophoblast of both types; Langhans' and syncytium. The careful microscopist will be rewarded by finding mitoses in the persisting, growing, Langhans' epithelium of a hydropic baby's placenta. Whatever the stimulus may be, probably fetal blood destruction owing to iso-immunization, the placenta remains immature even though it may reach the astounding gross weight of 2200 grams.

With respect to fetal syphilis,[6] the author has always been in doubt. He has spent many fruitless hours trying to stain spirochaetes in placentas from treated syphilitic patients. Few placentas from patients with untreated syphilis have come his way. The placenta is said to be large, pale, and fibrosed. It is probable that the fetal blood vessels are infected and thrombosed. If so, the villi will still be viable; fetal blood supply is not necessary to villous viability.

Speaking of thrombosed fetal blood vessels within the chorionic circulation, this offers a seeming paradox. If the fetus dies, the placenta still remains viable, and the thrombi of the larger villous vessels may undergo organization. It is the only example known to the author of a thrombus associated with a dead body undergoing organization. To be sure, the placenta is well nourished by the intervillous maternal blood and so is not dead, even though the fetus or baby may be macerated.

64. With respect to the apparent age of the placenta, its estimation is a matter of experience. As the functioning villi become older, they become smaller and better vascularized. The Langhans' epithelium disappears as a layer at about sixteen weeks' menstrual age, but isolated cells persist to term. The syncytium becomes thinner and the nuclei more clumped. Nucleated red cells disappear about the beginning of the middle trimester: the sixteenth to seventeenth week. The basal plate of the placenta becomes thinner and thinner as term is approached, as shown in Figures 176 to 178. The *decidua basalis* also becomes correspondingly thinner. Evidences of degeneration (such as subsyncytial and cell column fibrinoid) become more marked, but these are subject to individual variation. A good review of the progressing aging of the placenta as an organ may be read in McKay and associates.[97]

In summary, with these few simple remarks and bits of advice, the author wishes the potential placentologist well. The placenta is an interesting organ, pathologically, physiologically, and anatomically. It deserves a better fate than it is usually accorded. As a final paper, delightfully written by the master, George W. Corner, the reader is referred to *Exploring the Placental Maze* which was a lecture given in honor of the obstetrician, Karl Miller Wilson, of Rochester, New York on October 12, 1963.[18] Dr. Corner is one of the great anatomico-physiologic scientists of the present day. He is an accomplished writer, medical historian, and bibliophile. Incidentally, he and Willard Allen isolated progesterone in pure form.

INDEX

Infection
   bacterial, 171, 341
   viral, 120, 171
Infertility, 139 *(See also* Fertility)
Intervillous space, 50, 57, 58, 104, 116
   as arteriovenous aneurysm, 73
   blood in, 57, 62, 63, 121, 211, 307
   glycoprotein in, 112
   in invasive mole, 303
   maternal blood in, 211
   maternal blood vessels and, 50, 57, 62
   overdistention of, 160
Invasive mole, 238, 239, 258, 259 (T), 260, 265, 272, 274 ff., 297, 300
   chemotherapy for, 275, 276
   choriocarcinoma and, 274
   chorionic villi in, 272, 274, 300, 303
   complications of, 274
   crater formed by, 272, 274, 276, 300, 304
   curettage for, 300
   cytotrophoblast in, 303
   diagnosis of, 300, 307
      differential, 276, 277
      early, 276
   giant cell production and, 279, 288, 303
   histochemistry of, 278
   human chorionic gonadotropin in, 101
   implantation site and, 303, 304
   incidence, 265, 277
   intervillous space in, 303
   involution of, 275
   local excision of, 276
   location of, 272
   morphology of
      gross, 300, 303
      microscopic, 303, 304
   myometrium in, 303, 304
   silence of, 272
   syncytiotrophoblast in, 303
   trophoblast and, 260, 272, 274, 279, 288, 303, 304
Iron
   inorganic, 278
Isotopic labeling
   in organ culture, 104

K

Kaolin method for urine concentration, 320
Kidney disease, 211
   of fetus, 338

L

Labor
   fetal bleeding during, 220
   premature, 163 f., 184
   third stage of, 204
Langhans' epithelium, 42, 58, 81, 342, 343, 344
Law
   on abortion, 51, 165, 172
   on birth of twins, 216
   related to interpretation of bleeding in early pregnancy, 51, 124
   on premature delivery, 165
   on trauma
      congenital anomaly and, 191
   on unborn child, 191 *n.*
Leukocytes, 47, 57, 164, 341, 342
   in decidua of abortion, 171
   in *decidua basalis,* 341, 342
   trophoblast invasion and, 42
Liver cell
   trophoblast incompatibility with autologous, 105
Lung
   choriocarcinoma metastatic to, 105, 289
   molar villi in, 274
   trophoblastic compatibility with autologous cells, 105
   trophoblast deported to, 238
Luteinizing hormone, 320

M

Macaque monkey
   angiogenesis in, 81, 82, 86
   chorion, 219
      angiogenesis in, 9
   gestation time, 34, 86
   implantation in, 219
      time of, 34, 86
   ovum
      postimplantation stage, 34
      preimplantation stage, 34